Invocation Track
Chapter 20 - Pg

Four Pillars which represents the four
elements are: knowledge, courage,
volition & Silence i.e. IHVH - the
tetragramaton

The Practice Of
Magical Evocation

Volume II
Of The Holy Mysteries

Franz Bardon

The Practice Of Magical Evocation

A Complete Course Of Instruction
In Planetary Spheric Magic

The Evocation Of Spirit-Beings From The Planetary
Spheres Of Our Solar System

MMI
Merkur Publishing™ Inc.
Wisdom of the Occident

© 1956 Verlag Hermann Bauer, Freiburg/Breisgau, Western Germany –
Die Praxis der magischen Evokation

© 1967, 1970 Dieter Rüggeberg, Postfach 130844, D-42035 Wuppertal,
Germany
Translated by Peter Dimai, Graz, Austria
First English Translation Published 1967, 1970, 1975, 1984, 1991

© 2001 Dieter Rüggeberg
Second English Translation, Translated by Gerhard Hanswille and Franca
Gallo
Translated from the original German edition: *Die Praxis der magischen
Evokation*
Edited by Ken Johnson
ISBN 1-885928-13-0
First Printing 2001

Printed and bound in China by C&C Offset Printing Co., Ltd.
Cover design: Reed Perkins

Merkur Publishing,™ Inc., PO Box 171306, Salt Lake City, UT, U.S.A.
84117, (801) 272-9008 or (800) 204-2473
www.merkurpublishing.com

Dedication

I dedicate this work to my wife, Marie, my life's companion, in constant memory.

CONTENTS

PART II: HIERARCHY

PART III: ILLUSTRATIONS: SEALS OF THE PRINCIPALS, INTELLIGENCES, GENII AND BEINGS

Foreword

In our present times, Franz Bardon, the author of *Initiation into Hermetics*, was given the divine mission and the very important assignment by Divine Providence to lead those who are seekers of truth onto the path of perfection. With the publication of *The Practice of Magical Evocation* the author makes his second work available to the public.

In this second treatise, Franz Bardon conscientiously guides to the next level of their development all those readers and true students of magic who, on the basis of the first work, were granted the opportunity of embarking onto the only proper path. The author clearly asserts that there must be no lingering or standing still on the path of perfection. This would undoubtedly result in regression into one's old daily routine. It would lead the student back to ignorance and darkness. Therefore there is only one solution, and that is to move forward, forward to the brightest heights. These bright heights beckon anyone who is not afraid of making the effort and who courageously and incessantly continues to work on his spiritual ascent. It is the purpose of this book to provide this particular help.

The author, who in the meantime has become well known due to his large circle of readers, conscientiously makes all his students aware, in very simple language, of all the significant or insignificant dangers that lurk when a student digresses from the true path. And the author does everything within his power to prevent such a mishap, because the result would be that the student might be unable to return to the path of perfection for quite a long time, and some students might never get back at all.

There is presently not one single book available on this particular subject — whether from ancient times or from the present, and regardless of how promising it seems to be or how eloquently it has been written — that will give the reader a true guiding principle as clearly and distinctly as this book does. In this book the author describes every detail faithfully and in a fascinating manner; and with very simple words he explains the most peculiar occurrences and the most miraculous incidences that take place on our planet as well as the various different worlds and spheres.

We, the readers, the true students, and all others who are interested in the highest knowledge should not be remiss, to extend their most sincere gratitude to Divine Providence for Her great grace and for the author that She sent to us.

Every person who is able to obtain a copy of this book should consider himself very fortunate. May this book never leave his possession and may he follow the instructions, hints and teachings faithfully and conscientiously.

Otti Votavova
(1903 – 1973)

Introduction

Throughout the ages, and primarily during the past few centuries, many lengthy dissertations have been published on the art of higher magic. Unfortunately, they are for the most part such bewildering and incomplete remnants that very little of it can be taken as a point of reference for practical studies, and this only in small fragments. The original initiative for magic was known only to a very few lodges and was reserved for a particularly chosen few, while for the seekers of truth who searched diligently for any information, this subject matter remained dark and mysterious.

Various religions during the Middle Ages were severely hostile towards any magical knowledge. In our history, the most prominent examples are the well known Inquisitions. Later, in modern times, magic was regarded as mere superstition, and any person who showed some inclination toward this knowledge, let alone one seriously concerned himself with the study of magic, was regarded as a fool and was ridiculed. In the past, mystical and other sects maligned magic to such a degree that the word "magic" has to this very day an extremely dubious reputation. And any person who has had an appreciation or understanding for magical knowledge has been pilloried as a black magician.

In reality, true magic was initially taught in the ancient schools of the prophets, and then only in the highest circles. However, only a few select insiders had access to these institutions. In those days, only a few books occasionally disclosed scant bits of information about true magic. These books were deliberately written in such a way that they would disclose little or nothing even to the most astute reader, and hence they would not give the seeker of truth a complete understanding of the subject of magic.

In accordance with the ancient Egyptian Mysteries, the magic of the second Tarot card is represented by the High Priestess. I shall gladly continue to guide the serious, diligent reader and student of magic along the proper path, as long as this person is devoid of any fanatical religious beliefs and erroneous ideology. Furthermore, this person has to be prepared to penetrate further into the mysteries of the knowledge of magic or the Hermetic sciences.

As in my first book, *Initiation into Hermetics*, I shall endeavor to keep the language of this second volume in a style that is understandable to everyone. The subject matter of the magic of evocation is among the least known and least investigated branches of the art, and therefore I shall make certain that every person who reads this book will become completely familiar with this subject matter, not only in theory but above all with the practice, if he so chooses. However, it is important that the reader know that he will not achieve any results with the practice of magical evocation unless he has successfully completed Step VIII, at the very least, of my first book, *Initiation into Hermetics*, which is a description of the first tarot card, the Magician.

Should I be successful in assisting the reader who has successfully completed the entire practical part of my first book to achieve the same good results with this one, then I will have achieved my objective. Those readers who initially study the secret sciences only theoretically will find in this work a satisfactory broadening of their knowledge.

Part I
Magic

Chapter 1
Magic

Magic is the greatest knowledge and the highest science that exists anywhere on our planet. Not only does magic teach the metaphysical laws, but also the *metapsychical* laws that exist and which are applicable on all planes. Since time immemorial the highest knowledge has always been known as "magic." However, it was accessible only to particular circles of society, the members of which were predominantly the high priests and the most powerful potentates. The magi have always been considered to be the highest initiates. They knew the true teachings, but kept these teachings secret with all the means at their disposal. They knew precisely the synthesis of their own religion as well as of all other religions. By contrast, all religious knowledge furnished to the public at large was merely symbolic. Only after many centuries were a few morsels of the true knowledge made known to the public. And yet it was still very much concealed, and understandably so, since the majority of the people were uneducated in magic in accordance with the divine laws. They understood only a few morsels of this high knowledge and only from an individual point of view. As a result of this, they could only pass this knowledge on in an inadequate and one-sided manner. That is why the knowledge of magic has, without exaggeration, remained secretive to this very day. The comprehension of the true magical laws depends upon the spiritual and magical maturity of the individual. In order to reach the maturity required for this endeavor, a certain amount of pre-schooling is absolutely necessary. Therefore, the reader should now understand why I say that he must have successfully completed the teachings of the first Tarot card in *Initiation into Hermetics,* up to and inclusive of Step VIII, if he expects to succeed in higher magic. And that means the student of magic must have completed

Step VIII not in theory alone, but also in practice in every aspect mentioned in the first volume.

There are no miracles as such, nor is there anything that can be considered supernatural. This opinion is shared by the educated rationalists and by those who are unable to grasp or understand these kinds of occurrences. Magic is the knowledge that teaches the practical application of the lowest laws of nature to the highest laws of the spirit. Whosoever wishes to learn the laws of magic must first learn all about the effects of the lowest laws of nature before he will be able to understand those laws that follow, and then eventually he will progress to the highest of laws.

Depending upon how far the reader has progressed at this point of his development, or which laws he is presently studying, for the sake of an easier overview he can now divide magical knowledge into three categories:

1. *Lower Magic.* Lower magic deals with the laws of nature, their effects, how and where they prevail and how they can be controlled. Lower magic is also known as the Magic of Nature.
2. *Intermediate Magic.* Intermediate magic deals with the universal laws in a human being, the microcosm, their effects, how and where they prevail and how they can be controlled.
3. *Higher Magic.* High magic encompasses the universal laws in the macrocosm, namely the entire universe, their effects, how and where they prevail and how they can be controlled in the entire macrocosm.

In *Initiation into Hermetics*, I mentioned several times that the powers and laws between the lower, intermediate and higher magic are in an analogous context. These powers and their effect, and how and where they prevail, are described in detail in this second work.

Magical knowledge can be compared to a school system, where lower magic, the magic of nature, is the subject matter for elementary school, intermediate magic, the magic of the microcosm, the subject matter for middle school and higher magic, the magic of the macrocosm, the subject matter for high school.

In accordance with the *Tablet of Hermes,* the universal axiom that applies to magic is as follows: "As above, so below" and vice versa. Therefore, we cannot truly speak of lower, intermediate or higher magic, for in reality there is only one "magic" and the level of maturity of the particular magician determines the degree of his development. It determines how far he has progressed with his magical knowledge.

The universal laws always remain one and the same, regardless of whether they are applied or considered with good or evil intentions. The manner in which a law is applied depends upon the character and intentions of the individual. Should the magician use the powers for good purposes, then he is practicing "white" magic. Should he, however, pursue evil purposes, then he is practicing "black" magic. It does not matter whether the activities are good or evil — the laws that apply always remain the same.

It should be completely clear to the reasonable reader that in reality there is neither white nor black magic. These various concepts were brought into common use by mystical and religious sects so that they could accuse a person who was not like-minded, or anyone who simply did not suit them, of being a black magician. I shall give the reader an appropriate comparison from a universal point of view. For example, would it not be completely illogical to consider the night as evil and the day as good? One cannot exist without the other, and both of these poles had to come into existence when the macrocosm and the microcosm were created, in order to distinguish one from the other.

God the universal Creator did not create anything impure and evil. However, that is not to say that man should do both good and evil. The contrast exists for one reason: so that a human being may master it and learn how to distinguish the truth from its opposite. A true magician will never underestimate the negative, and neither will he avoid it. A true magician will always cede to the negative the place to which it is entitled, and therefore the negative must be just as useful to him as the positive. That is why a magician does not consider the negative powers to be evil. He does not consider good and evil from a religious point of view; rather, he considers them from a universal point of view.

Magic is quite often mistaken for sorcery. At this point I shall briefly explain the difference between magic and sorcery. A true magician relies completely upon the universal laws; he knows their cause and effect and he works consciously with these powers, whereas the sorcerer avails himself of powers the origin of which he knows not at all, although he does know that this or that will occur when he sets this or that power into motion. But he has no idea as to any other context of these matters, because he lacks the knowledge of the universal laws. Even though he may have partial knowledge of one law or another, he does not know the analogous context of the universal laws, their effects, how they develop and how and where they prevail, because a sorcerer does not possess the necessary maturity.

In contrast, a true magician, one who does not want to descend to the level of a sorcerer, would never embark upon any endeavor until he thoroughly understands what he is doing. Even a sorcerer can make use of the secret sciences and do one thing or another with good or evil intentions. In this case, it is irrelevant whether he employs positive or negative powers, for it does not entitle him to consider himself a magician.

By way of contrast once again, a charlatan is a person who is trying to deceive other people, and therefore he cannot be considered either a magician or a sorcerer. In common parlance such a person would simply be called a fraud or a con man. Charlatans like to boast of their high magical knowledge, which of course they do not possess, and they like to veil themselves in mystery, but only to conceal their ignorance.

These are the people who are responsible for true magical knowledge being so distorted and disgraced. A true magician does not identify himself through mysterious behavior or external splendor; on the contrary, he is modest and he endeavors at all times to help humankind and to explain magical knowledge to mature human beings. In order not to disgrace this holy knowledge, it should be understandable that the magician will not entrust any of the Mysteries to an immature person. A true magician will never display his true magical knowledge by any external demeanor. A true magician cannot be distinguished from an average citizen, because he adapts to every person, to every occasion and to every situation. His magical authority is internal, and therefore it is not necessary for him to shine externally.

There is also another variation of magic that is often mistaken for true magic, but in fact has nothing whatsoever to do with magic at all. It is the so-called art of the prestidigitators or illusionists. Through his dexterity and through deceiving peoples' senses the illusionist emulates a few phenomena, phenomena that a true magician achieves with the help of the universal laws. The fact that these prestidigitators and illusionists use the word "magic" for their tricks is proof again of how far the true concept of magic has diminished. However, it is not my intention to spend too much time with tricks or stage magic. It is a foregone conclusion that an illusionist or prestidigitator is not a true magician or indeed a sorcerer, even if he gives himself the most alluring names because of his dexterity.

In this book I describe the synthesis of that part of magic which up to now has not been revealed. It is the magic of evocation, which is the most difficult to comprehend. From the gloomy days of antiquity right to the present time, hundreds of books have been published which contain instructions on how to invoke beings for making pacts with the devil, etc. But not one of these books gives the reader true knowledge, much less assures success on account of the instructions that were recommended. It is, however, true that now and again, in isolated cases, an individual, on account of his talent and maturity, did achieve some partial success. A true magician, one who thoroughly concerns himself with the magic of evocation, need not worry that he will be unable to achieve any results at all or only partial success. He will reach the conclusion that, with the synthesis of evocative magic, he will be able achieve a successful evocation without any difficulties.

I shall not deal with matters concerning other kinds of magic such as mummial magic, sympathetic magic, spell-magic in cases of sickness, healing by sympathetic means, and so forth. To a genuine magician these kinds of magic happen to arise by themselves if he should occasionally want to make use of them. The initiated magician can modify the instructions that are given in conventional books and then possibly make use of them in practice.

Chapter 2
Magical Aids

Although a true magician can achieve everything with his own powers — which he has earned without any other help as a result of his spiritual maturity during his magical development — it is his choice to make extensive use of ceremonial magic and all the aids that belong to it.

Ceremonial magic offers the advantage that, when used continuously and frequently for one and the same operation, effects are produced without making use of one's own powers. With the help of various aids, ceremonial magic enables the magician to make his work with occult powers easier.

All magical aids, every single magical instrument, are basically mnemonic aids, aiding the magician's consciousness. When one directs his attention to a particular instrument, this triggers in the consciousness the particular ability or power symbolized by that particular instrument. Once a magician takes one or another magical instrument into his hand during the evocation, he immediately comes in contact with what this instrument symbolizes and he achieves his purpose without much effort.

For example, the magic wand represents the magician's absolute will. If a magician takes the magic wand into his hand, by making use of the wand he immediately establishes contact through his will with the spirit he wishes to evoke. The same applies to all the other magical aids because they symbolize spiritual powers, laws and attributes.

Should a magician decide to employ ceremonial magic, then he must dedicate a great deal of care to his magical instruments. He must treat them with an almost religious awe, because the more carefully, the more precisely, and the more attentively they are handled, the more effective they will be. Magical instruments are on the same level as sacred objects and they serve the magician to establish the necessary temple atmosphere for ceremonial magic. When the magician uses his magical instruments he must be in a state of complete rapture. If any magical instrument were to be used, even once, for any purpose other than that

20

for which it was intended, then that particular instrument will immediately cease to be magically effective and will be forever useless for its actual original purpose.

Since all magical aids bring forth a very special feeling of respect in every magician, they must be hidden from the view of any uninitiated person in order to avoid any profanation. Therefore, before a magician reaches for a magical instrument, he must under all circumstances undergo an internal cleansing process, whether through prayer or suitable meditation. He should never under any circumstances touch a magical instrument if he is not in the proper state of mind, which is absolutely essential for such a ceremony. A magician must always be conscious of the fact that all magical aids or magical instruments symbolize the most sacrosanct laws and must therefore be dealt with in the same manner as one would deal with sacred relics. Only in the hands of a magician who takes all this into very careful consideration will the magical instruments actually bring forth magical effects.

By exactly observing the guidelines which have been recommended here in regards to the appropriate attitude and the preparation of all magical instruments, the magician calls forth within himself an extremely strong state of manifestation of belief, will and all the attributes of the law. By so doing, he thereby increases his magical authority considerably and hence exerts the necessary influence upon a being or a power so that the desired results or effects are actually realized.

Even if the magician does not use his magical instruments for a long period of time, they are still constantly in contact with the particular attributes that they symbolize. Since every instrument is magically charged or, in other words, consecrated for a specific purpose, it will never lose its magical effect if it is handled properly, even if centuries have passed since the instrument was last used.

When the magical instruments are consecrated and charged for use for a particular magician, in other words, he for whom they were made, they cannot be used by any other magician. These instruments would not be effective even if they were to fall into the hands of a magician who is completely conversant with the holy sciences of magic, unless he charges and consecrates the magical instruments anew for himself.

21

In the chapters that follow, I shall describe the most important magical instruments and their symbolic analogies as far as their practical use is concerned, and how they are to be generally used in a ceremonial magical operation. If it seems desirable and necessary, any magician, on the basis of my instructions, can make his own additional magical aids for particular magical purposes, and I shall supply the guidelines as to how he is to proceed.

Chapter 3
The Magic Circle

All books that deal with the subject of ceremonial magic and give accounts of invocation and evocation of any kind of being stipulate that the magic circle plays the most important role. There are hundreds of instructions available on how to make magic circles for a wide variety of purposes. For example, instructions can be found in works such as the *Albertus Magnus*, the *Clavicula Solomonus*, the *Goetia*, Agrippa, *Magia Naturalis*, in the *Faust Magia Naturalis,* and in the ancient grimoires. In all these books the instructions given are always the same: all one has to do when summoning a being is to stand in the circle. But rarely is there an explanation for the esoteric symbolism of a magic circle. I shall therefore explain the magic circle in detail to the seriously aspiring magician in accordance with the analogies and the universal laws.

A true magic circle is a symbolic representation of both the macrocosm and the microcosm, in other words as far as the microcosm is concerned it is a representation of the perfect human being. A circle indicates the beginning and the end, and therefore the alpha and the omega. Furthermore, it depicts eternity, which has no beginning or end. As such, the circle is a symbolic diagram of the Infinite, of the Divinity, in all Its aspects, that can be understood by the microcosm, which means by a true initiate or a magician who has successfully completed all the exercises in *Initiation into Hermetics*. In other words, it is understood by a perfected magician. The drawing of a circle symbolizes the Divinity in Its perfection, to come into contact with the Divinity, namely when the magician stands in the center of the circle, whereby, symbolically expressed, the connection with the Divinity is graphically represented. For the magician it is a connection with the macrocosm on the highest level of his consciousness. It is therefore completely logical from the point of view of true magic for the magician to stand in the center of a magic circle with the awareness of being at One with his universal divinity. This clearly shows that the magic circle is not only a diagram for protection against undesirable negative influences, but it also expresses untouchability and unassailability as a result of connecting one's consciousness with the Highest. Therefore, a magician who stands in the center of a magic circle is protected from all influences, be they good or evil, because he symbolizes the Divinity in the universe. Besides, a magician who stands in a circle is God himself in the microcosm, who rules the beings which are created in the universe and he is the one who exercises his absolute powers.

Therefore the esoteric significance of standing in a circle represents something entirely different than what the conventional books on magic dealing with the matter of evocation, invocation or incantation claim it to be. If a magician, when standing in the magic circle, were not conscious of this esoteric significance — that he symbolizes God, the infinite Being — he would be unable to exert any influence upon a being. At that point, the magician is a consummate magical authority and all powers and beings must be absolutely obedient to this consummate authority. His will and the orders he gives are the orders of the Infinite, of God, and without exception these orders must be respected by the beings with whom the magician comes in contact. Should the magician fail to have this attitude during the magical operation, he will sink to the level of a sorcerer, and he will be merely a mimic, without actually being in contact with the Highest. His magical authority will therefore become questionable. Besides, he will face the danger of failing to gain any respect from the beings that he has summoned, or worse, he may be ridiculed. Besides which, there are all the other undesirable, accompanying problems to which he would be subjected by the powers he has summoned, especially when they are negative beings.

The design and preparation of such a magic circle depends solely upon the individual preference and level of maturity of the particular magician. The diagram, the drawing, and the manner in which the form of the Divinity is expressed in the circle is based upon the religious ideology of the magician. And that is also why the instructions regarding magic circles which an Oriental magus employs in his magical operations do not apply and cannot be used by an Occidental — because the concepts of an Oriental in regards to infinity and God are quite different from those of an Occidental. If an Occidental magician were to draw a magic circle following Oriental instructions with all the appropriate names of Oriental divinities, then for him the circle would be completely ineffective and the purpose strived for could never be achieved. A magician who is raised in Christian religions or beliefs should never draw a magic circle that is based on the Hindu religion or belief, or one based on any other religion, because it would be an exercise in futility; in other words it would be a wasted effort. The preparation of a magic circle always depends upon the notion and belief of one's own personal concept of God, which in this case has to be represented in a graphic manner. That is why a true magician would never think of drawing a magic circle, performing rituals and following instructions regarding ceremonial magic with which he cannot identify. A similar situation would arise if an Occidental were to wear Oriental clothes in the Occident.

The design of a magic circle should contain that which corresponds totally with the magician's point of view and which is on the same level as his individual maturity; that would be the best choice. A magician who is completely conversant with the harmony of the universe and knows the hierarchy of the universe exactly can also consider these facts when he designs and draws the magic circle. In accordance with the possibilities the diagram has to offer, a magician who is conversant with these matters can include the entire hierarchy of the universe in his circle, and thereby more easily raise his consciousness and more easily establish contact with the universe. It is entirely at the magician's discretion to draw several circles at certain intervals in which he records the hierarchy of the universe in the form of divine names, genii, princes, rulers, angels and all the other powers.

When the magician draws the magic circle, it must be understood that he must meditate accordingly and must also take into consideration the concept of the particular divine aspect. A true magician must know that divine names are symbolic descriptions of divine attributes and powers. It goes without saying that, when the magician draws the magic circle and records the divine names and the particular powers, he must also take into consideration the appropriate analogy. The analogies include the corresponding colors, numbers, and geographic directions. If a magician does not represent the universe in a completely analogous manner, he allows a gap to occur in his consciousness.

Every magic circle serves its purpose, regardless of whether its design is drawn in a simple or complicated manner, so long as the magician possesses the ability to bring his own consciousness into harmony with the universal consciousness, under which the cosmic consciousness is to be understood. In an emergency, even a barrel hoop could serve the same purpose, provided it is used with the proper attitude and with the complete conviction that this circle represents the universe upon which the magician has to act when standing in the center of this circle.

The magician will conclude that the greater his knowledge in literature, the greater his intellect and the greater his knowledge in any given field, the more complex the rituals and more complicated magical circles will he require in order to have sufficient points of reference. This will enable him to establish contact with the microcosm and macrocosm more easily when he stands in the center of the magic circle. Magic circles by themselves, whether they are drawn in a simple or complex manner, can be designed in various ways to suit the circumstances, the situation, and the possibilities that exist. Therefore they can be very complex magic circles which are based on the hierarchy of the universe, or they can be very simple.

The magician can also work outside in the open air. If that is the case, the magic circle can be drawn on the ground with a magical weapon, such as a dagger or a magic sword. Should the magician work in a room, a magic circle can be drawn with chalk on the floor. A magic circle can also be drawn on a large piece of paper. However, the most practical magic circle is one that is either sewn or embroidered on a flannel or silk cloth. A magic circle prepared in this manner can be used in a room as well as outside in the open air, whereas magic circles drawn on paper tear easily and they can also be damaged in many different ways, especially when used frequently. The magic circle must be large enough for the magician to move about quite freely. It is of great importance that the magician maintains the appropriate attitude and concentration when drawing the magic circle. If the magician draws a magic circle without the proper simultaneous concentration, he will have a circle but it will not be a magic one. When the magician has a magic circle that is sewn or embroidered on flannel or silk, the circle has to be retraced with his finger, his magic wand or magic weapon with the necessary concentration, meditation and proper attitude. When the magician retraces the magic circle, he must focus his attention magically on the fact that it is not the magical instrument that he uses to retrace the circle, but rather it is the divine ability which is symbolized by the particular magical instrument. Furthermore, while he is in the particular meditative state required for this operation, the magician must be mindful that it is not he who draws the magic circle but that it is the divine Spirit which, through the magician's hand and through the magical instrument, actually forms the circle. It is therefore absolutely necessary that a connection between the magician's consciousness and the omnipotence, the Infinite, has to be established through meditation and influence each and every time before the magic circle is drawn or traced.

A trained magician who has successfully completed the practical exercises of the first Tarot card in accordance with *Initiation into Hermetics* has learned, in one of the steps contained therein, how to become conscious of one's spirit and how to act consciously as a spirit. It is not difficult for a person who has successfully completed the aforementioned practical exercises to imagine that not he but the divine Spirit in all His highest aspects is drawing the magic circle which he desires. It is obvious to the magician that when two human beings perform the same task, the effects in the invisible world are not the same. For example: a sorcerer or a dabbler in magic who does not possess the required maturity will never be able to draw a circle in the true magical manner.

A magician who is well-versed in the Kabbalah can draw a second circle in the shape of a serpent inside the first circle. This inner circle should be divided into seventy-two sections, and the name of the relevant genius must be inscribed on each of the seventy-two sections. The names of the genii together with their analogies are to be drawn magically while pronouncing these names correctly and in the proper manner. Should a magician be working with a flannel or silk cloth, the names must be sewn on or embroidered in Latin or Hebrew. In my third book *The Key to the True Kabbalah*, the genii, their analogies, effects and how they can be employed are explained in detail in the practical part of that work. An embroidered magic circle has the advantage that it can easily be placed on the floor or ground and folded up without drawing and charging it each time it is used. The serpent that represents the inner circle is not merely a replica of a circle, but, most importantly, it represents the symbol of wisdom. In addition, the symbol of the serpent has several other meanings, as, for example, the strength of the serpent also represents the powers of the imagination, etc. It would, however, exceed the scope of this book to fully describe all its aspects.

A Buddhist initiate who draws his mandala by placing his five deities in the form of figurines or in the form of diagrams on their appropriate emanations meditates on each individual deity and thereby influences himself. This, too, is a magical ceremony which actually is a true prayer to the Buddhist deities, and from our point of view it can be considered a magic circle. However, it is not necessary to go into this matter any further, because enough information has been published in the Oriental literature about this practice of magic, some of which is available in exoteric publications, while other information is available in more secret manuscripts.

The magic circle offers many possible uses. It serves for the evocation of beings or entities, but also as protection against invisible influences. At times a magic circle does not have to be drawn on the ground or floor or placed on the floor in the form of paper, a flannel or silk cloth. It can occasionally be drawn in the air around oneself with a magic weapon, a magic wand or magic sword, with the firm conviction that this releases the particular universal attribute of protection which is desired. Should there for some reason be no magic weapon available, a magic circle can be drawn with the finger or the hand with the proper attitude and conviction, which means in connection with God.

The possibility also exists that a magic circle can be drawn merely with one's imagination. In accordance with the power and the effect of the imagination, the magic circle expresses itself either on the mental or astral plane and indirectly also on the physical plane. The binding power of the magic circle is commonly known in magnetic magic. A magic circle can also be produced with the help of the accumulation of the elements or with the help of the accumulation of light. Pertaining to the magic of evocation and the invocation of beings, it is advisable to draw an additional smaller circle or a pentagram with the point facing upward or facing the altar[1] in the center of the magic circle, thereby symbolizing the small world; or in other words symbolizing a human being as a true magician.

The instructions in books that describe the magic circle always warn that during evocations or invocations the magician should never step out of the magic circle. The significance of this warning is that a magician should never interrupt the contact or the bonding consciousness with the Absolute or with the macrocosm. Whenever a magic circle is employed or when the summoned being stands in front of the circle during a magical procedure, it should be a matter of fact that the magician should not physically step out of the magic circle until the being has been dismissed and not until he is finished with the magical operation.

It should be obvious by what has been said thus far that, when working with ceremonial magic, a true magic circle cannot be replaced with anything else. A magician will always see the magic circle as the highest symbol in every respect.

At this point, it would be superfluous to draw an actual diagram of a magic circle, because, on the basis of the information given here, every magician will know what to do. All that is to be done now is to put the information given here into practice. The magician should never forget what matters most: his entire attitude in respect to the magic circle. Only when he has achieved within himself the cosmic contact through meditation and imagination, i.e. when he has established his bond with God, only then has the magician the qualifications to enter the magic circle and only then is he ready to begin his work therein.

---

[1] See the picture of the Priestess, the second Tarot card. – ED.

Chapter 4
The Magic Triangle

In contrast to the magic triangle, the magic circle is the symbol of infinity, of a bond with God, the Alpha and the Omega. The triangle represents the symbol of manifestation, the symbol of everything created, in short, of everything that has come into being. It would be impossible to do any ritual or ceremonial work without the proper knowledge of the symbolism of the magic triangle as well as all the other magical aids.

In all the books on ritual invocation or in the grimoires you will find a general statement that the particular spirit, being or power summoned is to manifest in the triangle. However, the manifestation of a being in a triangle is only one aspect of ritualistic magic, because a being cannot completely manifest itself if the magician does not understand the entire symbolism of the magic triangle. In order to understand this symbolism properly, one must be fairly well conversant with the Kabbalah and have complete knowledge of the secret of the number three. The more that is known about the analogies of the mystical number three, the more profoundly can one penetrate into the symbolism of the triangle and what it represents, and hence the summoned power may manifest more easily. It would exceed the scope this work were I to detail the entire symbolism of the number three and all its correspondences. However, I shall offer some encouragement that may serve the magician as a guiding principle.

Above all, the triangle is a diagram of the three-dimensional world, by which we understand the mental, astral and the physical or material worlds. Any power that is summoned and that is projected outside into the physical plane must pass through the three planes mentioned above. The diagram shows an equilateral triangle where the tip of the triangle[2] faces upward, similar to a pyramid. And it gives us to understand, when looking at the triangle from above, that from one point two powers diverge sideways in two directions and each power ends up in a line that has its restriction. The overall picture of these two diverging lines represents the two universal powers, which are the plus and the

---

[2] Take a look at the triangle in the altar of the second Tarot card. – ED.

minus, electricity and magnetism. The two lines are then united by the base line. This symbolizes the manifested causal world, which, from an astrological point of view, characterizes itself as Saturn, as the number three. On the mental plane the number three symbolizes the will, the intellect, and feelings. On the astral plane it symbolizes power, lawfulness and life, and on the physical plane, as already mentioned, the plus and minus and the neutral. Therefore, the triangle with its lawfulness reflects itself in all things and in every respect, because it is the beginning of everything created, and the primary cause of everything comprehensible. The number three, the symbolism of the triangle, plays one of the most important roles in all religions. For example, in the Christian religion it represents the Trinity: God the Father, God the Son, and God the Holy Ghost. In Hindu teachings it represents Brahma, Vishnu and Shiva: the Creator, the Preserver, and the Destroyer. Hundreds more of these symbolic analogies could be listed. But in this case it has to be left to the magician's own discretion to penetrate more deeply into this symbolism and all the relevant analogies. For the magician the equilateral triangle always remains a most important and worthwhile thing to know, because the equilateral triangle represents a universal symbol in magic, next to the magic circle.

A magician could never summon a particular power or being into a circle — it must be in a triangle — because the circle represents the symbol of infinity, not the symbol of manifestation. A magician should never ignore this basic concept. However, he could summon a being or a power into a form or design other than a triangle, which is often the case with lower beings. But when it comes to higher powers and higher beings a magician will never omit to have the proper diagram drawn, in this case the triangle, right next to the circle. The aspiring magician now knows that a circle is the diagram without limits, whereas the triangle is the first diagram that is limited by space, into which a being or a power, etc., can be projected.

When the magician is engaged in a magical evocation, he must be certain that the triangle is large enough for the power or entity that has been evoked, so that it does not protrude or tower over and beyond the triangle. He must also be certain that during the evocation the powers that he evokes into the triangle are completely obedient to him, and that he himself, while standing in the circle, represents a higher and superior power, and that through the circle he also represents a divine universal concept. That is why a being that is summoned into the triangle cannot leave the triangle without the specific permission of the magician, or when expressed in the proper terminology of magic, without abdication. As for the shape of the triangle, it does not necessarily have to be an equilateral triangle; it can also be an acute or a right-angle triangle.

When the magician works outdoors, he can also draw the triangle with a magic sword or dagger in the same manner as described when drawing the circle. The triangle must be made of the same material as the circle. Should the circle be embroidered or sewn on flannel or silk, then the triangle must be embroidered or sewn on the same cloth as well. The triangle has to be traced magically with the consciousness of the astral and spiritual hand and not with the physical hand, similar to the procedure described in the previous chapter, "The Magic Circle." Otherwise the triangle will be ineffective and it will not exert the expected influence upon the summoned power or being. During this procedure, the magician must meditate that the manifestation of the summoned power or being will come about through the triangle as the highest symbol. The magician will soon conclude that the more he knows about the symbolism of the triangle, the greater the influence will he be able to exert upon the power or being summoned. Furthermore, a great advantage is offered by the certainty that the magician, when drawing the triangle, must be fully conscious of the fact that he has already bonded with the Divinity within himself, which is called forth through meditation or through the imagination. Therefore the magician does not draw the magic triangle himself; instead, the Divinity he has called forth within himself is doing so. It is highly recommended that the triangle be traced with a magic weapon each time it is used, to constantly revive the analogy in the triangle itself and in the consciousness of the magician. In the case of a triangle that is drawn on paper or embroidered or sewn on cloth, the lines of the triangle are gently traced with a weapon. In the case of a magical operation that does not require a magic weapon, the triangle can be traced either with a magic wand or with the index finger.

Usually the seal or talisman of the being to be summoned is placed in the center of the triangle. This is done because the seal or talisman expresses the symbolic significance of the being. In another chapter of this book I describe in detail how to make these seals and talismans. A competent magician can place an appropriately charged fluid condenser into the triangle instead of a sigil. The fluid condenser is to be poured into a shallow container or saucer. The magician can also use blotting paper that is impregnated with a fluid condenser, which has to be charged accordingly for the purpose of the manifestation of the particular power or being. It is left to the individual magician as to which of these two possibilities he cares to choose. These details do, however, depend upon the kind of powers or beings the magician wants to contact and make manifest.

In *Initiation into Hermetics*, fluid condensers, liquid and solid, simple and complex, are fully described. In accordance with their purpose and analogy, the magician may use either simple or complex fluid condensers.

The magic triangle is thus the connecting diagram for the power or being that the magician wishes to contact. At times the triangle serves several purposes. First of all, it serves to establish contact with the desired beings. Secondly, it evokes a very particular being from the macrocosm into our physical plane. Thirdly, it condenses or manifests the particular being to such a degree that this entity can even call forth effects on the physical plane. All this depends upon the wish of the magician, whether the being or power that is summoned is to be effective on the mental, astral or physical plane.

In accordance with the principle set forth in this book, and with which the magician is by now quite familiar, any being or power can only be effective in the sphere into which it is summoned and condensed. For example, a being that is projected into the mental sphere cannot influence the physical world; it can only be effective on the mental plane. The same applies to the astral and physical planes. The reader will find in the following chapter more details regarding the secret of materialization from one sphere to another.

Chapter 5
The Magic Censer

Many people mistakenly believe that the being or power to be summoned should materialize by the mere burning of incense and by uttering the names, and when their efforts are met with complete failure or only partial success, they become very disappointed. What is even worse, at times they even fall victim to their own fantasies as well as various kinds of hallucinations. For this very reason, I shall reveal to the reader the great mystery and the symbolic significance of the censer.

The symbolism of the censer conceals the mystery of the materialization of the desired being or power. Only a few initiates possess this knowledge; that is why so many evocations fail whenever an attempt at exteriorizing a being is striven for. A clear example of this kind of one-sided, inadequate procedure would be the analogy of a fish. What would happen if we take a fish out of its element, water, and assume that the fish will continue to live in the element of air? We should not be surprised that the fish must perish. This applies to the citation of beings and powers also. Should you wish to summon a being from the invisible world into our physical world, you must have the ability to create a compatible atmosphere for that being. It is likewise impossible for a human being to enter into a finer atmosphere with his physical body without the proper previous preparations. Should the magician possess the proper abilities, namely a strong will and a firm belief, he can call forth a vibration in his own microcosm that is appropriate for the being, and thus he may establish contact with that being. This is similar to the explanation I have given in my first work, *Initiation into Hermetics,* in the chapter dealing with mirror magic. Despite that, under these circumstances a being would never be able to transfer to our physical world and be effective here. Only high intelligences, i.e. high spirit-beings, have the ability to prepare their own environment where they can materialize; in this particular case, it is the magic triangle. However, they must know and understand how to use the laws of the physical world just as well as a high initiate who understands and is in control of the laws of the spheres that lie outside of our physical world.

In a case where a high spiritual being prepares all the conditions necessary to project by itself, the magician has no possibility of controlling that being with his will for his own use, not even if he has generated the form of the Divinity within himself. He will have to come to terms with the fact that such a being will never completely acknowledge his magical authority. Instead, it will have the freedom to choose to deceive the magician and refuse to obey him. This kind of evocation, in which the being generates its own atmosphere, is unfortunately used by sorcerers who, partly due to total ignorance and partly due to inadequate magical development or other reasons, do not understand how to prepare the so-called magic space for the summoned being. A being that is summoned in this manner will in most cases opt to refuse to obey the sorcerer. And it will deceive him or even compel him to enter into a pact, not to mention all the many other threats and dangers to which the sorcerer will be exposed and subjected by that being. The events that occurred in the case of Dr. Faust and Mephisto are and remain an unmistakable example of this kind of invocation. Later in this book, I shall explore this situation somewhat more. Similar situations and events have taken place hundreds of times or more over the course of centuries, when careless people have made such attempts. The only difference here is that they did not become as famous as Dr. Faust, and hence remained unknown. A true initiate who knows and considers all these guidelines as well as all the analogies necessary for ritualistic magic will never be subject to such a tragedy. It is therefore a prerequisite to be completely conversant with the symbolism of all magical aids and also to have a thorough understanding of this, in order to be in complete control of these entities.

The censer symbolizes the materialization of any particular being. Before the magician can proceed to summon a being, he must create the atmosphere that is required for it. Under no circumstances should he rely upon the being itself to generate its own particular atmosphere, for this might make the magician totally subject to the being's influence.

In the oldest mysteries, the "creation of an atmosphere" for any desired being, of whatever station, referred to the manner in which the magician prepared and created the appropriate atmosphere inside the magical working space. A variety of instructions were applicable to this procedure. There are today papyrus scrolls in existence from ancient Egypt which detail the practice of preparing such an atmosphere in the magical space. However, the ignorance of the people who deciphered the symbolism of these scrolls contributed to the fact that they remain either completely unnoticed or completely misunderstood.

In order to prepare the magical room, space, or place for the materialization of a being with the symbolism of the censer, the magician must impregnate that room or space according to the method described in *Initiation into Hermetics*. In this work, I describe the method of impregnating a room or space and charging it for one's own purpose (or that of someone else) on the physical plane. I also point out that the impregnation of a room or space — in other words, the preparation of the magical area in which the desired entity is to manifest — and the preparation of the censer is a matter of the utmost importance. The impregnation of the space itself and the location where the particular being is to manifest depends upon the kind of power with which one works. Surely, no one would entertain the thought of charging the space with the Earth principle if he is working with the Fire element, etc. Not only would this be foolish, but it would also be, above all, unlawful. For example, should the magician work with the beings of the elements, then the space in which these beings are to manifest must be charged with their particular element. Gnomes or Earth spirits, being of the element of Earth, can only manifest in an area that is charged or filled with the Earth element. Water spirits can manifest only in a room that is charged with the Water element. Air spirits or fairies manifest only when the spiritual astral Air element prevails in a room or place. Salamanders or Fire spirits manifest only in an area that is charged with the Fire element. Higher beings and intelligences require a room that is permeated with light. The light must have the color that corresponds to the being's planetary analogy. Beings that are outside our planetary system manifest only in a pure white light.

The magician generates the required color of the planetary light through the power of the imagination. For example, beings of the Saturnian sphere appear when the light vibrates in violet. The beings of the sphere of Jupiter appear only in a vibration of blue light. The beings of the Sun appear only in a vibration of golden light. The beings of Mars appear only in a vibration of red light. The beings of Venus appear only in a vibration of green light. The beings of Mercury appear only in a vibration of orange light, and the beings of the Moon appear only in a vibration of silvery light. When the magician works with positive beings of the individual spheres, then the color of the shining light should not be vibrant; instead it must be faint. The darker the color, the more difficult it is for a positive being to manifest. When the magician works with negative beings, the color has to be rich and considerably heightened. Should the magician coerce a positive being into an impregnated room where its color vibrates in a darker shade, even if it is the appropriate color, and should he expect the being to be effective there, it can easily happen that a negative being of the same planetary sphere may take on the shape of the positive being and pretend to be that being. The being that appears always has the character traits of the particular color. Lower beings require a darker color, a slower vibration than the higher beings, because the higher beings require higher vibrations and therefore a purer color.

When a magician works outdoors with the power of his imagination, he must create a room of a specific size, which has to be impregnated. Should he work indoors, then the entire room has to be filled with the appropriate element. The impregnation is carried out either by means of lung and pore breathing in conjunction with the powers of the imagination, or merely with the imagination alone. The inhalation of the particular element or the particular color of light is carried out through the physical body of the magician, who accumulates the particular element or light in his physical body. After that, he allows the light or the element to emanate directly through his hands, his magic wand, or directly through his pores into the room. In this manner he fills and enlivens the room and thereby prepares it for the entity to be summoned. This practice, the practice of the imaginative light accumulation through the physical body into the room, is used for the citation of beings and powers that serve the magician's own purpose. The same method is employed when the magician wishes to project and condense out of his own body, out of his own soul and out of his own spirit — in other words out of the microcosm — an attribute or power that corresponds with the planetary analogy. Should the magician work with beings that are to serve the purpose of others rather than the magician himself, then the impregnation of the room is carried out by the magician directly from the universe and only through the power of the imagination. Only when a room is prepared in this manner can the being or power work and condense itself. When the room is sufficiently impregnated, then the magician can carry out a specific accumulation in the triangle and form the shape of the summoned being with the aid of his imagination. The power of accumulation, also called "dynamism," of the appropriate element is of the utmost importance here, because the effectiveness of the being depends upon it. For physical effects or influences during the accumulation, the magician can burn a small amount of incense composed of ingredients that are harmonious with the particular planetary being.

Should the magician wish to bring forth especially strong physical effects, then accumulated electric fluid or magnetic fluid must be introduced into the created shape during the burning of incense. The magician can also banish either the electric or the magnetic fluid in a fluid condenser — or possibly even both together, the electromagnetic fluid — which the being can then make use of in order to be physically active. This method is explained in *Initiation into Hermetics* in the chapter dealing with volting. If, during the process of materializing a being, the magician does not insist on forming a particular shape for the being, then the being will work amorphously or even take on a shape of its own choosing. In this case, depending on what is required, either a liquid or a solid fluid condenser has to be placed into the triangle. Then the appropriate electromagnetic volt has to be formed on the surface of the particular fluid condenser that contains the wish, so that the being may make use of this power in order to call forth the desired effects. This wish is projected into the volt by concentration, called wish-concentration. The instructions on how to generate a volt in the shape of a sphere, where the inside is electric and the outside magnetic, can be found in *Initiation into Hermetics* in the chapter mentioned above. In this instance, all the laws must be taken into consideration, such as the length of time of the effect, and so on. The physical burning of incense with the appropriate ingredients only achieves a weak formation of the electromagnetic fluid. In the beginning, the magician makes use of this method if and when he requires the appropriate mental support in this respect. However, for a magician who is in control of all the laws, this procedure is not absolutely necessary.

The use of narcotic incense, which is mentioned in many books on invocational magic, is reprehensible from the proper point of view of a true magician, because apart from the fact that they contain poison, opiates do not summon the desired being. Instead, they produce hallucinations and subconscious projections of the desired being. On account of these effects, a magician will never endanger his health with such experiments.

If the magician wishes to summon departed human beings, or beings who are in the Akasha or the astral world, and have them appear before him, or if he wishes to use them for other purposes, he must impregnate a room with the Akasha and generate the electromagnetic fluid as a volt and use it in the manner described above. I shall describe the practice in another chapter dealing with necromancy.

Chapter 6
The Magic Mirror

In the literature which has been thus far available, magic mirrors have been recommended for use in ritualistic magic only now and again. This is because the use of fluid condensers in regards to magic mirrors was known only to a very few initiates who protected this knowledge as a great secret.

The magic mirror is not absolutely essential. However, the magician should not forego the opportunity of using such a good aid in his work, especially when he works with less intelligent beings or powers. The magic mirror can at times even replace the magic triangle, for a magic mirror that has been treated with a fluid condenser is by far more advantageous. If the magician does not have a magic mirror available, he can also make use of an optical magic mirror.

In *Initiation into Hermetics*, I dedicated an entire chapter to the various uses for which a magic mirror may be employed. That is why I here describe only briefly the purpose which the magic mirror serves to make the task of evocation easier. The magic mirror can be employed for the purpose of contacting beings and powers and making them visible. It can be used for ritual magic as follows:

1. To accomplish this, the magic mirror is placed either into the magic triangle or outside the triangle at its uppermost tip, which is by far more advantageous. This is followed by charging or impregnating the magic mirror with an accumulation of the desired power. This is then followed by the wish-concentration for the particular purpose through the imagination into the accumulated power, the volt, before the actual evocation.

2. The impregnation of the room can be accomplished with the aid of the magic mirror; all the while the required dynamism is automatically maintained during the entire evocation without the magician having to pay particular attention to it. This allows the magician to focus his attention completely upon other phases of the ritual, for example upon the materialization or viewing of the being. In this particular case, the mirror is placed in the corner of the room so that the influence pervades the entire area.

3. The mirror can also be employed as an attractive magnet for the summoned being. However, for this purpose the fluid condenser on the surface of the mirror has to be charged through the imagination accordingly. In this case the mirror has to be placed in the center of the magic triangle or at its uppermost tip.

4. The magic mirror can also be used as an accumulator into which, by means of the imagination and through accumulation, enough qualitative and quantitative powers are concentrated so as to enable the being to call forth the desired effects. At this point it is not important as to whether the being takes on a visible shape through the accumulated power, or whether another effect is to be brought forth. It all depends upon the wish and will of the magician.

5. The mirror can also serve as a telephone. To accomplish this, the fluid condenser has to be charged with the Akasha and with the wish-concentration (imagination), through which a timelessness and spacelessness is established. The evocation is uttered into the mirror, in which manner the magic mirror is transformed into an astral wireless

telephone. This method allows the magician to summon a power or a being that may also speak out of the mirror. The magician hears the voice as if through a loudspeaker, not only mentally or astrally, but at times physically as well. All this — how and in which particular sphere the magic mirror is to function — is at the discretion of the magician. A magic mirror that has been charged for the physical sphere may even allow those who are not magically trained to physically hear the voice of a spirit. As a point of interest, two magicians who are equally well-trained can converse by this method over the greatest distance, and they can communicate mentally and astrally and physically. They can hear everything with their physical ears just as if they were to use a radio transmitter.

6. The magic mirror also offers another possibility when practicing ritual magic; it can be used by the magician to protect himself from undesirable influences. The most common method used in this particular instance is the accumulation of light-energy. During charging, the wish-concentration must be focused on restraining all undesired influences. The magic mirror that is charged in this manner must have such emanating powers that undesirable beings (larvae, schemata etc.) cannot even come near the magician's sphere of operation, much less enter it. In this particular instance, the magic mirror must be placed in a position whereby it can emanate in the entire area of operation.

In most cases, the magician will only make use of one mirror, namely for the task which seems to be the most difficult. However, when it comes to ceremonial magic the magician can, if he wishes, make use of several magic mirrors as aids for his purposes in order to make his work easier.

Chapter 7
The Magic Lamp

Much has been written about the magic lamp, which is also known as the *laterna magica* in many grimoires and in the oldest books that deal with the evocation of spirits. The magic lamp is also a very important tool in the practice of ritual magic, and that is why the magician will certainly avail himself of this magical aid. The magic lamp is the symbol of enlightenment, cognizance, experience and intuition, and also of the inner light. In short, the magic lamp represents all symbolic analogies of the light. From a Hermetic point of view the lighting of the lamp denotes the lighting the magician's inner light and kindling it into a flame. By the color we understand the quality, vibration and oscillation of the light, and this also belongs to the mystery of the magic lamp. The quality of a being, of a plane or sphere, expresses itself in the quality of the color — it can be pure or mixed, depending always on the character of the being. The purer, brighter, clearer and more gleaming the atmosphere of a being, plane or sphere turns out to be, the higher, more intelligent and purer the quality with which you are dealing. Lower or negative beings make themselves known through dark and dull colors, i.e. through an impure color.

It is quite important for a magician who works with ritual magic to be well informed about these matters. By making use of the magic lamp he expresses enlightenment symbolically. When the magician works with beings, the light of the lamp has to emit the color that is compatible with the being; this can be achieved with appropriately colored glass or colored transparencies. For example, when the magician works with the beings of the Fire element, the light of the magic lamp must emit a ruby-red light; therefore the magic lamp must be fitted[3] with a ruby-red glass. In the case of the spirits of the Air element or fairies, a dark blue light is required, and therefore the lamp has to be fitted with a blue glass or blue silk so that it emits a dark blue light. The Water spirits or undines require a green light. When it comes to the Earth spirits, they require a yellow or brownish colored light. The Akashic color is the color of the universal light; therefore the magic lamp has to emit a violet light. High beings or intelligences from outside our planetary system require a white light, whereas planetary intelligences from our solar system require a light that corresponds to the color of their particular planet. Therefore, beings from Saturn require a light violet or an ultramarine light, beings from Jupiter a

---

[3] Some magic lamps can be filled with various colored glass which slides in. Or the lamp can be covered with colored glass, silk or cellophane, depending on what is available. – ED.

blue light; beings from Mars a red light; beings from the Sun a yellow light; beings from Venus a green light, beings from Mercury an opalescent light, and beings from the Moon a white light. Only under the rarest circumstances can operations in ritual magic be performed with everyday artificial light (electric light), because physical electricity has disturbing effects on the astral oscillations that vibrate in the room during these magical operations. Usually the *laterna magica* or magic lamp uses a candle or oil as a source of light. An ideal light is a spirit flame (alcohol). The fuel or alcohol is prepared by mixing one-third dry chamomile blossoms by volume to two-thirds alcohol. This mixture has to steep for eight or nine days in a well-sealed glass container, after which it has to be filtered. This fuel is also a good fluid condenser which the magician can charge with his will in order to achieve better results. When spirit of wine or fuel which has been charged is burned in the magic lamp, it produces a more favorable atmosphere and therefore also achieves better results.

This spirit flame can also be charged when practicing clairvoyance, or when the magician works with the magic mirror or other astral magical operations where electric light causes a disturbing influence. Should the magician work in a closed room, the lamp can either be placed into the magic circle or into a corner of the room. However, the best solution is to affix the magic lamp directly above the head of the magician, through which the entire room is evenly illuminated. While lighting the magic lamp, the magician must meditate, so that the inner light of his soul and spirit ignite simultaneously.

Chapter 8
The Magic Wand

In ritualistic magic the most important aid has always been and remains the magic wand. Since time immemorial, magicians (and sorcerers too) have been depicted with a magic wand. Charlatans, stage illusionists and prestidigitators make use of the magic wand to this day, using it in the performance of their tricks. Whosoever thinks that merely taking a magic wand in one's hand is sufficient to produce miracles is severely mistaken. I shall give the reader a description of the symbolic significance and the synthesis of the magic wand from the magical point of view, as well as its theoretical and practical applications.

Above all, the magic wand is the symbol of the will, the power and might with which the magician exerts his influence upon the particular sphere for which the magic wand was made and charged. That is why a magician possesses not just one magic wand for his practice, but as many as he requires, depending on what he intends to do and what he endeavors to achieve.

The actual purpose of a magic wand is to help the magician project his will through the wand to the outside in every sphere or plane. He may have magic wands for the following purposes:

1. To influence any number of beings, whether human or animal.
2. To heal the ailing and the afflicted and to remove unfavorable influences.
3. To summon high intelligences and for the invocation of demons and spirits.

The claim that the magic wand symbolizes the absolute might of the magician is completely justified. Whosoever completely understands the mystery of the magic wand to its fullest extent will never work in ritual magic without this tool. It would exceed the scope of this book were I to mention all the possible uses of the magic wand. The reasonable student should be satisfied with the hints mentioned here, and they shall serve as a guiding principle. However, he can increase his knowledge tremendously on this subject through meditation.

The material used to make the wand is of no consequence. A magic wand is a condenser which is charged with the magician's will and expresses a particular power. There are common or simple magic wands and there are complex ones. The common magic wands are made or carved from wood. The wood chosen for the wand must serve the particular purpose. Hazelnut and willow are used for divining rods (a divining rod is a variation of the magic wand). A wand that is made from the wood of the ash tree (*Fraxinus excelsior*) can be used for all magical operations. However, for ritual magic the magician prefers to charge this kind of wand only for the treatment of ailments. A magic wand that is made from elder wood (*Sambucus nigra*) is analogous to Saturn and as such is especially effective to summon, name or invoke spirits from the elements and to summon demons. Magic wands made from willow rods can be used for any purpose and for any magical operation, since willow is an excellent fluid condenser. Any observant reader will remember that willow, on account of its high water content and receptivity of water, attracts lightning. An old European proverb states that it is best to avoid willow trees during a thunderstorm or when there is lightning, and one should seek refuge under a beech tree instead. Oak and acacia are also excellent materials for making magic wands.

It is a simple matter to prepare a magic wand from the various woods mentioned here. Cut a branch off the particular tree, one that is approximately 1/2 inch to 1 inch (1 – 2 cm) in diameter and 15 to 20 inches (30 – 50 cm) in length; remove the bark and make the wand as smooth as possible. Quite often, the best time for these magic wands to be cut from the tree is calculated astrologically. This may be done at the discretion of the magician should he be knowledgeable in astrology; however, it is not necessary, because a magician is aware of the fact that the stars influence but do not compel, and a sage controls the stars. Therefore, every person has the ability to prepare such a magic wand from the aforementioned wood. Should it be the intention of the magician to prepare a magic wand for ritualistic purposes, it is highly recommended that one should use a brand new knife for cutting the branch from the tree. The knife can then still be used for other ritual purposes or magical operations. However, it should not be used for any other everyday purpose, for example in the kitchen, etc. Should the magician, after he has prepared the magic wand with that particular knife, be of the opinion that he does not want to use the knife anymore, he should bury it somewhere, so that no other person has access to it.

Another type of magic wand is one made out of a steel magnet and requiring an insulated handle. A steel rod of 15 to 20 inches (30 – 50 cm) in length, and which has a diameter of approximately 3/8 of an inch (1 cm), is required. The steel that is best suited for this kind of magic wand is electro-steel, steel for magnets. This electro-steel rod has to be highly polished and must then be nickel-plated to prevent it from rusting. Once the steel rod has been nickel-plated, it must be magnetized with an electric coil in the same way that horseshoe magnets and magnets for electric motors are magnetized. The more powerful the physical attractive force of the magnet, the better the magician can work with it. The magician does not merely have a very powerful steel magnet, he also has an excellent magic wand that can be used for many magical and magnetic experiments. It is important to know which end of the magic wand is the north pole and which end is the south pole. The north pole must be marked with a plus sign and the south pole with a minus sign. The center of the wand has to be insulated. Therefore, the magician can wrap silk around the wand as wide as his own hand, the average being approximately 3 to 4 inches (8 – 10 cm). He can also use a rubber hose or a hollow wooden handle, which he can slip over the steel wand. A wand of this kind allows the magician to call forth many different kinds of magnetic and magical phenomena. I shall now give the reader a few examples.

When the magician works with the electromagnetic fluid from the universe, and he wants to condense it physically to a very high degree, in order to accomplish this he takes the wand in such a manner that it rests with the plus pole in the center of his right palm, and the minus pole in the center of his left palm. In other words, the ends of the wand rest in the center of each palm. Whereupon he directs the electric fluid with his imagination from the universe through the right side of the wand into his body. The plus-radiation or Od-radiation that exists in the wand will condense to a tremendous degree as a result of the similar vibration of the plus pole. Therefore it will be easier to accumulate the electric fluid in his body. The magician has to follow the same procedure with the magnetic fluid through the left side of the wand, the south pole. The magician now condenses the electric fluid which he has accumulated in his body to such a degree into the plus space of the wand that he can assert his influence with the wand directly on the physical plane. This applies of course to the magnetic fluid as well, which he can accumulate in the left side of the wand; this is the negative pole radiation. However, the center of the wand, which is insulated, will remain neutral. If the magician now concentrates his wish through the imagination into the electromagnetic fluid that has accumulated in the wand, he has actually transformed this wand into a magical magnetic-electric wand. By means of the electromagnetic fluid which emanates brightly from this wand, anything can be realized on the physical plane. Initiates choose this kind of wand to influence people afflicted with ailments, to heal the ailing, and for all magnetic phenomena. The magical electromagnetic wand is, in accordance with universal laws, an excellent condenser with the same oscillations as the universe itself, but in a more refined form. Whosoever meditates thoroughly on this subject will, without much effort, come up with a number of other methods on the basis of the universal laws by means of the magic magnetic wand. For example, the magician, like an antenna, will be able to either draw the fluid from the universe and accumulate it in his body or pass it on to other people far and near through the imagination. The wand will become an indispensable aid for the magician, because the plus and minus energy which is concentrated into the wand will assist him in calling forth the same oscillations in his own electromagnetic fluid.

Furthermore, there are magic wands that are filled with solid, liquid or compounded condensers. Much can be said about the manner in which they could be prepared and the methods that could be employed. However, I shall only mention a few which will serve the magician best.

Take an elderwood rod of about 12 to 20 inches (30 – 50 cm) in length and 3/8 to 3/4 inches (1 – 2 cm) in diameter, remove the bark and use sandpaper to smooth it out. After that is done, remove the pith; this then gives you a hollow elderwood rod. Seal one side with a cork and sealing wax, and pour in a fluid condenser, i.e. a liquid condenser or whatever you may require, into the opening on the other side. This side has to be hermetically sealed as well. At this point, the elder rod is ready for use. You can prepare rods from other kinds of wood such as ash, hazelnut, willow, and oak in the same manner. However, these kinds of wood do not have pith, and that is why a hole has to be drilled through the center. A long, fine drill will be required, so that you have a hollow space through the entire length of the rod. And of course, instead of a liquid fluid condenser, a solid fluid condenser may also be used, the same condenser which is used for magic mirrors. There is a description of the preparation of all these fluid condensers in Step VIII of *Initiation into*

Hermetics. The magician also has another possibility: instead of a solid or liquid fluid condenser, he can use blotting paper that has been saturated with a fluid condenser. After the blotting paper has been properly dried it must be charged, rolled up, and carefully inserted into the hollow space of the rod. However, wood has one disadvantage over other materials, in that wood deteriorates with time, especially when it contains a fluid condenser and becomes porous. Therefore it is advisable that the magician replace the wooden rod with a metal one. Among the metals, the best are those which are good conductors for heat and electricity. The ideal metal for this purpose is a copper pipe, with a diameter of 3/8 to 5/8 of an inch (1 – 1½ cm). In order to avoid any oxidation of the metal, the magician can have it nickel-plated, chrome-plated or tin-plated before it is filled with the fluid condenser. One opening of the copper pipe must be immediately soldered closed, whereas the other opening must be soldered closed immediately after it has been filled with the fluid condenser. This copper pipe makes an excellent magic wand, because it can be used for any purpose. Magicians who alternately work with the magnetic and the electric fluid would do well if they prepared a metal wand made with an iron or a steel pipe with fairly thin walls for the magnetic fluid, and a copper wand for the electric fluid, as mentioned above. An experienced magician can work with two wands simultaneously by charging the copper pipe with the electric fluid and the iron or steel pipe with the magnetic fluid. A universal wand is prepared in the same manner, only instead of a copper or iron pipe, a nickel-plated brass pipe is used. Should the magician be financially comfortable, he can use a compounded condenser that consists of semi-precious stones instead of the fluid condenser mentioned above. This fluid condenser and the wand are prepared as follows:

For the electric fluid the magician uses the copper wand. He fills the hollow space with pulverized amber, which for the electric fluid is an incomparable condenser. For the magnetic fluid the magician can fill the steel pipe with pulverized rock crystal instead of the solid condenser, because rock crystal makes an excellent fluid condenser for the magnetic fluid. There is also another possibility whereby two individual small pipes can be soldered together, making one wand. Then one half is filled with the amber powder and the other half with rock crystal powder. In effect, one single wand contains both fluid condensers in two separate chambers. However, these separate chambers must be connected on the inside by a thin copper wire and a thin iron wire, which must go through the center of both chambers lengthwise. The wand can also be nickel-plated on the outside. With this method, this ideal wand has acquired a fluidal attribute and can therefore be used for any magical operation.

There is yet another possibility: a wooden rod can be adorned with seven rings. The rings must be made from the corresponding planetary metals. They can either be affixed to the wooden wand in the Kabbalistic sequence or the gold ring representing the Sun may be affixed in the middle of the wand while on each side of it are the three rings made from the other metals. The following metals are used in the manufacture of these seven rings:

1. Lead corresponds to Saturn
2. Tin corresponds to Jupiter
3. Iron corresponds to Mars
4. Gold corresponds to the Sun
5. Copper corresponds to Venus
6. Brass corresponds to Mercury
7. Silver corresponds to the Moon

In addition, these rings must be engraved with the sigils of the intelligences of the above-mentioned planets. This kind of magic wand is mostly used for the evocation of the intelligences or spiritual entities of the seven planets. Otherwise, this wand is not superior in its effect to the other magic wands. These examples should give the magician ample information to devise his own variations. The shape and size of the magic wand is of lesser importance. However, what is of the greatest importance is charging the wand for practical use, the description of which follows:

The magic wand can be charged for specific purposes with a fluid condenser, in the same manner as with the magic mirror. There are many possibilities of charging the magic wand. However, they all depend on the wish and on the intention that the magician pursues with his magic wand.

The magician must constantly be conscious of the fact that the magic wand symbolizes his will, his power and his might. Therefore, the magic wand represents a container or, so to speak, a fluid condenser of that power, quality etc., into which he can load the power he desires and also accumulate the power, quality etc., in the magic wand to a very high degree. It does not matter at all if the wand is merely a rod which has been cut from a tree or bush for this purpose, or if it is a complicated wand that is saturated or filled with a fluid condenser. A magic wand can be charged or loaded:

1. with the will,
2. with attributes, qualities etc.,
3. with magnetism — bio-magnetism etc.,
4. with the elements,
5. with the Akasha, and
6. with the aid of the light fluid.

I shall now give the reader examples concerning the six above-mentioned points:

Point 1: Charging Or Loading The Magic Wand With The Will

Take the wand which you have prepared accordingly into your hand, and concentrate your will as much as you can into the wand, and transfer yourself with your consciousness into the wand until you feel that you *are* the wand. Once you have reached this state, maintain this feeling and concentrate that your whole will power, your might etc., becomes incorporated in the wand. This concentration must be maintained in this manner for at least five minutes without interruption. While you incorporate your will into the wand, you must also think that your will power will set itself immediately into motion as soon as you take this wand in your hands, and that whatever you wish will occur. Once you have transferred your entire will power into the wand with the greatest of tension and your most vivid imagination, bring this procedure to an end by wrapping the wand in a piece of pure silk. Then store it in a safe place where you keep all your other magical aids.

It is advisable to charge this wand repeatedly, but each time you charge it you must increase the intensity of your imagination. Never forget that you incorporate your entire spiritual will in the wand. It is very important that you limit the time and, if possible, also the space of the power which you have concentrated into the wand. Therefore concentrate your will power into the wand so that as long as the wand exists it incorporates your entire will, your entire might, and remains effective. A wand charged in this manner can be effective until the end of your physical life and, should it be your wish, it can even remain effective beyond your physical death. This kind of magic wand can continue to retain its influence for centuries. The influence can even increase with time provided that, during the charging of the wand, the wish is expressed that this influence increase day by day automatically. In the beginning the wand will only be effective on the mental sphere. After a prolonged period of time and repeated loading the wand will be effective on the astral sphere, and eventually it will also be effective on the physical sphere. The length of time for the wand to be effective on the physical plane, after it has already been effective on the mental plane, depends upon the magician's maturity, development, powers of imagination, and the objective for which he strives and which he wishes to achieve. A magician who is conversant with the Kabbalah knows very well that a realization from the mental plane into the physical world must usually be repeated 462 times. By then the influence from above to below has made its way, i.e. it has condensed from the mental sphere, onto the physical world. Of course, this is not to say that the same success cannot be achieved earlier. As aforementioned, the ability of the magic wand to bring about the realization depends on the wish and the purpose for which it was made and charged. At this point the question could be raised as to why a magic wand has to be charged at all, since the magician's will power alone should actually be sufficient. However, it is a fact that the magician is not always in a position to be able to expand his will with the utmost effort to bring about its necessary projection. There are situations where even the best magician might be exhausted, and consequently his ability to concentrate in an expansionary way is not always the same, and therefore it would also not be immediate. Whereas a magic wand that is charged well is effective at all times. Hence the magician does not have to exhaust his will, and he can use the magic wand instead, and direct his thought upon the realization of his wish. However, there is one danger: even an uninitiated person is in the position to realize his own wishes with the magician's magic wand, at the expense of the magician and the magic wand's volt. Therefore the magician is well advised not to tell anyone, not even his best friend, for what purpose, in which respect, and in which manner he has charged his magic wand.

When a magician charges a magic wand with his will it mostly serves the purpose of influencing spirits, entities, human beings and animals, which the magician wishes to bring under his absolute will, so that they obey his might. It does not matter whether they are on the mental, astral or physical plane. Exerting influence is not limited to living beings; this can also be done to dead matter, provided that this was taken into consideration when the magic wand was charged.

Point 2: Charging Or Loading With Attributes, Qualities And So On

Charging with attributes is to be understood as charging with a specific universal attribute, for example omnipotence, or any other particular attribute which the magician requires for his realization on the mental, astral or physical plane. He can project any attribute into the magic wand in the same manner as described in the previous chapter. The same procedure used to charge the wand with the will can be employed when it comes to an attribute, not only by transferring one's consciousness into the magic wand and banishing the attribute into the wand with an accumulation of power, but through the imagination as well. With wish-concentration, the magician can also draw the attribute directly from the universe into the magic wand and compress or accumulate it there. By frequently accumulating or condensing the same attribute into the wand, the power or energy which has accumulated in the wand through the power of concentration eventually becomes a physical power or physical energy. At this point the magician has a magic wand that is an accumulator, very much resembling the kind of accumulator that is charged with high-voltage electric current. It is true that one and the same power or energy can be used for good and evil purposes. However, a magician who has reached this level in his development will never allow himself to entertain or pursue any kind of evil motives, especially if he always wishes to be respected and considered by Divine Providence as a faithful servant.

Point 3: Charging Or Loading The Magic Wand With Magnetism, Bio-magnetism Or Prana

In this instance the procedure is the same as described in the previous chapter. In this particular case, however, it is advisable not to transfer your consciousness into the wand when you condense the energy or power. Rather, it should be carried out either through the physical body by way of the imagination or else directly from the universe. The magician cannot forget that terms and time limits have to be set for the power or energy that is contained in the wand and the wish-concentration, for whatever purpose the wand has to serve, and must accompany the imagination. Through repeated charging, the energy or power in the wand becomes effective on the mental and astral planes as well as on the physical plane. Any experienced magician knows that the power from the wand can be transmitted over the farthest distances. When the magician begins to introduce the Akasha Principle between the subject and himself, he has the opportunity to span time and space immediately, and, by means of the magic wand, to transfer the power or energy without further ado upon the intended person with the same influence, intensity and success as if that person were standing right next to him. When the magic wand is charged with vital energy or magnetism, and if the terms or conditions have been properly introduced into the wand (in this case including the idea that the vital energy or magnetism is to increase automatically on a daily basis), then all the phenomena that can be achieved with the vital energy can be brought about by the magician without any great effort with the aid of the wand. With a magic wand charged in this manner, even an inexperienced person could perform miracles if he knew how to use the wand. Therefore it is in the interest of the magician to safeguard the secret of his wand. The magician can also charge the wand in such a manner that it will automatically draw vital energy from the universe without any effort on his part and then transmit it through the wand. Charging the magic wand in this manner with magnetism or bio-magnetism is a preferred method, especially for healing purposes. A magician whose calling is to heal the sick will make use of this method and use his wand, which has been prepared in this manner, to heal his patients from afar. In the hands of a magician a magic wand charged in this manner is truly a blessing for suffering mankind, especially when patients can be cured over vast distances.

Loading or charging the magic wand with the electric, magnetic or electromagnetic fluid requires the same procedure, except in this case the magician does not transfer his consciousness into the magic wand. When only a single wand is charged, the procedure of charging the wand becomes somewhat more complicated. When a magic wand is charged with only one fluid, be it electric or magnetic, the fluid has to be drawn from the universe through the imagination. At the same time, the wish-concentration has to be banished into the wand so that the fluid to be contained there will immediately realize the wish, even if it is hurled into the farthest distance, whether upon a particular plane or into the Akasha Principle. When the magician accumulates the fluid in the wand and makes it a condition that the accumulated fluid from the universe is to increase in its intensity automatically, i.e. that the fluid works on its own bio-electrically or bio-magnetically, then such a wand develops into an enormously powerful battery. It is highly recommended that the magician, before he makes use of the magic wand, accumulate the corresponding fluid within himself, so that the tension of the fluid within his body is at least equal to the tension of the fluid in the wand. Should the magician prefer not to do so, he must protect and insulate himself by wearing a pair of real silk gloves. It would truly serve this purpose if he made the silk gloves himself. In this case, only when he has insulated himself with the silk gloves can he take the wand into his hands. Since a magician usually works with both fluids, he should take the wand which is loaded with the accumulated electric fluid into his right hand and the wand which is loaded with the accumulated magnetic fluid into his left hand. It is always preferable to load two wands, one with the electric fluid and the other with the magnetic fluid, especially when one has ordinary rods or simple wooden rods that are not impregnated with a fluid condenser. Although it is not absolutely necessary, it is easier to work with two magic wands. If the magician has a magic wand which is filled with a fluid condenser but not partitioned in the middle, it would then be more advantageous for him to charge the wand with only one fluid, because it is considerably easier to work in that manner.

If the magician is dealing with an electromagnetic charge where both fluids are predominant in one wand, then he must make use of a wand that is not drilled all the way through from one end to the other. Instead, the wand has to be hollowed out from each end, leaving the center untouched. Each half of the wand is then loaded separately with a fluid condenser. However, the magician must mark which half of the wand contains the electric fluid and which half contains the magnetic fluid. The easiest way to identify this is to color-code the wand by using red for the half of the wand that is intended for the electric fluid, and blue for the half intended for the magnetic fluid. The charging of the wand has to be carried out in such a manner that the greatest tension of the fluids is concentrated at the ends of the wand, while the center of the wand, which is insulated with silk, remains free, i.e. neutral. The charging of each half of the wand has to be carried out separately.

For example, the magician can charge the wand first with the electric fluid which he draws from the universe and accumulates until it is duly loaded; then he can charge the other half immediately with the magnetic fluid. The magician should never charge the wand several times on different occasions with the electric fluid only, and then charge the wand several times on different occasions only with the magnetic fluid. The equilibrium of the fluids in the magic wand must be maintained at all times. Therefore the magician must first charge the wand with the electric fluid and then immediately with the magnetic fluid. However, the next time he charges the wand he must begin first with the magnetic fluid and immediately thereafter with the electric fluid. The magician continues to charge the wand in this alternating manner. As for all the other rules which have been recommended, they have to be adhered to as well.

A magician uses magic wands, when they are loaded with the electric or magnetic fluids or when they are loaded with both fluids, whenever he wants to be effective with these fluids, whether close by or far away, and whether he wishes to work in the Akasha or on the mental, astral or physical planes. I shall refrain from explaining particular variations of methods, for example working with volting or the treatment of ailing people or how these fluids can become carriers of the imagination, because whoever has followed my explanations carefully to this point has been given the possibility of devising his own individual working methods.

Point 4: Charging Or Loading With The Elements

Charging or loading with the elements can be carried out in two ways:

1. The first method is as follows: Regardless of whether it is a simple wand or whether the wand contains a fluid condenser, the magician loads his magic wand through the imagination with the powerful and mighty command that the elements must absolutely obey him whenever he uses the wand, regardless of the plane upon which he may be working. When the magic wand is duly loaded with the power to control the elements, then the beings of the elements bring about the desired effects. It would be wise if the magician would extend his powers or authority over all the elements, i.e. Fire, Air, Water and Earth, so that he is not limited to only one element. During evocation the magician must call the principals[4] of the elements, one after the other, in front of his magic circle, and he must compel each of them to take an oath on his magic wand that they will absolutely obey him at all times. As soon as the magician has completed the evocation, he can engrave the particular symbols or seals of the individual principals of the elements on his magic wand. However, engraving

---

[4] Also known as *Spiritis Rector*.

the seals is not absolutely necessary, because the magic wand in the hand of a magician represents his absolute will and his power over every being of the elements. The magician can find the particular seals of the individual principals through his clairvoyant vision in the magic mirror or by transferring his mental body directly into the kingdom of the elements. Some of the seals of the beings of the elements are described in this book. In accordance with his development and through contemplation, the magician also has the possibility of devising his own symbol for the particular element. He will then have the principal of that element swear an oath that not only will he obey the symbol that the magician has engraved on the wand, but the entire wand itself.

2. The second method is as follows: The magician draws the element with which he wants to work directly from the universe, i.e. out of the particular sphere, with the aid of the imagination, and accumulates it dynamically in his magic wand. When the wand is thus loaded, the beings of the elements do not bring about the effect, but instead it is the magician himself. This method has an advantage in that the magician has the inner feeling of satisfaction, because he himself is the cause of the magical effect. However, it is essential that a wand be made for each element. The wands must be kept apart and also stored separate from each other. These wands must also be identifiable from the outside in order to prevent one being mistaken for another. For easier identification, each wand can be marked with the color of the particular element. In the beginning, the effects will only be noticeable in the mental sphere. However, after prolonged use and repeated charging, the effects will also be noticeable in the astral sphere and, after continued use and repeated charging, finally in the physical world. The possibility exists, that with such a magic wand, spiritual beings, human beings, animals, yes, even inanimate nature can be influenced through an element, as is the case with the electromagnetic fluid. Experienced magicians call forth fabulous natural phenomena with such a magic wand; for example, they can influence the weather, accelerate the growth of plants and many other such phenomena.

Point 5: Charging Or Loading
With The Akasha Principle

The magic wand can be loaded with the Akasha Principle with the aid of the imagination, but it cannot be accumulated, because the Akasha Principle cannot be condensed or compressed. However, through repeated meditation on the attributes of the Akasha Principle with all the aspects contained in the wand, the magician may, with such a wand, produce causes directly in the Akasha Principle which have an effect on the mental, astral and physical planes. With a wand that is loaded in this manner the magician can imaginatively banish into the Akasha a power or attribute similar to a volt that has been created with the electromagnetic fluid and which exerts a direct influence from up above upon the three-dimensional world. Such a wand will instill awe upon the positive intelligences and fear upon the negative beings of every plane. This method of charging a wand is preferred mostly by magicians who work with negative beings, i.e. with demons, in order to make them submissive. There is more information on this subject in the chapter dealing with evocative magic, i.e. necromancy.

Point 6: Charging Or Loading
With Light-Fluid

The universal light, out of which everything has been created, has to be accumulated or compressed in the magic wand to such an extent that the wand radiates like a sun (i.e. concentrated universal light). This is accomplished with the aid of the imagination by taking into consideration the attributes of the universal light when loading the wand. A magic wand that is loaded in this manner is mostly used for theurgic purposes, i.e. when summoning high beings of the light and high intelligences. Such a magic wand is an excellent attractive magnet with which the magician can make relevant light-beings pay attention to him, to his desires and his will. Otherwise, all the other rules apply to this magic wand as well, such as insulating the wand with white silk, and a safe and good place for safe-keeping, and so forth.

Not only will the magician be able to work in the physical world with his magic wand, but he will also be in a position to transfer the mental and astral shape of the wand into the corresponding sphere with his mental or astral hand, or both. He can make his influence known in these planes without having to hold his wand with his physical hand. When the magician exteriorizes his entire mental body, not only can he take the mental form of his magic wand with all its qualities into the mental sphere, but he can also take the mental form of all his magical instruments and aids. He can work and be effective on the mental plane with his mental body, as he is with his physical body on the physical plane. The magician must never forget that the magic wand represents his true will in its perfection, in its absoluteness and in its power, and can be compared to a magic oath. For many magicians the magic wand not only symbolizes the will, it also symbolizes the magic oath. From the Hermetic point of view, the magic oath can never and should never be broken. Many magicians engrave the individual symbols that are analogous with their will and the loading of the wand onto the magic wand. The magician can choose for this purpose either universal symbols or specific individual symbols, signs and seals of the intelligences, divine names and so on, that express the magician's true will. The manner in which the magician chooses to handle this is left completely to his discretion, because it is an individual matter. On the basis of these instructions, the magician will know how to proceed in achieving his purpose. It is entirely at the discretion of the individual magician whether he chooses to engrave secret names which represent his will onto his wand. It goes without saying that such a name must be held in the strictest confidence and it can never be spoken.

Chapter 9
The Magic Sword, The Magic Dagger
And The Magic Trident

There are negative beings and entities that do not like to enter our earth atmosphere during evocations. If a magician insists on their manifestation and the magic wand does not suffice, then he must use the magic sword. The magic sword has several symbolic meanings, but as a rule, and so far as the magician is concerned, it represents a symbol of absolute obedience for every being, for every power. At the same time it is also a symbol of victory and superiority over any power and being. The sword is analogous to the light, for it is an aspect of fire and as such also of the Word. It is written in the Bible: "In the beginning was the Light, the Word, and the Word was with God." Anyone who is somewhat conversant with symbolism remembers how the Archangel Michael is portrayed with a flaming sword whilst slaying the dragon. The dragon represents the enemy, the negative principle. Even Adam and Eve were driven out of Paradise by an angel with a flaming sword. The symbolic significance is depicted in these cases in a very clear and succinct manner.

The magic sword serves as a magical instrument whenever the magician must exert a certain force, a certain compulsion upon a power or being, and mostly when the demands of the magician are against the particular being's will. The sword is an indispensable magical aid for a magician who concerns himself solely with demonology, because he can never achieve anything positive without the use of a magic sword. However, most of the time a true magician does not require anything more than a magic wand. Despite that, he will not fail to fabricate a magical instrument such as the magic sword in order to have it available should the occasion arise. The magic sword gives the magician a higher level of security and solidifies his authority. During certain procedures, especially during evocations, a true magician will only make use of the magic sword if a power or spiritual entity opposes him and refuses to obey him.

In some grimoires you will find that a dagger is mentioned instead of a magic sword. A magic dagger is really a small sword and it is symbolically identical. A dagger is fabricated and prepared in the same manner as a sword.

When the magician summons demons and lower spirits, he can replace the sword or dagger with a trident. The trident should be mounted securely on a wooden stick such as a broomstick. The trident belongs to the same category as the magic sword and dagger and it represents the means of enforcement. Besides that, in the grimoires it is recommended that the trident be engraved with various divine names. However, this is a very personal matter and depends upon the purpose of the evocation and the personal view of the magician. Symbolically, the trident is at the same time an extension of the magic sword. The three prongs represent the three-dimensional world, and with the trident the magician can coerce the beings to fulfil his wish, not only on the mental and astral planes but also on the physical plane or, for that matter, on all three planes simultaneously. It should also be mentioned that when demons appear they usually do so with a trident and they are thus depicted in various paintings. However, this does not mean, as is foolishly assumed by the majority, that demons spear souls in hell with their trident. In reality the trident only depicts that their influence extends to the mental, astral and physical worlds.

There is also another use for the magic sword, dagger and trident. With the tips of these magical instruments the magician can disperse or dissolve undesired and uninvited apparitions such as larvae, schemata, elementals, elementaries, etc., which force themselves upon the magician during an evocation. There is also another possible use for these magical instruments which is not very well known. A magic sword or dagger, and to a lesser extent the trident, serve quite well as magic lightning rods.

When the magician has completed his evocation, particularly an evocation of higher negative beings, demon princes, etc., and he is ready to retire for the evening, he can protect his bed with a magic lightning rod if he is in doubt as to whether these beings will disturb him during his sleep. This is accomplished in the following manner: a copper or steel wire is wound around the legs of the bed and the two ends of the wire are wound around the sword or the dagger, which is then thrust into the floor. The wire forms an enclosure around the bed in the shape of a square, and the dagger serves the purpose of diverting the influence that has been directed toward the magician into the ground. When the magician winds the wire around the bed, he must do so by imagining that it is a circle and with the wish that neither a being nor an unfavorable influence can penetrate beyond this circle, i.e. the bed, and that any influence regardless of who sent it is diverted into the ground by the wire. Then the magician can sleep undisturbed in his magically protected bed, and he can be certain that he cannot be attacked by any influence, regardless of its sphere of origin. If the magician under certain circumstances does not have a magic sword or dagger available or if he requires it for another purpose, then he can use a brand new knife which will only be used for this specific purpose. The magic lightning rod is also excellent protection against influences from black magicians, especially while one is asleep. An experienced, fully-developed magician can do without this kind of protection, because he has the ability to draw a magic circle around his bed with his imagination mentally and astrally with his magic wand, sword or dagger, and to protect himself in this manner against any undesirable influences.

The fabrication of a sword is entirely personal and depends upon the individuality of the magician. The instructions in the various books recommend that the magician use for his operations a sword with which a human being has been decapitated. The idea of having this type of sword serves the purpose of creating a certain feeling of awe, and it also creates a certain tension as soon as the magician takes it in his hands. However, it is mostly sorcerers or others who require external influences to put themselves into a raised state of consciousness that would make use of such a sword. From a Hermetic point of view these or similar kinds of prerequisites are not necessary, provided of course that all the other required abilities are present. A sword made of the best steel (electro steel = stainless steel) is more than adequate. Should the magician not be able to fabricate a sword himself, he can have it made by a blacksmith or by a sword cutler. The length of the sword depends on the height of the particular magician. Generally, the sword should be between 28 to 39 inches (70 – 100 cm). The grip can be made from copper, because copper is an excellent fluid conductor.

The design of the sword is not of major importance. The blade can have either one or two cutting edges, but the tip must be very pointed and must have very sharp cutting edges. It depends on the inclination of the magician as to whether he wishes the grip of the sword to be adorned with appropriate symbols or not. This explanation should suffice as far as the fabrication of the sword is concerned.

The sword is loaded by transferring the particular attributes into it with the imagination. These attributes can include power and control over all beings, absolute victory and the respect for victory as the symbol of battle, life, etc. These attributes are dynamically intensified by frequently loading the sword. The magician also has the option to condense light-fluid into the sword, so much so that the sword resembles a glowing sun, a flaming sword, similar to the well known symbolic representation of the Archangel Michael with the flaming sword.

However, the proper attitude towards the sword is of the utmost importance, and is to be accompanied by an unshakable belief of absolute victory on all planes. This bestows upon the sword the might that every power and every being will fear the sword and respect it under any and all conditions. After each use the sword must be wrapped either in black or white silk and kept in a safe place, just like all the other magical instruments.

Through mental travel the magician can transfer the spiritual form of the sword as well as the spiritual form of the magic wand onto the mental plane. He can visit the planetary spheres with his magic sword and he can make his influence known there with his magical instruments in accordance with his wishes. It is a foregone conclusion that in those spheres every being must obey him. Therefore, during magical operations, i.e. evocations, it is possible for the magician to transfer the mental form of the sword with his mental hand through the imagination into the particular sphere, and from thence to coerce the being to obey his will. This kind of coercion can only be accomplished without danger by a magician who is pure of heart and has a noble soul. If a sorcerer had the audacity to commit such an act, he would only incur the hatred of these beings and unmistakably subject himself to them and their influences. The history of the occult sciences gives us many examples of the tragic destiny and even more tragic demise of many such sorcerers. The scope of this book does not lend itself to quote any of these events, therefore I shall refrain from mentioning any such occurrences.

Chapter 10
The Crown, A Cap Or Miter,
A Magus Headband

The magician must always wear something on his head when he is carrying out a ritualistic magical operation, be it an evocation, an invocation or any other ritualistic magical operation. It can be a golden crown that is engraved with magical symbols. It may also be a cap, miter or some other headdress that is either adorned with the symbolism of the macrocosm and microcosm or the symbol of the Divinity with whom the magician is in contact or whose form he adopts or symbolizes. The symbols have to be applied with a high-quality paint or embroidered with silk or sewn on. For example, the symbol of the macrocosm and the microcosm is represented by a hexagon, which has to be placed in the center of two circles, and the microcosmic symbol of man, the flaming pentagram, which has to be centered inside the hexagon. If the magician embroiders the cap himself or if he has it embroidered by someone else, he should use a gold thread to embroider the two circles as a symbol of infinity. To create a uniform hexagon, the magician can merge two equilateral triangles. He should use a silver thread as a symbol of the created universe and, for the pentagram in the center of the hexagon, he may choose either a white or violet thread. Should the magician prefer to paint the symbol on his headdress, then the color of the paint has to be chosen according to the relevant analogies. Instead of a headdress such as a cap, a miter or a turban, the magician may use a silk headband, also called a Magus headband, the color of which can be white, violet or black.

    The part of the headband that covers the forehead should be adorned with the aforementioned macrocosmic and microcosmic symbols, which are either embroidered or painted on parchment paper with the appropriate colors. The macrocosmic symbol could be replaced with another symbol that symbolizes the magician's connection with the Divinity. For example, he may also choose the sign of the cross, which symbolizes the plus (positive) and the minus (negative), and the four ends of which symbolize the four elements. The magician may also choose as a symbol the cross of the Rosicrucians, which is a cross with seven roses in its center, through which the four elements, the plus and the minus and the seven planets with which the magician is in contact, are likewise symbolized. A magician does not depend on a particular symbol; he can express his spiritual development, his objective, his maturity and his cosmic relationship in accordance with his own discretion through several symbols and adorn his Magus headband with these symbols.

As aforementioned, the crown, the cap or Magus headband symbolizes the dignity of the magician's magical authority. It is a symbol of the perfection of his spirit, a symbol of his relationship with the macrocosm and microcosm, therefore with the large world and the small world. Thus it is with the highest expression of his magical power that the magician symbolically crowns his head. All these utensils, whether crown, cap or Magus headband, must be made of the finest materials and must exclusively serve ritualistic purposes. As soon as his chosen headgear is fitted for size and ready for use, it must be sanctified through meditation and a holy oath. And the magician should only wear it when he is "at one" with the idea of the divine connection, and he should only wear the crown, cap or Magus headband during magical operations which require this symbolic manner of expression. When the magician administers the oath, he must place his right hand upon his headdress, depending of course upon the one he selects. Then he must concentrate with a firm imagination that, at the moment he places the head covering upon his head, this act immediately brings about the connection with his Divinity or with the symbol that adorns his headdress. When the magician is finished with this magical operation, he puts his headdress safely away with his other magical aids.

When the magician has made all the necessary preparations for evocation through the appropriate meditation and puts on his headdress, he will immediately be placed in touch with his Divinity. Not only will he perceive this holy temple atmosphere within himself, but it will also permeate the entire room or wherever he wears his headdress. Therefore, the magician will realize that his headdress is also a very important component of his magical utensils, and one to which he must also pay the greatest attention. Even sorcerers make use of a cap. However, these caps are adorned with the magic symbols of demons, and only very few sorcerers know the true significance and proper use of the cap, and they know much less about the actual symbolism. However, a magician that does everything consciously will never stoop to the level of a sorcerer, and he will never do anything he does not understand. For the magician, every action has a particular purpose.

Chapter 11
The Magic Robe

The magic robe has to be dealt with in the same manner as the headdress. The magic robe is a long garment made of silk, which is buttoned from the neck down to the feet. The sleeves of the magic robe must be long enough to extend to the wrists. The robe resembles priestly robes, and it symbolically expresses the absolute purity of all ideas and the purity of the magician's soul. The garment is at the same time the symbol of protection, similar to regular clothing protecting us from external influences such as cold, rain, etc. The magic robe serves the magician as protection against undesirable external influences that might somehow attack his body through the astral and mental matrices. It has been mentioned previously that silk is the best material for insulation against any kind of astral and mental influences. Consequently, an excellent means of insulation is a robe made of silk. A magic robe made of silk can also be successfully employed in operations which are not directly connected with ritualistic magic, for example as protection for the astral and physical bodies while on mental and astral travels, so that no being can take possession of the magician's astral or physical body without his permission. And the magic robe can also be successfully employed in similar operations where an insulation of the mental, astral and physical bodies is required. However, this is at the discretion of the magician, if and when he makes use of his magic robe. However, under no circumstances can a magic robe be used for ritualistic magic or for evocation if it has been used for conventional purposes such as Hermetic exercises or common everyday magical operations. A special garment must be prepared for this exalted form of magic, and the color of the magic robe must serve the purpose. It is important to know that the magic robe can be worn as an insulating garment over one's everyday clothing when performing ordinary mental and astral work or when practicing certain experiments. However, when performing ritualistic magic or evocation the magical garment must be worn over one's naked body. In some climates it might prove too cold were the magician to wear only the magic robe on his otherwise naked body. In this case he can wear a shirt and pants made of the finest silk under his magic robe. In this case, the shirt and pants must be the same color as the garment. The magician may also wear slippers on his feet; again, the color must be identical to that of the garment, whereas the soles can be leather or rubber.

The color of the robe should always correspond with the work, idea and purpose pursued by the magician. However, he also has a choice of three universal colors: white, violet or black. Violet corresponds with the color of the Akasha and can be used for almost any magical work. A white magic robe is used only for exalted and positive beings. A black garment is used for negative beings and powers. If the magician has the financial means to afford magical garments in these three colors, he can carry out at least one of each of the aforementioned rituals. Should the magician be blessed with earthly wealth, he can obtain all the garments that correspond with the colors of the planets, i.e. the corresponding spheres with which he works. And they are as follows:

> for the beings of Saturn, the color is dark violet
> for the beings of Jupiter, the color is blue
> for the beings of Mars, the color is crimson
> for the beings of the Sun, the color is yellow, gold or orange
> for the beings of Venus, the color is green
> for the beings of Mercury, the color is opalescent (taffeta)
> for the beings of the Moon, the color is silver or white

Should a magician not have the financial means, one magical garment will suffice, but it must have a light violet color and the head-dress must be of the same color, too.

When the garment is ready to wear, the magician must first wash it under running water in order to remove the Od, so that no foreign influences remain on the silk. The magician must iron the garment himself, so that only his hands come in contact with the magic robe. The magician will find that this measure is completely justified, because a sensitive magician finds it disturbing when someone else simply touches his magical utensils, even if it is a member of his own family, a relative or a friend. After the silk robe has been washed, dried and ironed, the magician places it in front of him, and imaginatively he unites with his Divinity and then blesses the garment, not as a person but as the evoking Divinity Itself. He administers an oath upon the garment and he swears that it will be used only for rituals. A garment that has been influenced and impregnated in this manner truly contains magical powers and offers the magician absolute security during his operations. Before the magician prepares his garment magically, he can embroider it with universal symbols at his discretion, similar to the cap. However, everything is in accordance with the magician's wishes. A magician who has reached this level in his spiritual development can be certain that he will not make any mistakes in this respect.

Chapter 12
The Magic Belt (Girdle)

The magic belt, which is worn around the waist to keep the entire garment together, is necessary for the magic robe. The belt is either made from the same material as the garment or cap, or else it can be made of leather in the same color as the garment. Ancient magicians preferred belts, or, as they called them, girdles, made from lion skin, which they turned into leather first. Lion skin was considered to be the symbol of power, strength and control. The symbolic significance of the belt actually points to the control of the elements, in other words to magical equilibrium. And since the upper and lower halves of the human body are kept together at the waist or in the middle, the belt symbolizes a scale. The symbol chosen by the magician can be crafted or painted on the leather belt, whereas if he chooses a silk belt it would have to be embroidered. It is at the discretion of the magician as to how he expresses the equilibrium and control of the elements in a symbolic drawing. For example, he can draw a circle, in the center of which he can draw a pentagram with the tip pointing upward; and in the center of the pentagram he can draw an equilateral triangle as a sign of control over the elements in the three worlds. In the center of the triangle he can draw a Greek cross (an equilateral cross) as a sign of the plus (positive) and minus (negative) principles and of the equilibrium. The procedure is the same as it was with the magical garment and cap. The magician must bless or sanctify the magic belt and give an oath that he uses it with the magic robe only for rituals. The magic belt is kept with the magic robe and all the other magical instruments in the same safe place.

Chapter 13
Additional Magical Aids

With any additional magical aids that he intends to use for ritualistic purposes, the magician must use the same procedure as he did with all the other magical instruments already described. There are still quite a number of these additional aids, and it would be too voluminous to mention them all, because the number of magical aids always depends upon the purpose and the objective for which they are made. For example, the magician requires the following supplies: writing utensils, ink and engraving needles for writing and engraving talismans; embroidery needles, wool or silk for embroidering, parchment paper and paint. For particular operations he also requires sacrificial blood, also known as holy oil, with which the magician embrocates his instruments and anoints specific areas of his body. He also requires salt, frankincense and other incense, as well as a scourge, which he employs in a similar manner as the magic sword and according to the same symbolism. Furthermore, the magician also requires a chain, which symbolically represents the bond of the microcosm and the macrocosm with all its spheres. At the same time the chain is a symbol of integration into the great Brotherhood of Magicians and into the hierarchy of all the beings of the macrocosm and microcosm. The chain can be worn as jewelry, like a necklace, which indicates that the magician is a member of the Brotherhood of all the genuine magicians.

For particular magical operations a goblet is used as a symbol of wisdom and life. During certain magical operations, the magician takes the sacrificial feast (the Eucharist), the sacrament of communion. The goblet, which is filled with wine, serves the purpose of charging the wine with the divine power (quality), similar to the procedure which is employed at the Christian communion. The wine in the goblet must be blessed. This is accomplished when the magician transforms himself into his Divinity and blesses the wine and turns the wine into divine blood, wisdom, strength and life. During intermittent interruptions of his work the magician drinks the transformed wine and in this manner partakes in the holy sacrament. The chapter on the Eucharist in *Initiation into Hermetics* deals with this matter in more detail.

Another magical aid is a bell which can also be used for evocation. This bell must be made from electro-magicum, which is a mixture of all the metals that correspond to the seven planets, in accordance with the description in Chapter VIII of *Initiation into Hermetics*. The magician uses this bell only when he wishes to make the invisible world pay attention to him through a rhythmic ringing of the bell. The rhythm and the number of strokes of the bell correspond to the number of rhythms of the particular sphere with which the magician wishes to communicate. True magicians rarely use the Oriental method of bell ringing, whereas in the Orient, mostly in Tibet, summoning with the ringing of bells, striking of cymbals, etc., is quite often practiced. I have frequently mentioned that these magical instruments must be new and can only be used for the particular purpose the magician has chosen. Every magical aid must be safely stored immediately after use. Should a magical aid no longer be required and should the magician have no intention of ever using it again, the instrument must be destroyed or rendered harmless. Should a magician use a magical instrument for any purpose other than that for which it was intended, it would be a desecration and the instrument would be rendered magically ineffective.

All magical aids must be handled as if they were relics. The more meticulously the magician handles his magical instruments, the greater will be their magical effect and the greater influence will they be able to exert.

Chapter 14
The Pentacle, Lamen Or Seal

A pentacle represents the universal symbol of power. It is charged with the attribute of a particular power with the help of the magic wand or the imagination. The pentacle serves the purpose of exerting an influence of respect and obedience upon a particular being or entity, so that it obeys the will of the magician. The universal symbol is chosen in accordance with the magician's religious beliefs. For example, it can be the same universal power symbol that the magician has embroidered or engraved on his headdress (the crown, cap or Magus headband). It can be a hexagram, which is formed by two equilateral triangles, in the center of which can be a pentagram. In the center of the pentagram a Greek (equilateral) cross can be placed. Even a Greek cross by itself can serve as a universal symbol.

Many magicians can avail themselves of the Pentacle Salomonis as a symbol of coercion for all beings. However, it should be a foregone conclusion that the magician should not choose a symbol whose graphic representation he does not understand, because it could not express the authority that he requires for his purposes. Only when the magician comprehends the entire significance of his symbol will he be able to tune in to the symbol, which will then be properly effective magically. Therefore, to represent the idea of his power he should only use symbols which he comprehends.

In contrast to the pentacle, a seal is a graphic representation of a being, a power or a plane that corresponds to the quality of the particular being and which is expressed through the symbol.

There are the following kinds of seals:

1.   Traditional seals are seals which were elicited either through clairvoyance or through astral travel in the individual spheres and which were reproduced by the beings of these spheres. However, these spirit-beings only react to these seals if the magician possesses the ability to transfer himself into their sphere of power. The magician increases his influence and exerts it upon the particular being on account of the reservoir of energy which is at his disposal. This energy is replenished and stockpiled due to the frequent use of the seal.

Over the years, many errors have arisen due to frequent copying of these seals from various sources. Therefore, these seals have become distorted and incomprehensible; at times this was done intentionally in order to make it difficult or even impossible for magicians who worked with them to achieve any success. However a magician whose astral senses are intact can, by introducing the Akasha Principle (trance) and by focusing his attention upon the seal, verify its authenticity. This then gives the magician the ability to make the proper corrections.

2.   There are universal seals that symbolize the quality and the sphere of activity as well as the attributes of the being. The magician can produce these seals himself through graphic representation by taking the laws of analogy into consideration. He can charge these seals through his imagination with the particular attributes of the spirit. The being has no choice but to react to these seals without any resistance.

3.   Then there are seals which every magician can produce himself in accordance with his own discretion, without following any analogous relationships. However, these seals have to be approved by the spiritual beings. The acceptance of such a seal or sign occurs when the magician travels with his spirit into the sphere of the being and has the being take on oath mentally on his seal, as to its form, its design etc., in order that it reacts to this seal.

4. A lamen resembles a universal symbol, but it does not represent the symbol of the microcosm and macrocosm. Instead it symbolically expresses the spiritual and psychic authority, the attitude and the maturity of the magician. Usually a lamen is sewn onto the magic robe in the area of the chest or engraved on the appropriate metal like an amulet or painted on parchment paper and carried separately. Through its symbolic drawing a lamen expresses the absolute authority of the magician.

5. A talisman is mostly used during magical operations where protection against undesirable influences is necessary or where the magician wants to achieve a sweeping success with his magical operation. A talisman can be a graphic representation of the attributes or capabilities with which it is charged or loaded. The charging of the talisman is carried out either by the magician or by a being that he summons for this purpose. When a being carries out the loading of the talisman, the energy that is expended is at the expense of the fluidal energy substance of the particular being or its own reservoir of energy. In this case traditional signs or symbols can be engraved, and they can be signs which are passed on from one magician to another or which are offered by the being itself. Furthermore, they can be appropriate signs which the magician has had approved by the being.

The fabrication of pentacles, lamens, seals or talismans for rituals can either be analogous to the plane of the being, to the elements, the planets, or the signs of the zodiac, with the appropriate metals onto which the signs or symbols are engraved. Or the signs and symbols can be carved into small wax plates, which the magician can make out of pure beeswax. Once the work has been completed, these engraved wax plates can be charged or loaded. Seals, pentacles and talismans can also be made out of parchment paper upon which the appropriate color of paint or ink the symbols can be drawn or painted.

The ancient grimoires recommend virgin parchment, which is a form of paper that is obtained from the hide of a prematurely born calf. A true magician does not require this kind of parchment, for a piece of regular parchment paper serves exactly the same purpose. However, he must remove all negative influences which might be attached to such

paper. This is achieved through the imagination. In order
or a pentacle, the magician may also use blotting
impregnated with a fluid condenser. It is also advisable the
use a soft color pencil instead of liquid paint when drawing the symbol, so
that the colors do not bleed.

The loading of a seal, pentacle, lamen or talisman is accomplished by using one's finger. The sign or symbol is traced with the finger while concentrating the attribute into the seal, pentacle, lamen or talisman, using the imagination. It goes without saying that the union with the Highest, with one's Divinity, must take place, so that it is not the magician but the Divinity who, through him (meaning through his body) loads the seal, pentacle, lamen or talisman. The magician may also use his magic wand instead of his finger to load the seal, pentacle or talisman. There is no doubt that such a talisman etc., is actually effective magically, because through this procedure a talisman, pentacle etc., is consecrated to the level of a relic and the magician is completely convinced of its magical effect.

I shall describe the different seals of the spiritual beings in the chapter of this book dealing with the hierarchy of the spiritual beings together with their attributes and effects.

Chapter 15
The Secret Book Of Formulas

All the books that have been published thus far on ritualistic magic assert that the magic book, the book of formulas or books that contains incantations with which the magician summons or invokes a particular spirit or being, is usually considered the most important component in the magic of evocation. However, the content of this subject matter is constantly misunderstood to such an extent that I deem it absolutely necessary to explain it from the Hermetic point of view.

I should like to make it perfectly clear from the very beginning that it is completely erroneous to believe that all one has to do is obtain a journal in which he records the incantation and enforcement formulas for articular spirits, then merely recite these formulas to make the particular beings promptly appear.

All the grimoires which I have had the opportunity to examine, whether from ancient or present times, contain without exception the same mistake as far as the explanations are concerned as to the content and purpose of the book of formulas. True initiates find the mystification somewhat ridiculous and consider those who do not meet with success unfortunate because of their erroneous assumptions. In one respect it is completely correct that whatever has been written thus far about formula magic was written in an obscure manner. As a result, the true secret has thus far never been revealed in order to prevent any profanation. I have decided to speak quite openly about this matter since *The Practice of Magical Evocation* is only intended for those who are ethically on a high level and who are highly developed, and only mature human beings will be able to achieve success. There is also another consideration, namely to understand true initiation properly and to acquire the content internally.

Above all, the book of formulas is not to be taken literally, because the title "magic formulas" as mentioned in the grimoires serves as a cover, a disguise for a particular order of thoughts. Moreover, it served to bring the consciousness of the operator out of its normal mode and to transfer it into a certain ecstatic state through barbaric expressions, words and names. It was assumed that, while he was in this ecstatic state, the operator would have the ability to exert an influence upon the spiritual being. As a rule the successes achieved by an inexperienced operator are either in the form of hallucinations, schemata, phantoms or incomplete mediumistic results, and there is no need to describe them in more detail. In most cases they are mediumistic phenomena; provided that you are actually dealing with these phenomena, they are the end result of an exteriorization of the operator's subconsciousness. Occasionally, due to an operator's strong ability of emanation, elementals are created and sometimes even elementaries. A true magician is well informed as to their existence and how they come into being in practice. This is all explained in *Initiation into Hermetics*. These kinds of elementaries are mistaken for true spiritual beings that were summoned or evoked. A human being whose astral senses are not developed does not possess the ability to examine and distinguish the beings properly. This explanation may serve anyone as a warning not to practice any ritualistic magic unless he is properly magically prepared. Aside from the tremendous disappointment, such a person could suffer severe health problems affecting his spirit and his soul, which is even more regrettable. However, a true magician who has completed his magical training can safely practice ritualistic magic without endangering himself. This kind of magic is not the place to indulge in experiments of any sort. Instead, what should be practiced at this point in time is a systematic working procedure, whereby only a mature magician with his powers already developed can operate more effectively and with fewer difficulties.

The book of formulas, which is also mistakenly called the book of spirits, is actually a true magical diary of the magician who is practicing ritualistic magic. In this diary he records his working procedures step by step, so that he can proceed point by point in a conscientious manner and thereby reach his objective. Many readers might now ask how such garbled formulas, citation phrases and the like have come into being. Since time immemorial the great mystery of magic has always been the property of the higher castes alone, of potentates and high priests, so that the real truth and ideas, spiritual advice and so forth did not get into the hands of the general public. Hence the people who had this knowledge devised various code names, the so-called formulas, whereas, on the other hand, only the initiates had the key to decipher these formulas.

The key to deciphering these formulas was passed on only to the mature and only by word of mouth, and any profanation could only be atoned for by penalty of death. Consequently these teachings have remained a secret to this very day, and in the future they will remain occult and mystical even though they are published for everyone to read, because the immature and uninitiated will consider these writings to be mere fantasies and fallacies and, in accordance with their degree of maturity and spiritual receptivity, each of these people will have their individual opinions and explanations. That is why even the most secret things will never lose their occult tradition and only a few human beings will be able to draw benefits from these teachings. Should such a book of formulas ever fall into the hands of an uninitiated person without knowledge of the key to decode them, he will take everything at face value. In other words, he will take everything literally, without having any knowledge that these formulas are really only memory aids for a true magician, in other words they are diagrams for his ritual work.

This then explains why, at times, the most nonsensical words were considered to be magic formulas or so-called spells with which particular beings could be summoned or invoked. Instead, the book of formulas is an actual diary in which a true magician records his entire working procedure or entire magical operation from beginning to end. Should the magician be uncertain as to whether this book might fall into the hands of other people, then he will use code names. I shall give some guidelines which a true magician may adhere to on an individual basis in accordance with his train of thought.

A book of formulas contains the following:
1. Purpose of the operation.
2. The being or spiritual entity, power, plane or sphere etc., which is to be evoked or summoned.
3. The location where the magical operation is to take place.
4. Preparation of all magical utensils which are to be used for the particular operation.
5. The actual magical operation.
6. Assuming the form of the Divinity which controls the particular being, i.e. bonding with the particular Divinity, including all the attributes etc.
7. Drawing the circle when united with the Divinity. When working with a silk, flannel or linen cloth where the circle is either sewn on or embroidered, then the circle has to be traced.
8. Drawing or tracing of the magic triangle.
9. Setting up the censers and the burning of incense.
10. Igniting the magic lamp while concentrating meditatively upon intuition and enlightenment.
11. Loading or charging the seals, pentacles or lamens of the beings to be summoned or evoked.

12. Loading or charging the magic mirror, or even several mirrors, depending upon the circumstances when more than one is required for particular purposes.

13. Dressing in the magic robe and assuming meditatively the attitude of protection, purity etc.

14. Donning the headdress and meditating on the bond with the Divinity.

15. Girding the magic belt while concentrating from a position of strength on the control of all powers, especially the control of the elements.

16. Attaching the magic sword to the magic belt with the meditative attitude of absolute victory; repeat loading while employing the magic wand at the same time, which the magician holds in his right hand, so that his absolute will can be realized.

17. Entering the magic circle with the perception of being bonded and symbolizing the microcosm and macrocosm.

18. Focusing on the magic space or location, i.e. by eliminating the concept of time and space.

19. Renewing the bond with one's Divinity.

20. Transferring one's entire personality into the particular spiritual plane with all the magical utensils.

21. Commanding the power or might of that plane or the being that is evoked to appear in the triangle or magic mirror and also forming the shape of the desired being imaginatively.

22. Returning with one's consciousness to the workroom.

23. The order or wish that is to be directed to the spirit, i.e. the information he demands from the spirit or the work the spirit has to perform, regardless of which plane.

24. After the work is complete, dismissing the being with one's consciousness into the sphere from whence it was summoned, and then concluding the magical operation with a thanksgiving prayer.

25. Returning all magical utensils, the circle etc., to their place of safekeeping.

26. Recording the course of the entire operation, the time, the success etc., into the book of formulas (the magic diary).

A true magician must understand the book of formulas in this or a similar manner and he must act accordingly. Whosoever is conversant with the Kabbalah can use the appropriate divine name of the particular sphere when he transfers his consciousness into that sphere. These divine names only serve as memory aids for his consciousness. However, a true magician can do without these divine names. When a magician performs his first evocation he is always somewhat uncertain, but in time he learns everything that is associated with the evocative procedure and he will progress to the point that he masters this aspect of the science of magic. There are no rewards without diligence.

Chapter 16
In The Sphere Of The Beings

Before I commence with the description of the actual magical operation and evocation, I shall first acquaint the magician more closely with the sphere of the spiritual beings. A true magician must not undertake anything regarding which he is not thoroughly informed. He must also have a completely concise picture of the purpose of his objective. The magician has already learned from the previous chapter, which dealt with the book of formulas, how extremely important it is to know the analogies of the magical instruments thoroughly and to know how to use them in the magical operations. Without the knowledge of the symbolism and the analogy of these instruments, the magician will be unable to use them with the proper magical effect. He will also be unable to focus meditatively with the proper attitude and rise with his spirit into the spheres of the spiritual beings. His magical aids will be completely illusory, and he will sink to the level of a mere sorcerer and be unable to exert his magical authority over the spiritual beings or to influence them. A magician does everything with total awareness — every procedure, every method. He carefully and systematically records everything in his book of formulas before he begins any magical operation, ritualistic magic or evocation. His spirit, his consciousness, is connected with his magical instruments and with their attributes, and with what they are loaded with etc. As the magician has a proper overall view of his magical instruments, he must also be completely informed about the sphere of the spiritual beings with which he intends to work. He must be in a position to give a clear account of the existence and activities of the spiritual beings, and in this respect his own experiences will be, for the most part, his best teacher, because the magician has visited the individual planes with his mental body as described in *Initiation into Hermetics*. This dissertation is simply a brief summary of a magician's experiences that he gathers on his visits to the planes.

Only an incorrigible materialist, who perceives only the material world with his physical senses and believes only what he sees, hears and feels, will doubt the existence of other spheres besides the physical world. A true magician will not judge or criticize a materialist, and he will not attempt to change his personal point of view. The materialist occupies the level of maturity on the physical plane that corresponds with his level of development. Therefore a magician will not make any effort to enlighten him, because a materialist will always present the same argument, namely that he has never seen a spirit and consequently he can only believe what he perceives with his physical sensory organs. The materialist does not deny that matter or substance exists, but he admits to the existence only of that substance and energy in which he resides. To believe that finer layers of substances and energies exist is far beyond his horizon. That is why a magician should never attempt to influence the belief of another human being — because the uninitiated will always have his own opinion of higher concepts from his own point of view, and will therefore always judge this subject matter accordingly.

Just as in our physical world solid, liquid and gaseous substances exist that form our earth, there are in accordance with the laws of analogy so-called aggregate conditions in a finer form, which are not accessible to our normal senses but which are, however, connected with our physical world. In the Hermetic sciences these finer aggregate conditions or states are called planes and spheres. In these finer planes the same proceedings take place as they do on our physical earth, and even there the law of Hermes — the Hermetic axiom "As above, so below" — applies. The same powers or energies are at work there as they are on our planet. The same influences make themselves known there as well as here. Consequently, in every plane the same interaction of the elements is in effect, the electric and the magnetic fluids. They are maintained and governed by Divine Providence in the Akasha Principle. A person who relies solely upon the impressions of his five physical senses has only one area of receptivity that corresponds with his physical senses, and he cannot go beyond that limit. Everything else is incomprehensible, untrustworthy and supernatural to him. A true magician, one who has refined and developed his senses through the magical schooling of the spirit, soul and physical body, considers the physical world only as a point of departure for his development.

Hence he will never deny the existence of higher planes, since he can personally visit them and see for himself. A true magician knows from his own experiences that these planes have finer and more condensed aggregate states. With his spirit, a magician will be able to visit the particular sphere that corresponds with the development of the senses of his mental body, and he will also be able to be active in this sphere. The magician must consider all of this when he practices evocative magic. These finer planes are not subject to time and space, but in accordance with our concepts one plane can go into another. For example, a room which we visualize graphically or which we somehow demarcate, actually contains all kinds of planes imaginable.

There are infinitely many planes and intermediate planes, depending on the degree of density. It would be impossible to mention them all. However, I shall mention those planes which are important for the magician in the practice of magic. The step-by-step order of succession of the degree of density is called "hierarchy." Before a magician commences working in these planes, he must have a graphic picture of the hierarchy in his mind. Above all he must be theoretically well-versed in the plane in which he wants to work, and later on he must also be conversant with these planes practically. Above all he must first be in control of the coarser planes before he commences to the next finer planes. Based on the laws of analogy, each plane in the hierarchy exerts a particular influence upon our physical world. The synthesis of astrology is based upon this relationship to the planetary planes. Unfortunately, nowadays astrologers use astrology mainly for mantic[5] purposes. What is less known or not known at all is

---

[5] Foretelling the future or having the power of divination. – ED.

that astrology is actually only a partial aspect of the effects of the planes, planets and signs of the zodiac. That is why astrology cannot give us complete but only partial information. I shall not deal with the astrological part of the higher planes, since it is not within the scope of this book. However, a true magician who is interested in or who practices astrology will find a more profound relationship to the planes, and he will know the exact time of the appearance[6] of these influences from the particular spheres regarding cause and effect upon our physical world.

In the Kabbalah the order of succession of the planes, taking into consideration their degree of density and their attributes, is called the Kabbalistic Tree of Life. I shall deal with the analogies and practice from a Kabbalistic point of view in detail in my third book, *The Key to the True Kabbalah*. However, the purpose of this book is to interest the reader in the spheres of the Kabbalistic Tree of Life in regards to magic, i.e. in regards to the spiritual beings. The planes are in the following order:

1. The physical world is the point of departure from whence the magician works and upon which every human being, initiated or not, lives and moves through his senses, his spirit, his soul and his physical body.

2. The sphere that follows and which is located beyond our physical world is the earth zone. It is also known as the zone girdling the earth. This zone has various degrees of density, the so-called sub-planes, into which human beings enter after they leave their physical bodies. This is the astral world that individuals enter into with their astral bodies after their physical death. Ordinary persons stay in the lower degrees of density, whereas the initiates are in the higher levels in accordance with their development. The more mature, the more developed and the more ethical a magician was on earth, the more refined will be the plane of the earth zone where he will stay. His place in the astral world will be the one which he has attained here on the physical plane during the course of his life. Heaven and hell do not really exist in the astral world. These are limited, religious concepts and teachings of the various religions, which, out of sheer ignorance, describe life in the astral world as heaven and hell.

---

[6] Time and otherwise. – ED.

However, if you consider the lower, coarser levels of the astral world to be hell and the higher and brighter levels to be heaven, then a portion of these statements made by the various religions can be considered true. A magician who understands how to interpret every symbol and every idea correctly will immediately find the proper explanation for heaven, hell and purgatory.

It would be too extensive to describe the entire spectrum of life in the astral world, because it would fill the pages of many books. However, I shall mention a few things which will be of interest to the magician. During his mental and astral travels, when he separates from his physical body, the magician experiences the fact that the concept of time and space do not exist in the astral world, because in a single moment he can travel any distance, and there are no material obstacles which he cannot penetrate with his mental and astral bodies. Every person will experience this after his physical death. An initiate has the advantage in that during his life on earth he has already become acquainted with life in the astral world, and while on earth he has one less concern, namely the fear of death. He knows exactly where he will be after his physical death, the level he will occupy in the astral world. He also knows that departing from his mortal shell is only a transition from the physical plane into a more refined plane, similar to changing one's place of residence.

The magician will also gather yet another experience here on earth, namely that all interests which a normal person, an uninitiated and undeveloped individual, has in the physical world will cease to exist in the astral sphere. Therefore it is not surprising that a true magician who is at home in both the physical and in the astral worlds will gradually lose all interest in the physical world, and he will use the physical world only as a means for his development. A true magician will realize while he is still on this earth that fame, honor, wealth and all other earthly conveniences cannot be taken into the astral world and are therefore completely meaningless. A true magician will never be attached to anything transitory, and he will be constantly mindful that he must use the time he has at his disposal on the physical world for his development to the best of his abilities.

Therefore it is a matter of course that all bonds that shackle a human being to the physical world, whether love, faithfulness or the like, no longer apply in the astral world. Those who were much attached to each other here on the physical world, but who are not on the same level astrally and spiritually, cannot occupy the same degree of density in the astral world after their departure from the physical world, because in the astral world they no longer feel the same bond that kept them together on earth. For example, when a husband and wife are on the same level in their development, then after their departure from the physical world they can move about in the same sphere in the astral world and they can be together through a bond of inner sympathy. However, in the astral world they will no longer feel the love they felt for each other in the physical world. The instinct for self-preservation, the carnal sexual love and sexual lust, do not exist in the astral world. In the higher levels, equally developed beings are linked to each other through a fine vibrating cord but with different sympathetic feelings than on earth. In our physical world, sympathy or attraction between two beings is usually caused and maintained by external stimuli. However, this does not apply in the astral world. In the astral world the concept of beauty is entirely different than it is on our physical plane. Since the astral body of a departed human being does not possess the concept of time and space in the astral sphere, it also does not posses any mental points of reference with which one can measure one's development. Therefore his soul yearns to return to earth — not only for the reason that he must equilibrate all the mistakes he made in his previous life due to the karmic law, the law of cause and effect, but above all because he yearns for a new opportunity to further develop astrally on the physical plane, and to gather new experiences in his spirit for the higher levels in the astral world.

After having passed on, a less developed person will come to yet another realization — that he cannot communicate with beings that are on a higher level than he. He will find that he cannot contact them, because he is not allowed to stay or move about in their sphere of light — he will not even be able to go there. If the possibility did exist to transfer to a higher level, he would not be able to endure the vibration for very long. He would have no choice but to return to the level in the astral world where he belongs in accordance with his development. Whereas a more highly developed human being can transfer to a lower sphere in the astral world by assuming the vibration of that particular sphere in his spirit.

Therefore, if a less developed spirit wishes to contact a higher spirit, the lower spirit must ask the higher being through the imagination to come to his sphere. Whether the higher being complies with the wish of the lower one always depends upon the purpose that the lower being pursues. All this clearly explains why a lower being cannot enter the higher levels of the astral world, while a higher being can enter the lower levels. A highly developed magician can transfer himself into any sphere because he possesses the ability to assume and to call forth any vibration and therefore also any form of the particular sphere which he wishes to contact. Many readers will now be reminded of a verse in the Bible and understand its meaning: "And the light shineth in darkness; and the darkness comprehended it not."

Any experienced magician knows that the physical body is maintained by nourishment (i.e. condensed elements), and that the astral body is connected with the physical body by the astral cord through breathing. It is therefore obvious to him that as soon as a human being dies all breathing ceases, and the separation of the astral and mental bodies from the physical body occurs immediately. It is therefore completely logical that a magician, through his magical development, may consciously loosen his mental and astral bodies from his physical body and thus enter into a state of ecstasy resembling a state of apparent death. While in this state the magician does not breathe. However, in this case there is one enormous difference: the physical body is not subject to any decay, because the connection with the mental and astral bodies can be reestablished at any time. A magician can be the master over life and death, if Divine Providence so permits. Therefore, a magician can reestablish the connecting link of a departed human being and thereby bring a dead person back to life. In the history of mankind there are some examples of this event taking place; there were some saints who accomplished this feat. There are some more details about this matter in my first work, *Initiation into Hermetics*.

When a magician dies, he no longer has a good reason to return to the physical world. He also does not entertain any wish to reestablish the material-astral cord from the astral world. There are of course also less developed magicians, sorcerers and the like, who make attempts to consciously reestablish the connecting link between the astral and physical bodies from the astral plane. However, they have only partial success because they lack the necessary development to condense the light to the necessary degree as well as the complete analogy, and thus they fail to transfer the realization into the physical world. Beings who are very devoted to their physical bodies usually evade the prerequisite necessary for realization. They vampirize the electromagnetic fluid (the vital energy) from living physical bodies and store this energy in their own physical bodies which they have left behind, in the belief that in due time they may succeed and bring their physical body back to life. A physical body that has been left behind by such a being can be preserved for centuries in the above-mentioned manner by this being, and during this time the body does not decay. History has recorded many such cases where the physical bodies of people who passed away were preserved and did not decay. However, to this day science does not know the real cause. From the Hermetic point of view these kinds of vampires are very pitiful beings, and the religious beliefs that prevailed in the past were correct when they decided to destroy bodies which did not decay. As a rule these vampiric beings were not set free from the bondage of their physical body until their physical body was destroyed. This was done with a wooden peg that was driven through the body, or by decapitation, or by simply burning the body. From a Hermetic point of view even the legends of werewolves can be explained. The process is the same, except that the astral body takes on an animal shape when the vampirizing occurs. In this manner, the so-called vampire disguises himself as an animal in order not to be recognized by a more sensitive person whom he vampirizes.

In order to briefly reiterate the process, in the physical world the physical body and the astral body are maintained through nourishment and through breathing. All three components that make up a human being, namely the physical body, the soul and the spirit, are invigorated from the higher spheres by the finer substantive elements during sleep. On the other hand, however, in the astral world the astral body is enlivened through impressions, which the being on the astral plane receives through material vibrations. When a human being reincarnates into physical matter from the astral plane, the cord between the mental body and the astral body severs and the being dies there, to be born again on our earth. The process of dying in the astral world is the same as when the physical body dies on earth. The astral body is no longer nourished by the mental body through the impressions of the astral world.

The decomposition process of the astral body is considerably slower than that of the physical body. In accordance with our calculation of time, an astral body can exist for many more years without being maintained or nourished by the particular spirit. Other beings, usually demons, take possession of these astral corpses in order to deceive people. In many seances, astral bodies of departed human beings appear in which the spirit of that particular person is no longer present, but instead the body is controlled and moved about by a demon. Only an experienced clairvoyant who, with his spiritually developed senses, can distinguish the astral body from the mental body, will be able to determine and expose the true facts. These demons like to fool human beings and play tricks on them, and they also like to haunt human beings. All spirits that haunt — poltergeists, phantoms, schemata and the like — follow the same concept and proceed in the same manner. I have written extensively about this subject in *Initiation into Hermetics*. Under normal circumstances an astral body dissolves gradually into its elements. The so-called astral corpse is absorbed by the elements and becomes more and more transparent, similar to a sieve, until it eventually dissolves completely into the individual elemental substances.[7]

---

[7] The earthly human being is a trichotomy: body + soul + spirit, namely the material carnal body, the substantial body of the soul or astral body, and the essential spirit body. The substantial soul consists of the energy of substantial warmth and light that warms and illuminates matter. The essential spirit consists of the essential warmth and light that warms and illuminates substance. After we leave our material body our substantial soul becomes our outer body with which we live in the substantial beyond or the astral world. It would be completely dark and cold on the substantial plane of existence, the astral plane, if the substantial reality were not warmed up and illuminated by the essential warmth and light. – ED.

In addition to those who, after their physical death, proceed to the astral plane, this zone girdling the earth is also inhabited by many other beings. Apart from all those beings which I already mentioned — for example, elementals, larvae, schemata, and phantoms — there are also the beings of the elements on this plane. In the chapter in this book titled "Hierarchy," I describe the individual beings of the elements and their principals in more detail. Any being that wishes to somehow make its presence known on our physical world, regardless of where it comes from (even if it comes from the highest spheres), must without exception pass through the astral sphere, because the zone girdling the earth is the first zone that is located directly next to the physical world. The zone girdling the earth is called Malkuth (The Kingdom) in the Kabbalah. The reader will find further explanations in *The Key to the True Kabbalah*.

In the astral world, the zone girdling the earth, the same powers prevail and are at work in the same manner as they are in the physical world; however, they are of a finer substance. Here, too, you find the Fire element with its salamanders or Fire spirits, the Air element with its fairies, sylphs or Air spirits, the Water element with its nymphs, undines or Water spirits, and the Earth element with its gnomes or Earth spirits. As fish move about in the water in the physical world, even so do all beings in the astral sphere of the zone girdling the earth move about in the other elements. Every element has positive and negative beings. For example, you could say that there are good and evil salamanders. This also applies to all the beings of the other elements. In reality, good and evil do not exist, because Divine Providence created nothing that is bad and disharmonious; this is only a human concept. From the Hermetic point of view, one type of being has to bring forth positive influences, whereas another type has to bring forth negative influences. In an astral respect these beings are the tools of the effects on our physical world. They are also the cause of all effects in the astral body of every human being, whether they are initiated or not.

The activities and effects of the Fire and Air elements in the astral sphere call forth the astral-electric fluid, and the activities and effects of the Water and Earth elements call forth the astral-magnetic fluid. The spirit-beings use these fluids to create the effects or rather the causes in our physical world. The Akasha Principle of the astral sphere maintains the harmonious equilibrium of the elements in the entire astral sphere. If a being of the astral sphere wishes to exert an influence on our physical world, it does not matter whether it is a spirit-being of the elements or a human inhabitant. This being must possess the ability to condense both the electric and the magnetic fluids to such a degree that the fluids can be realized on our physical world. An experienced magician can bring about the condensing process with the aid of his imagination by controlling the elements and the fluids. When working passively, the condensing of the elements and the fluids can be brought about by a medium from whom the spirit-beings withdraw the necessary electric and magnetic fluids vampirically in order to achieve the desired effects.

It is well known that the difference between a being of the elements and a human being is that a being of the elements consists of only one element, the very principle which preserves it, whereas a human being is composed of all four elements plus the fifth element, the Akasha Principle. An elemental being can only work with the one element and one fluid to which it belongs, whereas a human being can become acquainted with all the powers and can also control them. However, this applies in both cases to a human being as well as the elemental being; the determining principle is Divine Providence or the Akasha Principle. A human being can incarnate, whereas a being of the elements cannot do so by itself. In contrast to the human astral body, the astral body of a being of the elements dissolves into its element, whereas the human astral body dissolves into all four elements. There is also another difference: the being of the elements ceases to exist through its death, because it possesses a mortal spirit. However, a human being, who, since he was created in the image of God, is the macrocosm on a small scale, possesses an individual immortal spirit. Through a particular magical practice it is possible to modify the being that has only one element into a being with four elements and to give it an immortal spirit. But a magician will seldom intervene without good reason, because he is responsible and must justify his actions before Divine Providence.

The Akasha Principle of the astral sphere determines if and when a human being that lives in the astral world reincarnates on our physical world. The astral light-substance, also known as astral light, is the highest divine emanation in the astral world. To initiates who focus on the divine principle in the astral world, this light principle appears to them as a gleaming sunlight or as a sun, provided that they are able to see the Divine in the light of the physical world and that they do not materialize their Divinity or give it a particular form. The religion of every individual takes its course in the astral sphere in as far as he has given his God a form and a name on the physical plane in accordance with his religious ideology. Atheists have no need for God on the astral plane and, while they are there, they do not even have the ability to imagine God, despite the fact that they yearn for something Higher, similar to a person who is thirsting for water. For those who simultaneously believed in several religions and divinities while on earth, the effect in the astral world is utter chaos. These people have a somewhat more difficult position, because they cannot decide on a particular form. But in the course of their development on the astral plane, their concept of God clarifies and they confess to the idea of God which was always closest to them. This concept of God is many times the determining factor as to where they will incarnate next.

During his lifetime a magician who explores the astral sphere of the earth zone knows about the activities and effects of the powers and beings of the astral sphere from his own experience. In addition, the spiritual beings with which he works can provide him this information as well.

A magician who has not quite achieved an absolute magical development will use his spiritual guides to learn about the astral plane. He will take their advice, be it in the form of passive communication through automatic writing, or by whatever means he may choose. When the magician reaches the astral plane for the first few times, he is guided by his spiritual guides who, in accordance with our earthly concepts, teach him and support him while on that plane. Highly developed spiritual beings of the zone girdling the earth condense themselves on the particular astral level and in this manner become the guides of individuals or entire groups. They initiate the astral beings who are under their care into the higher laws. In the astral sphere these guides should never be coerced and, in accordance with their maturity and development, Divine Providence assigns them to each astral being. In the astral sphere the guide teaches his protégé the laws, and he also assists him in his development as a whole. These guides could also be called "guardian spirits" or "tutelary spirits." It sometimes occurs that an astral human being sets out to undertake something on his own. However, at the critical moment his genius or guide warns him not to act independently. The guardian spirit intervenes immediately when an astral human who is not sufficiently developed undertakes something that is contrary to the laws of Divine Providence. The guide instructs his protégé on the laws of the physical world and prepares him for his next incarnation. All these preparations clearly show that a human being must perfect himself in the physical world through his magical development in order to be prepared for the higher world.

All acts of fate that lead a person in the physical world to purify his spirit and which help him to gather the experiences he requires for his spiritual development are already prepared for him in the astral world by Divine Providence in accordance with his maturity and development. The being that is to incarnate again is well informed about the conditions that await him in the physical world. In addition, the being agrees to these conditions while still in the astral world; yes, he even wishes to go through this ordeal, this learning process. However, the very moment a human being incarnates, he or she loses all the knowledge of what Divine Providence has in store for that person. If a person that lives in the material world were to know in advance exactly everything that is ahead of him, then he would no longer have any free will in the physical world. Then he would be in all his actions no more than a stereotype or a mere robot, and the task which he would have to carry out on this world would be impossible to accomplish. Only an initiated magician of higher rank, one who has become a master over karma and a master over cause and effect, one who feels at home in the material world as well as in the astral world, is mature enough to know everything in advance without influencing his free will in a detrimental manner.

Beings from the astral world incarnate on our planet, limited by time and space, in order to continue to work on their development, because the physical laws of the material plane offer by far more obstacles to every individual than in the astral sphere. The obstacles of the material world strengthen the spirit and consequently the spirit's development is much faster on earth than in the astral sphere. That is why human beings in the astral sphere feel the urge to incarnate again in the material world as soon as possible. In return they accept the most difficult conditions, for no other reason than to continue to pursue the path of spiritual development.

Each individual can attain the level of perfection, because the entire evolution of humankind leads towards perfection. The spiritual guide who has been assigned by Divine Providence in the astral sphere to each human being for his initiation guides and supervises the spiritual development of his protégé, and continues to do so in many instances even after his protégé has incarnated in the physical world. That is why a magician should make every effort to contact his guardian spirit immediately at the onset of his development. The practice regarding how this contact can be made is described in *Initiation into Hermetics*. It does happen occasionally that a few individuals who, on earth, were already highly developed do achieve the completion of their spiritual perfection in the astral world. However, these human beings have been chosen by Divine Providence to fulfil one or more missions on earth. These spiritual guides are magicians and initiates at birth who, after a certain period of time during the physical development of their human body, suddenly become aware of their state and their level of development. This generally occurs immediately after puberty. At this point in their spiritual development they require only very little to be mature enough to fulfil the mission given to them by Divine Providence. These missions do not always have to be of a magical or spiritual nature; they may also concern other fields of endeavor in the material world. This explains the birth of brilliant human beings and inventors, so-called geniuses, in all fields of material knowledge or science. A magician knows that all of this is determined in advance and directed by Divine Providence, i.e. the Akasha Principle of the astral world. A magician can find the explanation for everything that occurs by employing the universal laws.

This is a general outline of the astral sphere, inclusive of its most important aspects. The astral sphere is also known as the earth zone or the zone girdling the earth, and it is on a higher level than our physical world in the order of things. The earth zone, even though it is set above us in the order of things, is, in accordance with human concepts, not the densest form, because it contains the most diverse intensities of light, oscillations and vibrations that correspond with the level of maturity of every human being. The earth zone is not limited — not only does it extend over our globe but over the entire cosmos. The lawfulness of the earth zone is not to be understood as an area in space, rather it refers to our entire microcosm and macrocosm and is analogously connected with the entire microcosm and macrocosm. This is the reason why a human being can achieve his perfection, his highest magical maturity, his bond with God, only in the earth zone. From a magical point of view this clearly indicates that the earth zone contains the lowest levels but also the highest emanation of the Divine Principle.

Subsequently I shall explain that there are other zones that correspond with the hierarchy and with which a magician can come into contact. Of course, as a perfect being, as the personified image of God, he can also inhabit the earth zone. On the earth zone the entire creation manifests, beginning with the highest perfection of God and continuing down to the lowest and coarsest forms. A human being can make contact with every sphere that is above the earth zone, but he can never become a permanent inhabitant of these higher spheres, because the earth zone is a reflection of the entire creation. It is the world where everything manifests in a density that has the greatest variety of degrees. The ancient Kabbalists were well aware of this truth, and they correctly identified the earth zone as Malkuth, which does not stand for "globe," but rather means "kingdom."[8] This is to be understood as the principle of creation from the highest to the lowest manifestation. The principle of creation contains, in accordance with the Kabbalistic Tree of Life, the Kabbalistic number 10, which indicates the beginning of the ascent. The number 10 is the coarsest form, but for a Kabbalist the number 10 is the reflection of the number 1, which means God, because the number 10 can be reduced to a 1 by simply deleting the 0. An intuitive magician immediately realizes the true relationship between creation and his physical body, and he comes to the conclusion that he has ten fingers and ten toes with good reason.

---

[8] Kingdom = *Reich* in German. – ED.

However, the reader will find more information about this subject in *The Key to the True Kabbalah*. Furthermore, the intuitive magician will find a certain relationship between the earth zone and the muladhara center; however, I leave the considerations regarding this subject to the magician himself.

3.   The Moon zone is next to the zone girdling the earth. The Moon zone is the zone with which the magician must become acquainted immediately after he has become acquainted with the earth zone.

4.   Next to the Moon zone we find the Mercury zone, which is followed by the Venus zone.

5.   Once the magician has become sufficiently acquainted with the hierarchy of these zones, he continues and begins to learn about

6.   the Sun zone and later on he becomes acquainted with

7.   the Mars zone, which is followed by

8.   the Jupiter zone, and finally with the last zone,

9.   the Saturn zone.

Besides the aforementioned zones, there are many others. But for the magician, these zones should suffice. He should first become acquainted with these zones which correspond to the planets, and he must also gain the ability to control them completely.

The following chapter contains the analogies and the hierarchies of each zone. Any sphere that lies above the earth zone from the Moon to Saturn has a threefold effect, namely upon:

1.   the mental world,
2.   the astral world, and
3.   the physical world.

Depending in which plane of the earth zone a certain effect is to be released, the creation of the cause for that effect in that particular plane must be taken into consideration, because the zones mentioned exert a very particular influence upon our earth zone. Therefore, when working with these beings, the magician must form an exact impression in his mind of the analogy of the laws of each zone regarding his own microcosm as well as the influence they can exert on the microcosm of any other human being. A magician must be completely conversant with every analogy of these zones as they apply to the microcosm and macrocosm, and he must understand how to bring about the cause that is analogous to the correspondences by means of the beings. The magician will not only imagine that every zone above the earth zone is a clearly defined limited plane, but he will also imagine that all zones in the macrocosm and microcosm are interconnected in accordance with their density and with their influences and effects. These zones carry astrological nomenclatures, but directly they have nothing to do with the individual stars of the universe, even though a certain relationship exists between the stars and the constellations, from which astrologers draw their conclusions for mantic purposes or for the determination of unfavorable influences. I have previously mentioned the synthesis of astrology.

Each zone is populated, as is the already familiar earth zone. The beings of the zones have their particular tasks, and they are subject to the laws of their zone in respect to cause and effect. In accordance to our concepts, there are millions of beings in each zone. It is impossible to categorize these beings by level. Every being is on a certain level of spiritual development, of maturity, and on the basis of this he has been given a specific task.

It is impossible for a human being who has not quite reached the required level of magical development and the necessary maturity to contact an astral being beyond the sphere of the material world, let alone establish a connection with beings who inhabit the higher spheres. There are only a few individuals on our physical world who tower with their spirits above the borders of human existence and who possess the ability to penetrate through the earth zone into another zone beyond. In the Hermetic sciences, human beings who are capable of consciously bringing about these feats are called initiates. An initiate is a "chosen one" who, after numerous years of spiritual development, has reached the level of maturity necessary for the tasks he has to fulfil. A true initiate is not a philosopher; he is not a person who has attained his maturity through mere theoretical knowledge. Instead, he has broken away from the masses of the ordinary after a very rigorous, persistent and continuous schooling, and he has acquired his knowledge through practice. Here the verse in the Bible applies, "For many be called, but few chosen." There are no limits, and that applies to everyone on earth. Therefore, a student who seriously aspires to succeed in magic can, after conscientious schooling, attain the level of perfection and become a chosen one. Any person on our earth can attain the most exalted levels of maturity.

Hence there are only a few who possess the ability to mentally travel beyond the normal sphere of the zone girdling the earth and to visit the next sphere with their spirit. In the magic sciences, these human beings are the principals or heads, the initiators and teachers. They have the holy task and duty to assist those who are under their tutelage on their spiritual path. In accordance with the universal laws, the same procedure applies to the seven zones that are located above the earth zone. And these few individuals among the millions of beings on these populated zones, who have reached the necessary state of maturity, hold the rank of principals or potentates in these zones, and they are also the initiates. As in the zone girdling the earth, the appropriate honor is bestowed upon an initiate in accordance with his level of maturity and knowledge by giving him the rank of a baron, count, prince, duke etc. This also applies to the principals of all the other zones — they also have their rank, their dignity and their titles. Every magician is well aware of the fact that these nomenclatures of rank and title symbolically represent the level of maturity of a particular being, and they know that this ranking order cannot be compared with that in our physical world. Therefore, only the principals, in other words the initiates of the individual zones, are capable of making their influence known on our plane with their causes and effects, be it in the mental, astral or physical world.

The kind of influence that every being analogous to our world must and can achieve on our world will be explained in "Part Two: Hierarchy." As there are in our earth zone, and in accordance with our human concepts, positive, good beings, and negative, evil beings, so it is in the other zones as well. The positive powers and beings are commonly referred to as "angels" or "archangels," whereas the negative powers or beings are referred to as "demons" or "arch-demons." The same ranking order also applies to the negative beings; there are the common demons and there are also barons, counts, and so forth. The average person will visualize these beings in accordance with his powers of perception and in his imagination he will see the angels and archangels with wings and the demons and arch-demons with horns. Whosoever is conversant with this kind of symbolism will be able to interpret this point of view in the correct manner. It is a well known fact for every magician that angels in the true sense of the word do not have wings. And he will interpret the symbolic significance correctly in that wings are analogous to birds, which can move about freely in the air above us mortals. Wings are the symbol of that which is higher than us, the symbol of lightness, freedom and the lack of restraint. At the same time wings are the symbol of that which is lighter and which floats above the earth and therefore they also represent the all-penetrating principle. The negative beings or demons are portrayed with animalistic symbols, with horns and tails, and furthermore as creatures that are half-human, half-animal. Their symbolism is the opposite of good and it indicates the subordinate, the imperfect, the flawed etc. It is of course another question, as far as the uninitiated are concerned, as to whether these beings, both positive and negative, actually possess the forms which are attributed to them by human beings in their respective spheres, and whether they appear to one another in that particular form. However, a magician who has the ability to personally visit the individual zones via mental and astral travel and who influences himself with the vibration of that particular zone in order to become an inhabitant of the particular sphere for the duration of his temporary stay, will find that this is untrue. He will find, without losing his individuality, entirely different forms in these spheres, but this cannot be expressed with words. The beings and principals which he will perceive there are not personified beings. Instead, they are powers and vibrations which are analogous to the names and attributes. Should a magician, from his individual point of view, decide to materialize one of these powers, or if he were to give this power a form that is accessible to his receptivity, then this power would appear to him in the form which corresponds to his symbolic abilities of perception. It is irrelevant whether they are positive powers or angels, or negative powers or demons. When a magician works with beings, these beings implement the causes in those zones upon which the magician asserts his influence, whereas a Kabbalist transfers his spirit into the zone in which the cause and effect are to be produced. Even though a Kabbalist is completely conversant with the laws of that zone, he achieves his purpose not through mediation with the beings that live there, but accomplishes everything himself with the help of the Kabbalistic word. The reader will find more details in *The Key to the True Kabbalah*.

The procedure when working with the Kabbalah is quite different from that employed by the magician. However, at this particular level of development and until he reaches a higher one, a magician can do nothing else but make use of these beings. One must first become a magician before he can become a Kabbalist. As a Kabbalist, one works differently and more advantageously.

When a magician summons or evokes a being from another zone into the earth zone or into our physical world without having any knowledge of its form, then the being must, if it wants to assume a visible form, choose one that symbolizes its attribute in order to come into contact with the magician. An ordinary demon does not have this ability, because for a demon which does not possess the necessary maturity, it is impossible to condense or materialize himself from his sphere into the earth zone or into our material sphere. That is why most books on the subject of invocation do not mention any kind of common demon, but deal exclusively with beings of rank and title. However, not one single book contains any precise details on this subject matter.

Here the question might arise as to whether a being that inhabits another zone would be in a position to evoke an initiate, a human being of spiritual rank, into its zone. From the Hermetic point of view the answer is no, because a human being, especially an initiate, is a Godlike being and therefore symbolizes the macrocosm on a small scale and represents absolute authority in the microcosm and macrocosm. Consequently, a magician cannot be coerced to do anything by any being regardless of its rank. The only exception is Divine Providence. All principals, without exception, regardless of their rank and zone, be they good or evil, are only partial aspects of the macrocosm. And without the permission of Divine Providence they cannot force their will or someone else's will upon a perfected magician who has achieved within himself a bond with God. Instead, all beings must unconditionally obey the magician's will. The magician gathers from this and from many other things the true value of a human being and his significance in creation, especially a human being who has a bond with God.

Should a being of another zone wish to descend upon the earth zone, particularly upon our physical world, either upon the orders of Divine Providence or at its own discretion, be it in the mental, astral or physical form, then the being or principal must, regardless of its rank, assume the symbolic form that is analogous to the attributes of its inherent sphere. For example, an angel would appear as a flawless beauty because his main attribute symbolizes love. A being whose attribute is strictness would appear in accordance with that attribute. This rule also applies to the negative beings; these beings will assume the forms that symbolize their negative attributes when they make their appearance on the earth zone or even on our physical world. A magician who is well-versed in symbolism can, on the basis of a being's appearance, immediately determine the being's attributes, whether it is a positive or negative being and regardless of its zone of origin. The attributes of a being, its appearance and symbolic representation, are precisely analogous to its name and, in accordance with the law of analogy, also with all the other analogies. Even a being of the highest rank cannot give a name that does not correspond with its attributes. A magician who is well-versed in the Kabbalah can, in accordance with the law of analogy, examine the correspondences exactly and determine whether any statement made by such a being is in accordance with the facts. There is not one being, not even the greatest liar or most evil being, that would dare give any other name than its true name to a perfected magician, nor will it assume any form other than the one that corresponds with its attributes. It is of course at the discretion of a perfected magician to order a being who has appeared in its actual true form to assume another form that best serves the magician's purpose. A being will always obey a genuine magician and it has already been mentioned repeatedly that a true magician represents the absolute authority, for he is a God-man.

Regardless of which zone a being inhabits, every being, good or evil, angel or archangel, demon or arch-demon, has been limited by

Divine Providence in its attributes and is dependent upon these attributes in its zone. Therefore, a magician is well advised only to ask a being what it can achieve on the basis of its attributes and what lies within the scope of its zone. A magician must be well-versed in all the attributes, qualities, causes and effects, powers and influences of the individual zones. He must also be in complete control of them to avoid making the mistake of demanding something from a being that is outside the range of its zone. Should a magician neglect to take these details into consideration and demand an effect from a being that does not lie within that being's sphere of influence, then the magician runs the risk that the being will enter another zone in order to fulfil the magician's wish and will. And while there, the being will make the necessary arrangements with another being which is capable of achieving the desired effect. This effect is not achieved by the being the magician summoned, but by another being. In this particular case the absolute will of the magician is not expressed, because the effect was accomplished without his knowledge. In "Part Two: Hierarchy," I shall give an in-depth description of the individual forms of the beings and how they generally appear.

It would also be of interest to the magician to know the method a being from another zone employs to achieve the desired effect on our plane, be it mentally, astrally or physically. Since the magician's will and desire is analogous with the attributes of the zone with which he works, the being which is charged with the task creates the particular cause with the electric and magnetic fluids in the causal world of its own zone in order to achieve the particular effect. The method is similar to the method of volting, as described in *Initiation into Hermetics*. Or the magician accomplishes this through the word, the cosmic language, and directs it through the causal world of the particular zone and imaginatively condenses it in the causal world of the earth zone into the mental, astral and physical world, depending upon the effect he wishes to achieve. This is the actual working procedure of beings that have the ability to assert their influence on our plane from their zone. However, there is not one being that can, on its own accord and at its own discretion, assert any kind of influence on our plane. Only upon strict orders from a magician who has absolute authority can a being from its zone assert its influence with an effect upon our plane. In this case the being is not responsible for anything, because all responsibility rests upon the magician. In other words, the work of a being is the same as the work a servant does for his master. In this case a servant is not responsible for the task he has to carry out on his master's orders.

A true magician will never dare demand that a being, especially if it is a negative one, carry out any effects that may have detrimental consequences. Although the magician has become master of life and death and master of the laws, Divine Providence still rules above him and he must pay dearly for evil deeds that he cannot justify.

The questions may now arise: Why would a magician employ the services of an elemental, an elementary, an astral being or a physically condensed being for his work on certain spheres or planes which he uses mentally, astrally or physically? Why does he not prefer to work with the help of his own powers that he has acquired and produce the effects magically? The main reasons why a magician evokes beings are: (1) he wants to confirm and establish his authority over the beings and make them aware of it; and (2) he wants to obtain accurate knowledge from the beings about their zone.

For certain operations performed by the magician on the mental plane, he can produce the effect through elementals or through volting i.e. the electromagnetic fluid. Furthermore, a magician possesses the ability to produce a physical energy and physical effects through various practices with elementaries. The difference in these operations lies in the fact that the powers or energies, entities and beings, the elementals and elementaries which he created, cannot act independently, because they do not possess their own intelligence, whereas the beings of every zone fulfil tasks with their inherent intelligence. These are, of course, tasks that require a certain degree of intelligence. Whenever a magician, during his work, can dispense with the services of a being in order to achieve his wishes, he will certainly refrain from employing a being from a zone for his purposes.

Every experienced magician who leaves the physical world either with his mental or astral body, and travels to the various levels of the earth zone or the zones beyond will observe that all the beings of all the zones, regardless of their particular qualities and attributes, speak only one universal language. This language is called "the picture language" and it is the language of the imagination. And that is the reason why all beings can communicate with one another. Every human being will have the same experience as soon as he leaves his physical body and departs from this world. He will be able to immediately speak or communicate with every other departed human being regardless of what nation he belonged to on earth or what language he spoke. Should a magician wish to speak, i.e. form ideas, in any sphere other than our physical plane, he would naturally do so with his voice, but no sound would be produced. Instead he would produce vibrations, which immediately would manifest as pictures that can be perceived by every being.

When a being embodies on our physical world, i.e. leaves the zone it inhabits and condenses on our earth so that it can be seen and heard, then the picture language immediately turns into audible speech and into a language the magician speaks or understands. Any religious person or one who is conversant with the Bible probably remembers the passage where Christ's apostles and disciples, after the Savior's death, were shadowed by the Holy Ghost and could speak any language that was spoken on earth. The Bible expresses it as follows: " ...filled with the Holy Ghost!" which means that Christ's disciples had access to the astral world through the spiritual shadowing or enlightenment by the Holy Ghost. Therefore they received the ability to turn the picture language of the astral world into any language they were required to speak. Hence this is not a miracle, because every being has this ability. Every person who is somewhat conversant with the Hermetic sciences knows that the cosmic language is the language of pictures, and he also knows that the ancient nations mostly communicated in that language. The best example of those times still exists today in the form of the Egyptian hieroglyphs. There is no doubt that words that are spoken in the picture language have an especially strong magical effect. It is not without good reason that people in the Orient, as well as other regions of the world, have made use of the picture language, and that this was the cradle of the Hermetic sciences.

Chapter 17
Advantages And Disadvantages
Of Evocative Magic

Many individuals who somehow manage to obtain a book on evocative magic succumb, because of the various methods described in these books, to the temptation of immediately trying to implement the recommended practices without having attained the magical development required for evocative magic. They believe that if they follow the inadequate preparations recommended in the instructions, it will be sufficient to ensure success. There are usually various reasons as to the motives for a rash decision to engage in evocative magic without any previous magical training. It could be mere curiosity that urges someone to see for himself whether these spheres truly exist. Someone else might wish to see real spirits, spiritual beings and demons. Another person might hope to gain some advantages through magical operations, and yet another might want to summon a being to obtain certain powers and abilities, gain the favors of women, gain fame and honor etc. Another person might want to obtain certain information or harm a person who stands in his way or whom he dislikes. Countless other motives could be mentioned which could tempt a careless person to pursue evocative magic. This chapter is written especially for those people who pursue evocative magic solely for the above-mentioned reasons and similar purposes, so that they may take these warnings to heart. Because ignorance does not prevent a person from the danger, disadvantages or misfortunes which are part of any magical operation if undertaken without any previous schooling and proper development.

If someone dares to practice evocative magic without being magically developed or prepared, he can be certain that he will have no success at all. And as a result he will probably not pursue this matter any further, or it could happen that his failure will even make him more of an unbeliever than before. Being bitter about his failures, he will declare that all magic is nothing but a lie, without looking first for the cause of his failures within himself and without realizing that magical knowledge must be more closely and more thoroughly pursued before any success can be achieved.

A person who has attained at least partial spiritual development and a certain power of the imagination in his present or previous incarnation can attain at least a partial success in evocative magic, even though it will not be a sweeping success. From the Hermetic point of view, these types of people are considered to be, and rightfully so, sorcerers and necromancers. And they are the ones who fall victim to the invisible powers. There are enough examples in history, the most famous and most prominent of which is the Faust tragedy chronicled by the German author and scientist, Goethe. I refrain from describing Faust's character, because every true magician knows what happened in this case.

Every true magician works consciously or from a point of knowledge with these spiritual powers. As a result of his magical development and maturity, a true magician represents a particular authority, power and might to these powers, and his attitude towards these spiritual beings is entirely different than that of a sorcerer. The influence that a magician exerts upon a spiritual being is entirely different and the dangers to which he is exposed are so minimal that they do not even have to be mentioned. A magician might only be subjected to some temptation by the spiritual beings, but since he has achieved a magical equilibrium, nothing can deter him from his path, not even the most alluring temptations. The beings acknowledge his authority and consider him to be the master, the image of creation and therefore the image of God. They serve him gladly and they dare not ask for anything in return for their services. It is, however, quite a different matter when it comes to a necromancer or sorcerer, because he is incapable of summoning the necessary authority in respect to the beings. A necromancer or sorcerer is always at risk of losing his equilibrium, at the expense of his individuality and magical development.

Should a necromancer or a sorcerer have a fairly good fantasy at his disposal, and should he have the ability to elevate his consciousness, then it could happen — at least in part — that by using magical names during a magical operation (even though they might be barbaric) one of his invocations may actually change into the language of that spiritual being, and the being he summons will hear this language. However, the question still remains: Will this being react to this invocation and will it comply with the wishes of the sorcerer? The being immediately senses whether the sorcerer has reached the necessary maturity and development to be able to compel it to fulfil his wishes, or whether it can ignore the sorcerer altogether. Should the power summoned be a positive being, a good being, then this being will have nothing but pity for the sorcerer. Should the being be of lesser importance and a less active being, and provided the wish of the sorcerer will not cause any harm if it becomes reality, then a being may occasionally make an exception and comply with the sorcerer's wish.

However, should the sorcerer entertain wishes which could harm himself as well as others, and if he has not reached a level that allows him to take full responsibility for his acts, then the being will not react to the sorcerer's invocation. All methods of coercion listed in the various books used by sorcerers to obtain the services of beings to fulfil their wishes, are powerless and empty words and exert little or no influence at all upon the astral beings. Negative beings are more likely to react to negative or evil intentions, and they may help a sorcerer realize them. A principal of demons knows very well that he does not have to carry out the wishes of a sorcerer who entertains the notion of fulfilling wishes that would place a heavy karmic burden upon himself or is unable to take the karmic responsibility. In such a case not even a demon would dare to fulfil the sorcerer's wish, because a being is dependent upon Divine Providence, even if it is negative. Such a being cannot, at its own discretion, call forth any vibrations which would cause a chaotic state in the harmony of a plane.

Therefore, it must be emphasized repeatedly that a particular magical development and maturity is absolutely necessary for the evocation of spiritual beings from any sphere. This maturity also extends to transferring one's consciousness into a particular plane or zone, and to changing one's thoughts into the picture language, the cosmic language, in order that a spiritual being can understand our language.

On the basis of these instructions, the magician now has the knowledge to attach the proper value and importance to his book of formulas. Now he realizes that it is actually a book containing the cosmic language in which he records his entire working procedures employed during evocative magic. He records it in the symbolic picture language, not in his native tongue.

A necromancer or a sorcerer who works with these weird rituals and carries out barbaric invocations and incantations is incapable of systematically carrying out an orderly incantation, i.e. of speaking with the spiritual being. Nor does he have the ability to represent an authority, because a sorcerer or a necromancer lacks the magical maturity and development. At best, a necromancer might achieve an ecstatic state during such an operation, but it cannot be considered any more than simply a mere shout into that particular zone, even when his citations are most terrifying and appear very promising to him.

In most cases the sorcerer is subjected to the most corrupt hallucinations due to the ecstatic state in which he finds himself. Under the most favorable circumstance, an elemental or elementary could be created involuntarily as a result of the ecstatic tension of the sorcerer's nerve energies during his inadequate invocation. However, this depends on how much nerve energy the sorcerer projects from his magic circle into the magic triangle. Unbeknownst to the sorcerer, this elementary will assume the form of the desired being, because the sorcerer cannot distinguish this being from the one he is trying to evoke and thus considers this being to be the one he summoned. Such a being is capable of arousing particular wishes or desires in its creator and is also capable of satisfying these wishes. In my first book, *Initiation into Hermetics,* I describe in detail the dangers connected with these kinds of evocations.

In connection with this, I must draw your attention to the fact that a magician must completely understand what a pact is, how a pact comes about, and what the disadvantages are. I shall now give the reader more information in this regard.

Should a sorcerer or a necromancer be successful in elevating his spirit to an ecstatic state during an invocation and actually summon a principal from a particular sphere into the physical world, then, provided it is a negative being, this principal will always endeavor to control the sorcerer's soul and spirit and make him completely dependent. It is usually during the second or third operation that the sorcerer realizes he is no longer capable of bringing about the same ecstatic state which helped him to exert a certain influence upon the particular sphere. These feelings give the sorcerer a deep sense of inner insecurity which causes him to literally seize the being he has evoked in order to have his wishes realized. The principal spirit-being that now appears to him will not react at all to the sorcerer's words if it is not certain that the sorcerer's soul and spirit are mature enough to serve it. Because the principal of the spiritual beings can see the many karmic developments which the sorcerer has already undergone, and he can determine whether it is a worthwhile endeavor to strive for the sorcerer's soul and spirit. He can also determine whether the sorcerer has achieved a certain degree of intelligence and maturity, and whether, after his death, the sorcerer will serve him well in his sphere. While the sorcerer performs his invocation the being, while still in its sphere, is already in possession of all these facts. If the being determines that the sorcerer can serve its purpose, then a principal or head (namely one of the negative powers) will appear to him and will attempt anything that is within its power to obtain the sorcerer for its own purposes. Such a being employs various methods depending upon the sorcerer's character traits, and because it also knows the sorcerer's weakest character flaws, i.e. where he is most vulnerable. Should the sorcerer be timid by nature, then the being will try its utmost to intimidate him and make him submissive. However, should the sorcerer be somewhat aware of the strength of his soul and spirit, then the being will make all kinds of promises to him, for example that it will grant him every wish or initiate him into everything etc. At the same time it will point out to the sorcerer that it can only fulfil these promises if he consents to a mutual agreement, and then it makes the sorcerer aware of all the advantages of such an agreement or pact. At this point it is up to the sorcerer to resist the temptations of the being and to oppose him. Now a battle ensues with one's own conscience, and it is quite a formidable struggle, because a human being's conscience is the subtlest form of Divine Providence. Should the sorcerer choose not to listen to the divine warnings of his inner voice, i.e. his conscience, and should he knowingly and repeatedly suppress these warnings, then he falls victim to such a being and usually enters into a pact.

Since this subject matter is probably of interest to almost everyone, I shall spend more time on it and examine it more closely from a

Hermetic point of view. Why does a being yearn for the soul and the spirit of a sorcerer? The reasons are several. First of all, there is not a single spiritual being, especially a negative one, that will do anything for a sorcerer unless it receives something in return. A sorcerer is compelled in accordance with the terms of the pact to leave the earth zone[9] after his departure from his physical body.[10] As legend has it, such a person is actually taken by the devil and must enter the sphere of the being with which he made the pact, in order to be a servant there.

The principal with whom the pact has been established usually sends these departed sorcerers to the various regions of the earth zone, whether that be the mental, astral or physical plane. There they have to carry out tasks for their master that correspond to the negative sphere of the particular being. A principal likes to form an alliance with a sorcerer, since a sorcerer, as a human being, is created in the image of God and as such is tetrapolar and has by far more possibilities than the principal himself. A principal turns his human servant in most cases into a so-called *spiritus familiaris* or *factotum* and puts him at the disposal of other similar sorcerers. As a *spiritus familiaris*, the sorcerer is bestowed with all the powers of the principal spirit-being, because from this point onward the sorcerer becomes a representative of the principal. This transfer of power either happens by receiving an *ankhur* from the principal or the demon prince, or by receiving the power to influence the zone; thus he calls forth the effects with which he is charged and achieves the desired results. Or other servant spirits are placed at his disposal to fulfil his wishes. Whether these servant spirits are also victims or whether they are actual inhabitants of the zone and underlings of their master is difficult to determine, because they cannot disclose anything about themselves. This matter is usually handled in such a manner that undesirable phases are expunged from the memory or consciousness of the servant spirit through a magic word or other practices. The sorcerer, in spite of his tetra-polarity, is dependent upon the sphere of the principal, his master. This prevents him from liberating himself from the fetters that exist between him and his principal

---

[9] The zone girdling the earth. – ED.
[10] After his physical death. – ED.

107

and acting in accordance with his own will. And therefore he becomes a tool of the principal and must carry out all the principal's orders.

Upon conclusion of the pact, the sorcerer does not commence with the actual work for weeks, sometimes even months, because he has to be initiated and instructed by the principal in the various practices and shown how to employ the powers that are given to him. The conclusion of a pact does not differ too much from those described in the grimoires or books of sorcery. There is, however, a lesser known fact which is not mentioned in these books. The being himself does not draw up the pact; rather, it is composed and written down by the sorcerer and the procedure is very similar to the book of formulas. The text of the pact is written in regular ink — or perhaps in special ink, depending on the rituals that apply in this case. Of course, this circumstance is not of great importance. The pact clearly stipulates the kind of services the being has to provide, the kind of wishes it has to fulfil, the possibilities and opportunities the pact offers the sorcerer, and all the other conditions which the being has to keep in so far as the sorcerer is concerned. On the other side of the pact are the obligations that the sorcerer has to fulfil and which he takes upon himself, the obligations he has to carry out and the kind of obligation which the being itself stipulates. Furthermore, the pact also contains the manner in which the principal is to be summoned, whether he is to appear visibly or invisibly, and how the sorcerer must deal with servant spirits if they are at his disposal or when they are to be part of the pact etc.

The most important point is the duration and expiration of the pact, and when the sorcerer is obliged to enter the sphere of the demon. Even the method by which the sorcerer dies and how his departure from the physical world into the sphere of the principal will take place are established and agreed upon in the pact. Then all points and conditions are confirmed and acknowledged by both parties. The being usually draws his seal in a mediumistic manner by using the sorcerer's hand. This serves as its signature, i.e. the confirmation of a mutual agreement. It can also happen that the being may attach great importance to the sorcerer's signature being written in his own blood and may even insist upon it. However, there were and are pacts where this is not a condition. Usually these pacts are executed in duplicate whereby one copy goes to the sorcerer and the other copy to the being. It is said that the being takes possession of both copies. However, this occurs rarely, and only when a sorcerer deals with a certain category of beings. It is customary that the sorcerer fold the second copy and burn it. Through this burning procedure the ideas and thoughts contained in the pact are transmitted to the zone of the being.

There might be some minor variations by which pacts are signed and sealed, especially with negative beings. A pact cannot be breached either by the sorcerer or the being, and all the terms of the pact must be met by both parties. It often happens that the victim does not know that he has fallen prey to such a pact, and he enters the sphere of the being without being aware that he has to repay it for services rendered. Should the sorcerer's conscience gain the upper hand before the expiration of the pact and he attempts to release himself of his contractual obligations, then under these circumstances the being does everything in its power to harm the sorcerer in a most treacherous manner and attempts to destroy him. Many witch trials of the past are undeniable proof that this happened, when sorcerers regretted entering into a pact with a demon and tried to liberate themselves from it. This usually resulted in severe suffering at the instigation of the being for the breach of the pact. In antiquity many sorcerers did not seek to escape burning at the stake, because within them the thought and the divine spark gained the upper hand and they chose death rather than to remain in contact with the demon until the expiration of the pact. Whereas sorcerers who strictly adhered to the pact and did everything in accordance with the terms of the pact until it expired were always under the protection of the dark forces and no power in the world could harm them.

The terms of the pact described here are those which are mostly in use. Through his pact, the sorcerer maintains an effortless direct contact with the spirit-being or his subordinates.

Now the question might arise: Is such a sorcerer at the mercy or in the service of a being or principal forever? For a magician who is at home in all the spheres, the answer to this question presents no problem. As soon as the sorcerer has repaid his principal demon with compound interest for the services provided by the principal on earth, then the sorcerer's conscience begins to stir to an increasing extent and his tetrapolar nature gradually feels the liberation from its bondage. In accordance to our calendar, the time the sorcerer spends in the demon's sphere could last several centuries, since time and space do not exist in those spheres. And, of course, as soon as the sorcerer has paid his debt to the last penny, he is master of his time again. Should the sorcerer at this time choose to suppress his conscience even though it makes itself known, or if he prefers not to listen to his conscience, then he will continue to remain in the sphere of his principal.

He will begin to gradually lose his tetra-polarity and identify himself to such a degree with the plane in which he presently resides that he will accept the vibrations of that plane forever, and thus condemn himself. The sorcerer ceases to be a human being in the image of God and he becomes a being of that sphere and sinks to the level of a demon. That is the most regrettable state a human being can stoop to, and from a religious point view it can be called eternal damnation, and that is a true sin against the Holy Ghost.

This is the entire procedure of an agreement between a sorcerer and a being of another zone. However, if the sorcerer follows the voice of his conscience, he leaves the zone of the principal and finds his home in the earth zone, where he once again has the possibility of inhabiting that zone as a tetrapolar being and beginning again with his spiritual development. Should he require an incarnation on our physical world for his spiritual development, he will be given this opportunity, because the possibilities on the physical world to purify oneself are much greater, and also to pursue his magical development, like any other being. A sorcerer who incarnates again on our world can acquire great magical powers since he already worked with the powers of the negative sphere. Sorcerers that are born again are born as magicians; they do not have to acquire much knowledge nor do they have to undergo any specific magical schooling, because they already possess inborn magical powers.

There can be no doubt that the temptation to misuse these powers on earth will again appear. It is also indisputable that perhaps the same principal, probably under a different disguise, might again endeavor to entice its former victim over to its side, so that upon his departure from the earth the demon can drag him again into its sphere. It is a foregone conclusion that a sorcerer with that experience has a much freer will than he had before and he also has the ability to better resist these kinds of temptations. The conscience of such a sorcerer works much more penetratingly and warns him considerably more intensely than the conscience of one who has not had the same experiences as a sorcerer. It happens rarely that such a sorcerer falls a second time. His experiences usually purify him to such a degree that he enters upon the true magic path and is much less inclined to establish any contact with demons or negative beings.

This description of true events may serve as a warning for anyone who strives for knowledge, so that he does not enter upon the path of sorcery. It is obvious from what has been said so far that such a fall represents a giant step backward in the evolution or spiritual development of a human being. The events which are quoted here are not based on pure fantasy, but are very sad, true occurrences, based on fact. Any magician can ascertain whether these events are fact or fantasy. A sorcerer who has reincarnated and who has entered upon the true path of initiation is exposed to far greater temptations than the average person, because the average person must develop from the very beginning. The planes that held him prisoner before will continue to try to get their former victim under their control again and they will employ any devious method at their disposal.

I shall refrain from mentioning any cases from ancient or modern history where human beings have entered into a pact with spiritual beings, except for those notorious cases which are already known to the public at large such as Johann Faust (Dr. Faustus[11]) and Urbain Grandier.[12] There are countless others, of which the public has no knowledge.

There is another kind of pact which is known to only a few initiates. This shall serve as a warning to those who establish contact with various beings. This kind of pact is not a direct pact, instead it comes about through the mediation or procurement of an already existing

---

[11] Dr. Faust sold his soul to the devil in exchange for power and knowledge. – ED.

[12] At age 44, after his legs were crushed on August 18, 1634, Urbain Grandier was burned alive at Loudon by French witch hunters. – ED.

human body. Which of the various pacts offers the greatest advantages is left to the opinion of the individual. This lesser known method may be preferred by departed human beings, as well as beings from the earth zone and even beings from the higher zones.

Establishing contact with a departed human being in the spirit world requires control over the elements, the light principle and the Akasha Principle by that human. Whereas the being who endeavors to establish this contact, i.e. the one who strives to enter into a pact with the departed human being, must be a higher intelligence and must have the necessary magical maturity. This kind of pact is absolutely feasible from the Hermetic point of view. Some sorcerers practice this kind of sorcery and they do not distinguish themselves from the average person by something unusual or supernatural. It is only possible for an experienced clairvoyant and the eye of a true magician to detect that a pact has been established. Usually the sorcerer is made aware of this kind of pact by the beings of the elements that are closest to the earth and offer these kinds of pacts to the sorcerer.

It is a very simple matter to proceed with such a pact, provided all conditions are met. The method is based on the following procedure: The high intelligence searches in the material world for a physical body which is on the threshold of death. Preference is given to a healthy body, where a minor cause, an accident etc., consequently causes the immediate death of that human being. Even physical bodies who succumb on account of fast progressing pneumonia, meningitis, or sudden heart failure are sometimes used for this purpose, whereas physical bodies who succumb to tuberculosis or other infectious diseases whereby vital organs are destroyed are avoided because they are not suitable for this purpose, especially when these diseases cause the death of that particular human being. It would be very difficult and take a great effort to reestablish the harmony in a body that has been ravaged by ailments that eventually destroy the body. The very moment the cord between the physical body and the soul and spirit (i.e. the life matrix) severs, the spiritual being takes possession of the human being. And through the method which is described in *Initiation into Hermetics*, it can create a new cord between itself and the physical human body with the help of the light-fluid. It is of course a foregone conclusion that, before the being unites with the physical body, it must form an astral body from the element-substance in the size and shape of the particular human body and bring into harmony the two life-cords i.e. the mental and astral matrices.

A being who seizes a human body in this manner becomes a complete human being in a borrowed body. Externally, and in the eyes of family members, it seems that the person who was expected to die has awakened from his agony and made a miraculous recovery and is now convalescing. This is how the entire procedure is perceived by family members or by those who are ignorant in these matters and who also do not possess the ability to observe clairvoyantly when the astral body leaves the physical body. These spiritual beings also possess the fabulous ability to adapt to any situation. Furthermore, a spiritual being in this situation retains all the abilities and powers which it possessed while in its zone, and it knows everything. Therefore it continues to play the role of the person who in reality has died and departed. And without attracting any attention it waits for the first opportunity to leave the vicinity of the family members of the departed person in order to be in the vicinity of the sorcerer. As aforementioned, the being retains all the abilities and powers which it possessed in its own zone and it puts these abilities and powers at the disposal of the sorcerer. With the exception of a genuine magician, no one would ever look for anything out of the ordinary and discover the truth about such a situation, regardless of whether this occurs to friends or paramours, etc. The services which this being, in its human life, renders to the sorcerer are exactly the same as if a sorcerer established direct contact with a being of the planes. Should the sorcerer wish to achieve something through the being in the astral world or in the mental world, then the being puts itself into a trance and fulfils the sorcerer's wishes.

The details of the physical contact between the sorcerer and the being are discussed as soon as the sorcerer makes the first contact, i.e. during the initial evocation with the high intelligence, and the sorcerer is made completely conversant with the entire procedure. It is a foregone conclusion that the sorcerer cannot breathe a word about this pact, under penalty of death.

In this manner sorcerers have many times prompted mermaids (undines) to take over the bodies of beautiful earthly girls in order to have physical contact with them, and at times these sorcerers will even enter into marriage with these beings. Under these conditions there is no difference between a normal female and an incarnated undine, because an undine in a physical body is subject to the same laws as any other person. However, the undine retains the abilities and powers of the Water element and she can make use of them in her human incarnation. An incarnated undine can even bear children. However, there is a condition, which if not met is fatal: the undine requires the absolute fidelity of her husband, the sorcerer, because with her physical body she is in contact with the physical body of the sorcerer. If the sorcerer endeavors to have sexual intercourse with another woman, he is exposing himself to the danger by paying for this trespass with his life. Under these circumstances the incarnated undine can no longer remain on the physical plane and she cannot establish another contact here. Soon after the demise of the sorcerer who has become her friend and husband, the undine dies. After an undine dies, she does not enter the earth zone like any other human being; instead she returns to her Water element where she continues to live as an undine.

If a magician has reached a high level of spiritual development and has a divine bond with God, he can bring about such a process. And with his creative powers, he will also have the ability to establish in the undine the same harmony of the elements that is inherent in every human being. The magician would in this particular instance create a new human being, whose spirit is as immortal as the spirit of any other person. However, a true magician would never undertake such an operation without a sound reason. The reason I mention this is to confirm that it is within the realm of possibility for a magician to accomplish such a magical act. To the uninitiated person this might seem utopian and incredible, but in spite of that it is well-founded and feasible from the Hermetic point of view. A true magician has no doubt that these possibilities exist.

In contrast to spiritualism, there is another kind of evocation called necromancy. The difference between a sorcerer and a necromancer lies in the fact that the sorcerer endeavors to contact the higher beings of the earth zone, the principals of the elements or the principals of other zones, whereas a necromancer's interest is limited to evoking departed humans. The method employed in necromancy is a fairly simple one: a magician who is not fully developed would be more successful with this method than a sorcerer who practices invocations. The dangers are the same for a necromancer as they are for a sorcerer, because even a departed being can gain complete control over the necromancer and make him totally dependent. When a necromancer becomes so dependent upon a being from the astral plane that he does not undertake anything without the counsel and support of the being, then this may also be considered a kind of pact, even though it does not have the same severe consequences as the aforementioned pacts.

A magician can summon any being from the astral plane without endangering himself, without becoming dependent upon that being and without falling victim to necromancy. A necromancer is one who is at a very low level in his spiritual and magical development and whose main attention is focused on astral beings of the earth zone, but mostly upon departed human beings. In most cases a necromancer avails himself of a being from the astral plane. It is not important whether he demands that this being serve him on the physical, astral or mental plane, or whether it serves him merely to satisfy his curiosity. A necromancer will choose for his purposes a human being that has departed from our earth and who, during his lifetime here, was engaged in some area of the secret sciences and who has perhaps reached a certain degree of development. If such a being were a true magician who followed the true path of initiation and learned all the laws on earth and attained a particular degree of maturity, who above all was noble of mind and more inclined toward the positive powers and had total control over the negative powers, this departed magician may, if he wishes and if he deems it to be good, appear to the necromancer and inform him about all the advantages and disadvantages of his plans and intentions (projects). But a true magician will never stay in permanent contact with a necromancer, nor will he exert any influence upon the necromancer to become dependent upon him. However, he will always warn the necromancer and allow him to contact him, but only when absolutely necessary. Furthermore, the departed magician will give the necromancer good advice and initiate him into the laws of the astral plane. But he will never agree to serve the necromancer, or feel obliged to help him or to fulfil the necromancer's material wishes. Only sorcerers and evil magicians who are in the beginning stages of their development and who are partial to the negative forces will strive for a contact with a necromancer and help him to realize his every wish as well as satisfy his curiosity. Should a necromancer get into the sphere of such a being and become dependent upon him, he takes on the same vibration that the being has in the earth zone; and this will affect the necromancer. The astral being sees to it that the necromancer does not progress spiritually or develop magically or achieve any form of enlightenment, and that the necromancer does not ascend. At this point the being becomes totally permeated with *schadenfreude*[13] because it has succeeded in being an obstacle to a human being on earth. The being then thinks back to the time when it was on earth itself, where it was plagued with obstacles and difficulties and when it fell victim to temptations, when it misused powers and had no opportunities to enter upon the true path of initiation. And because of envy, it now endeavors to impede the necromancer's development as well. I do not think the danger that develops for the necromancer from this contact has to be explained in detail — not to mention the fact that in many such instances the necromancer is vampirized by this being, who, with the energy it has taken from necromancer, realizes its own egotistical projects in the astral plane.

That is why every seeker should heed this warning and not entertain the thought of making such a contact, and one should especially never make himself dependent on any being. The manner in which a necromancer summons a being from the astral plane is twofold. The first method is based on spiritualism, where the being is prompted by employing meditation, i.e. through mediumistic writing or a trance medium, to make itself known in order to establish contact. Employing this method requires great perseverance until the particular being is able to establish a direct contact and appear before the necromancer. The second method is the evocative method, where the necromancer establishes contact through a picture from the being's previous incarnation

---

[13] Deriving pleasure from the misfortune of others. – ED.

or by enlivening the picture, whereupon the being steps out of it, similar to an elementary, and assumes its former form. A necromancer does not see his efforts rewarded immediately. However, if he continues with his efforts, then in accordance with his maturity and development, strength and imagination, as well as his will-power, he eventually forces the being to appear visibly before him.

It is difficult for a necromancer to distinguish whether he is dealing with his fantasy, or if he has involuntarily created an elementary, or if a visible contact with the desired being has truly been established. A necromancer with limited abilities does not really care who or what has called forth the desired effect — whether it was his fantasy, or an elementary which he created by repeatedly tensioning his nerve-energy, or if it was actually the being he evoked from the astral world.

Should it be a magician who is more inclined toward negative powers, then this so-called black magician welcomes this summoning and projecting into the astral world, and he himself will endeavor to establish contact with the necromancer. The necromancer receives everything — such as practices and instructions — that will satisfy his curiosity or lead to the fulfillment of his wishes from the particular being. However, the entire responsibility rests upon the shoulders of the necromancer, who burdens himself through these activities with more karma, especially if he demands the realization of wishes which he cannot justify. The end of such necromancers is always very tragic. Usually they die an unnatural death or of a sudden incurable disease.

What remains to be mentioned is that there is also the possibility of passive contact with beings of the astral plane and of the higher zones. However, passive contact is not as effective as the evocative contact and does not produce any great magical results, therefore I am of the opinion that I should not pay too much attention to it. Yet even in this particular case it could unexpectedly come to a pact, because the person who establishes a connection through passive contact is quite often in a worse position than a sorcerer or necromancer, since he has no control over the being with which he is in contact nor over the effects which it causes.

There are two main methods when it comes to passive contact. The first method is the spiritistic, where the spiritist himself is the medium who contacts and communicates with the being. This is accomplished through writing, listening or visual contact. The second method of communication is when a hypnotist or magnetopath makes contact with a being through a somnambular medium and remains in constant contact with that being. In this case it does not matter if he uses the being only to satisfy his curiosity or if he gains the cooperation of the being for particular effects in the mental, astral or physical world. When the hypnotist or the spiritist is not schooled in magic and does not have the requisite magical maturity and development, it will always take its toll on the health of the particular medium. Many mediums and spiritists who are constantly in touch with the same being and who make frequent use of that being become dependent upon it, and these activities eventually result in an indirect pact and severe ailments of the mental, astral and physical body. Many mental hospitals are the best witness for these kinds of unfortunate cases.

Everything that has been mentioned here so far applies to the negative activities of sorcerers and necromancers with negative powers and the dangers connected with them. Now I should like to address the true magician who has pursued the path of true development and who endeavors to contact good beings, irrespective of their rank and their zones. I should like to draw his attention to the fact that a true magician never becomes dependent, even upon positive intelligences or beings. However, he can at his own discretion contact a positive being at any time, though he cannot associate with it, no matter how much that being may appeal to him. For this could also lead to a pact, as is the case with negative beings, although the dangers would not be as great and as fateful for a true magician who works with good beings.

There are also instructions and methods as to how a pact can be made with the genius of any zone. This genius will give the magician advice and support in every respect. A true magician, during the course of his development, will establish contact with good beings, because he must get to know them and be in control of all spheres. However, he cannot allow himself to be dependent on any one single being, be that an angel or a highly developed intelligence. Were this to occur, the magician would be similar to a sorcerer, because he would incorporate within himself the vibration of the plane from which the being originates. And in time he would be influenced by that vibration to such a degree that he would gradually assume the entire make-up of that being. Naturally, this being would not want to enter into a written pact. However, there are methods which could lead a magician into a written association or pact with a particular higher positive intelligence. Through this pact the magician gains the certainty that he is protected at all times and in every respect, that he is helped in every way, that he is forewarned, and that the positive higher intelligence performs all kinds of good services for him. Despite all forewarnings, some magicians do enter into pacts with positive entities, and after his departure from earth, the being will automatically draw him into its zone. While the magician is in this zone he will serve his guardian angel on a voluntary basis, without coercion. A magician who finds himself in this situation, whereby he is constantly in contact with good powers, becomes a part of that plane and loses the need to rise higher or to proceed to other zones. He becomes satisfied with his existence and his evolutionary ascent ceases temporarily. However, when this magician is sent by Divine Providence to the earth zone or is reincarnated in the material world to fulfil a task as a human being, only then does he begin to yearn again to learn about a zone which is above the one to which he is accustomed. When a magician who was associated with a genius in a particular zone incarnates on our physical world, then the association shows itself in a special brilliance, whether that be in area of the Hermetic sciences or other sciences, for example art, literature, etc. Therefore the procedure is the same, whether it be negative or positive. A true magician will never allow his development to be hindered by a pact with a genius or an angel and thus impede his higher ascent. A magician maintains his consciousness when he perceives himself as having the same affection for all beings. This allows him to become a perfect human being, created in the image of God, and he represents his perfection by reflecting the Divinity, and he is no longer bound to or influenced by any sphere. Then he can achieve true perfection, provided that not one single element is predominant and he has developed within himself the absolute equilibrium of the energies and powers and he maintains this equilibrium permanently in the course of his further development.

It is decided in the higher spheres whether the magician wishes to attain the highest perfection or if he wishes to become a saint. A magician who strives for the highest perfection is the highest and greatest lord in creation, because he actually symbolizes the complete and entire image of God in all its aspects. A saint remains with one aspect and he perfects himself in this aspect. He becomes a part of this aspect and, when the perfection of this aspect eventually comes into being within him, he loses his perfected individuality. The highest perfection that a human being can ever achieve is that of a true sovereign, a true magician, thus actually representing a perfect image of God, whereby he never loses and never relinquishes his individuality.

When a true magician has acquired the knowledge of the entire hierarchy of the beings, their zones, causes and effects, this allows him to control every being in creation, whether good or evil, which eventually becomes his assignment. Control over the beings does not always have to be coerced, because the beings, whether good or evil, will serve a true magician willingly, obey his will at all times, and fulfil all his wishes without asking for any repayment. Even the principals of the zones serve a true magician gladly, and, if the magician wishes, they will provide him with subordinate beings and with the necessary *ankhur* without taking the liberty to ask him to enter into a pact with that particular zone. A true magician can place as many servant spirits under his will as he requires; it does not matter from which sphere they come, they will acknowledge him as their highest master. A true magician who is noble of mind will not make any distinction between a positive and a negative being, because Divine Providence did not create anything impure. A true magician knows that the negative principals, the demons, are as necessary as the angels, because without these opposites it would be impossible to establish a hierarchical difference. He will respect every being, whether positive or negative, in accordance with its rank. He himself will travel the golden mean, the path of perfection.

Chapter 18
The *Spiritus Familiaris*
Or Servant Spirits

Most grimoires and books dealing with evocative magic quite often mention servant spirits, which are also called *spiritus familiaris*. In accordance with these books, the servant spirits are placed at the disposal of the magician by high spirits, mainly by demon princes, for his personal use, so that the magician does not have to bother the demon prince on every occasion or with every minor detail. Furthermore, these books also state that the *spiritus familiaris* are assigned to the magician, or rather the sorcerer, by the demon prince or principal of a zone with whom he has entered into a pact. A *spiritus familiaris* is provided by his principal with an *ankhur* which gives it the same powers, attributes etc., which the principal possesses in his own zone. It is not of importance to the magician who causes the effect he desires, whether it is the principal himself or one of his servant spirits. What is important is that the magician — or in this case the sorcerer — carries the karmic responsibility. As I mentioned in the chapter regarding pacts, when the pact expires on the physical sphere and as soon as the magician departs from his physical body with his soul and spirit, he must follow the demon prince to his sphere and repay it with compound interest to the very last penny for the services he performed for him. Reimbursement is of course not material; it must be understood that repayment is made in a strictly spiritual manner.

The *spiritus familiaris* are not to be mistaken, from the Hermetic point of view, for the so-called family spirits of the primitive nations of antiquity. The family spirits were in most cases departed human beings of a tribe. They were either ancestors, heroes, etc. They were the objects of the so-called fetish cults which, in a primitive manner, practiced a kind of necromancy because they remained in constant contact with their departed relatives or heroes. In accordance with our present-day concepts this kind of necromancy could be compared with spiritualism. Since every initiate is familiar with the practices, cult rituals etc., which lead to a contact with one's ancestors, i.e. family spirits, I shall refrain from writing more about it. Not only did individual families have their family spirit or house-spirit, it is also a well known fact from historical accounts that there were also countless nations who had their particular guardian spirit. A true magician knows, from the Hermetic point of view, the difference between an actual *spiritus familiaris* and an ancestral or family spirit.

The approach and attitude of a true magician towards establishing contact with a higher being, or rather a higher intelligence, is entirely different than the approach and attitude of a sorcerer, or rather a black magician. A black magician attempts to bring spiritual beings under his control without any effort, without the proper preparation and without any magical development, for the sole purpose that they may serve him and help him to realize his wishes.

However, he does not take into consideration that he burdens his karma and furthermore that it is at the expense of his own evolution and more so that it severely impedes the progress of his magical development. Spiritual beings that serve a black magician will not serve him unless they receive extraordinary reimbursement. From a material point of view these services are nothing more than a kind of temporary loan. As I mentioned before, a sorcerer is in reality only a slave of the being, because once the pact expires the sorcerer must return everything. These beings are well aware of this fact, and the submissiveness they demonstrate toward the sorcerer assures him that they are willing to serve him and fulfil his every wish. Unfortunately, this gives the sorcerer the wrong impression — that he has become the master over these beings. His wishes and demands increase during their relationship and gradually the sorcerer develops an insatiable character. Shortly before the pact expires, the sorcerer realizes what he has done. And he also realizes the extent of his karmic responsibility and the great burden he has accepted. At this point, however, it is already too late. All possible advice and direction which could have been recommended regarding how to break a signed pact is no longer feasible or useful from the Hermetic point of view, and to a true magician it is absolutely absurd. Once causes have been created, no matter what kind, they must be properly discharged and balanced in accordance with the law of cause and effect.

Perhaps the objection could be raised as to why Divine Providence could not make an exception once in a while in Its aspect of mercy and divine love. A true magician knows that when causes are created, effects must follow; otherwise the law of karma, i.e. the law of retaliation, the entire lawfulness of the universe would prove altogether untrue and only a mere illusion. Naturally, it does not have to be emphasized that this is not true — everything is regulated in accordance with the true laws and with admirable meticulousness. Divine love and mercy with all Its other aspects, as for example goodness or grace etc., goes so far that It allows a human being to recognize that he himself is the cause of all the sufferings and problems that have overcome him, which cognizance alleviates his burden and suffering. Divine Providence cannot intervene any further in the aspect of love, goodness, grace etc., from the proper universal point of view. Every experienced magician who is conversant with the universal laws considers this to be a matter of fact. Therefore, every genuine magician must be extra careful and be on guard *never* to enter into a pact, because it would put a sudden halt to his magical development and evolution. A true initiate would not entertain any thought of entering into a pact, even with a high and positive principal, in spite of the fact that it could result in tremendous advantages for him. If a magician — or anyone else, for that matter — were to tie himself or commit himself to the beings and their respective spheres, it would result in a loss of freedom.

The objection could be raised that it is not necessary at all to concern oneself with evocative magic and it would be of greater advantage to work on one's further development and completely disregard the evocation of beings. The answer to this point is that a true magician may endeavor to establish contact with all beings, whether positive or negative, and he should deem it an absolute necessity to pursue true evocative magic. But it should never serve as an encouragement to bind oneself to or associate with any being routinely. A magician should establish contact only to increase and enrich his knowledge about the individual spheres, learn about their laws, and express his authority as a magician to those beings with which he works evocatively. There is no doubt that these beings gladly supply the magician with all the information he requires. They also serve him gladly, because to them a true genuine magician is their master and a true initiate and he is the one to whom they must pay tribute in the form of faithfulness and obedience. A being would never dare to petition a genuine magician who has been properly initiated into magic and who is completely evolved with a pact. A magician may make use of servant spirits from one sphere or another if he deems it necessary because he knows that he does not owe anything to these spirits, and because he knows that whatever a being does for him, he brings about through his own powers and on account of his systematic magical development. The magician will employ these beings above all to help his fellow man rather than himself, and to utilize the precious time saved for his further development.

This is the proper attitude, and it cannot be compared with the attitude of a sorcerer. A magician does not have to concern himself constantly with evocative magic. However, he must be able to master these practices and carry them out successfully whenever the need arises. A magician enriches and increases his power over the beings in the universe and solidifies his magical authority through a precise knowledge of evocative magic. A true magician must reach the level of perfection in every respect. He must pay close attention and observe the hierarchy of the beings when he practices evocative magic. This must be every magician's agenda, in the following order:

1. contact the principals of the elements and their beings, and perhaps their servant spirits, i.e. their subordinates,
2. contact all the principals of the earth zone, i.e. the zone girdling the earth, and also their subordinates,
3. progress to contacting the beings of the Moon in accordance with their hierarchy,
4. progress to the Mercury zone and contact the principals there,
5. progress to the Venus zone,
6. progress to the Sun zone,
7. progress to the Mars zone,
8. progress to the Jupiter zone, and
9. progress to the Saturn zone.

Chapter 19
Magical Evocation

When a magician studies a book on evocation — or perhaps he has several books in his own library — he will find that as far as the instructions are concerned, there exists a certain association of ideas. All these books together will give him instructions on how to summon a being, which formulas to use, etc. But he will not find the prerequisites that are necessary for a successful evocation in one single book. It is therefore not surprising that, up to that point, almost all attempts to establish contact with a being will end in failure. From the Hermetic point of view, any attempt to establish contact with a being, regardless of its sphere, can be considered a type of evocation. It does not matter if the methods employed are based on spiritualism, necromancy or something else. It is, however, questionable whether the desired being actually appears when these various methods are employed; only the one who makes these attempts would truly know the truth. Should an attempt now and then be successful through applying the methods quoted in these books, it could be that it was not necessarily directly an attempt to evoke a being. The possibility exists that, besides these methods, other methods could also have been employed. For example, apparent success can be achieved when employing spiritualistic methods to evoke, but in reality this is something entirely different, even though the claim will be made that success was achieved through the methods of evocation that were recommended in these books. When it comes to spiritualism, the subconscious of the medium who verbally relays the information to the operator can contribute to this, provided of course that a medium is employed. Furthermore, it could also be that schemata, elementals and elementaries are being produced unknowingly during the evocation due to the increasing excitement of the operator through the power of his own imagination. Effects that are achieved through these kinds of operations cannot be attributed to the being, but must be attributed to the individuality of the operator; however, this fact will hardly ever be admitted by him.

Therefore, I have concluded that I shall describe everything that is required for a successful evocation in detail, from the Hermetic point of view; in other words, what is absolutely essential to achieve an actual magical contact with a being, regardless of the sphere. Above all the magician or the person who intends to occupy himself with magical evocation must have the knowledge that without proper development of the astral senses, especially clairvoyance and clairaudience, a successful evocation is unthinkable. As an example, it is the same if a blind person enters upon an unknown path without reliable guidance. In order to establish contact with a being in an active manner, the first prerequisite is astral vision and astral hearing. Should a magician ignore this prerequisite or should someone dare to practice evocation without having his astral senses developed, he can assume with certainty that he, like all the other operators, will experience disappointments and all his labors will be unsuccessful. At the same time, should he attain a partial success in a heightened state, regardless of how partial that may be, he exposes himself to the danger of degrading himself to the level of a necromancer or sorcerer, regardless of whether his intentions were noble.

During the operation the magician must make use of his astral senses, because it gives him the opportunity to scrutinize all procedures and he never runs the risk of being deceived or working unsuccessfully. A magician who has his astral senses developed knows immediately whether he is dealing with a being that was formed through his imagination or whether it is a being from the desired sphere. From the Hermetic point of view, an evocation is the conscious establishment of contact with the desired being, namely through passive communication. The magician has learned the practice as described in Step V of my first book, *Initiation into Hermetics*, under passive communications. Passive communications are not accomplished with the magician as the medium; however, they are accomplished outside of the magician's body.

A being or a power from any sphere that is evoked outside the magician's body can be evoked either into a magic triangle, into a magic mirror, or into any kind of material which is impregnated with a fluid condenser. It can also be condensed or materialized at the discretion of the magician. In the beginning stages the magician cannot do without his magical aids. Later, when he has gathered enough experience and when he has a particular sphere completely under his control evocatively — when the beings of that sphere pay tribute to him in the form of faithfulness and obedience through which they acknowledge his magical authority — then he can do without his magical aids. This places an experienced magician in the position of summoning any being from the sphere which he has under his control, and working with it without the use of any magical aids. He can summon a being from that zone without a magic circle or triangle at any time and to any place, however and whenever he wishes, without any special preparation. Whereas a beginner has no other choice but to work with magical aids, because they are his memory supports and hence absolutely necessary for a successful evocation. Once a magician has a sphere under his control without his magical aids, then he proceeds to the next higher sphere, where he again makes use of his magical aids until he completely controls that higher sphere as well.

If a magician wants to carry out a successful evocation he must always bear in mind the three following principles:

1. Should a magician intend to summon a being from another sphere into his sphere, it is irrelevant whether he summons this being into a triangle, into the mirror or onto a fluid condenser. He must know that the being can only move about in an atmosphere that corresponds to its own sphere. Therefore, he must form this atmosphere artificially by accumulating the light, i.e. the sphere substance, through the imagination into the triangle. It is even better if he were to accumulate the sphere substance in the entire room in which he works. Should he work with a magic mirror, the loading of the mirror must take place with the corresponding light-substance of the sphere, i.e. the magic mirror must be impregnated with this light-substance. Should the magician work outdoors, then the impregnation must be limited to a particular space so that the beings or powers that are to manifest outside have enough space to move about. The light-accumulation or the light-impregnation has to have the color that is required by the color laws of the individual planet. In the first book, *Initiation into Hermetics,* in Step III and in the chapter dealing with room impregnation, the reader or student is thoroughly informed about the practice of impregnation or light-accumulation in a room. For example, when the magician evokes a being from the Moon sphere outside of his

body, then the light or rather the substance that is to be accumulated must be imagined in a silvery-white color. Should the being be a Mercurian being, the light-substance must be opalescent. When it is a Venusian being the color of the light-substance must be green, for a Sun being the color must be a golden-yellow, a Mars being requires red, for a Jupiter being the color must be blue, and for a Saturn being the color must be violet etc.

For example, should the magician summon a being from the Earth element, he must project the Earth element into the magic triangle or into the magic mirror with the aid of his imagination. Should the magician wish to summon a being from the Moon sphere, he must produce the vibration of that sphere. There is not one being that can remain in a sphere that is not suitable for it. Whenever this principle is not considered, the being has to create the necessary sphere-vibration by itself, in spite of the fact that it can still be coerced to manifest in our physical world. In such a case the magician loses his power over the being, and his authority suffers severely because the being will consider him to be imperfect and it will not show him the proper respect, apart from the fact that it will refuse to obey him. When it comes to evocation, the precise observance of this principle is of the utmost importance and cannot be ignored by any true magician.

2.   In order to be noticed by the being during an evocation, the magician must be able to transfer his consciousness into the sphere of the being whom he summons. This transfer of consciousness occurs by employing the Akasha Principle, with which the magician introduces a state of trance in which he is subject to neither time nor space. While the magician is in this state he summons with his will, with his authority etc., the particular being. The magician will be unable to achieve the appearance of the being without this capability.

3.   The magician must command reverence and obedience from the being with his magical authority, otherwise these beings, be they positive or negative, will not respect him.

A magician does not exert his magical authority or influence upon the being through his personality. Instead, he achieves this in conjunction with an intelligence that is higher in rank than the being, or he approaches the being directly as a divinity in an aspect that is of great importance to the being. In this case it is not the magician who exerts the essential influence upon the summoned being; instead it is the authority of the being that is higher in rank or the Highest Intelligence, namely the evoking Divinity. At the time of the evocation, the first task the magician undertakes is to influence or contact the higher intelligence. And only under the most severe circumstances, when the being to be summoned opposes the magician, will he assume the form of the highest quality to state his claim as an authority and make his influence felt. If the magician influences the evoked being with his own personality without connecting with a superior intelligence, Divinity etc., the being may refuse to obey the magician, or worse still, it may deceive him in every conceivable manner. However, if the being receives its order from the superior intelligence or from even a higher form, namely some aspect of God, and not from the magician, then the being has no other choice but to obey the order. The magician has already learned the practice of connecting to or influencing an intelligence or a divine aspect from my first work, *Initiation into Hermetics*, where I gave a detailed description about the individual communication or bonding with God.

The three basic points given here cannot be found in any instructions that have been available up to now, because without exception the authors have lacked the necessary personal experience in evocative magic and therefore endeavored to draw their teaching methods from other inadequate sources of literature. However, without these three basic conditions a successful evocation is not possible.

Before a magician begins with the evocation of beings, he must precisely record the entire procedure in his book of formulas. He should actually know the entire procedure inside out, so that during the evocation he does not have to look at his book of formulas to reassure himself. Only in the very beginning of his practice will the magician experience some difficulties, but in time and through frequent evocations he will gain more and more experience and all uncertainties will disappear. He will also realize that an evocation is not merely the summoning of a being. Instead, it is a regular ritual which consists of a complete sequence of magical operations. During the ritual the magician must be certain that there is no gap in his entire operation, because every gap causes a disturbing effect not only for the magician but also for the summoned being. A flawless operation is what the grimoires depict as a "perfect circle." This term does not refer to the magic circle which the magician draws for his protection and so forth; rather it refers to the entire continuity of the magical operation. Before the magician begins with the evocation, he must put the purpose of the operation in writing so that no additional queries come up during the evocation.

Anyone can gather from the entire procedures of these preparations that a carefully prepared and precisely executed magical evocation requires quite some time. Once the magician has established a good contact with the same being through frequent visits, so that the being obeys and acknowledges his authority completely, the magician can come to another agreement with the being in order to save time and establish contact in the future. It can either be an abbreviated individual ritual or a word etc., with which the magician determines to evoke the being, which ritual or word must be approved by the being. Or he can see to it that the being chooses an abbreviated method whereby it commits itself to appear at any time with all its servants. Even this abbreviated method must be conscientiously recorded in the book of formulas, so that during the practice of magical evocation the magician avoids making errors, especially if he has already established several such contacts with other beings. Should the magician be given an abbreviated version by a being, and if it is the being's wish that the magician not record this method but memorize it instead, then the magician must respect the being's wish. Even when the magician has permission to record the abbreviated version of the evocation, he must be certain that his notes never fall into the wrong hands, not even into the hands of another magician. An exception can be made only when the being is the author of the abbreviated method and it agrees that it can be given to another person, or when the being itself even advocates such an undertaking. A magician should never dare to circumvent or to break an agreement if he does not want his authority severely undermined. The consequences that the magician will suffer do not have to be more closely examined.

In the beginning, the being appears to the magician in the same manner to which it is accustomed to moving about in its own zone. Should the form in which the being appears not suit the magician, then on the basis of his authority he can see to it that the being takes on a form in accordance with his wishes. There are no limits as far as this is concerned, and it is at the discretion of the magician as to the appearance the summoned being will assume. The magician accomplishes this changeover with the aid of his imagination. Even the gender that the being assumes is not important. However, when for example a being is female in its own zone but appears as a male, the magician would be well advised not to insist that it change back to a female form, even though the being would have to oblige if the magician insists. It is advisable, during early operations, to leave the being in the form which it has in its own zone and in which it appears to the magician.

The magician communicates with the being in his own language. In this particular instance he is already in an exalted state, in a state of trance, wherein his language changes automatically into a spiritual language, the so-called picture language, and this is what the being perceives. The summoned being also speaks in the spiritual language which, in turn, changes automatically into the language spoken by the magician. Consequently, in the beginning the magician has the feeling that the answers of the being come out of his innermost, similar to the way in which the "inner voice" is perceived. In time the magician becomes accustomed to this condition and perceives the being outside of himself; and eventually, through repeated practice, the magician will discover that it is the same as speaking to a fellow human being.

The undesirable occurrences mentioned in the grimoires and which presumably accompany an evocation, as for example noise, rumbling, banging, creaking and knocking, are attributed to these beings. Thunderclaps, flashes of lightning and similar disturbances are completely unknown to the true magician. They only occur in the operations of necromancers and sorcerers who have not undergone any magical schooling, or whenever the essential prerequisites are ignored, or when the preparations for a proper evocation leave much to be desired. A true magician does not experience any undesirable occurrences when he summons beings or high intelligences. His evocations are executed as smoothly as any other physical, astral or spiritual operation. In the beginning, a magician would be well advised not to ask too many questions of the being. Rather, he should ask a few pertinent questions which concern the being's sphere. Under no circumstances should questions be asked that oppose the dignity of the being. Later the magician can see to it that the being, the intelligence, the principal or his underlings which are placed at the disposal of the magician, are actively effective, because the magician does not have to limit his demands strictly to obtaining knowledge from them. The beings gladly serve a true magician and help him in an unselfish manner as much as it is within their powers. A magician will certainly never be so foolish as to demand that beings bring him treasures and carry out heavy physical work, because the effects of their expression of power on our physical world are dependent upon the energy substance, i.e. the condensation substance, which the magician must place at their disposal.

At first these spiritual beings will only be able to carry out mental work. As time progresses, and when the magician possesses enough experience, they will be able to perform astral work, and in time they will even be able to perform physical work. However, it is advisable not to burden these beings with physical assignments, because they have to solve these assignments and carry them out in exactly the same manner as the magician would have to do with his acquired magical abilities. The beings make use of the same energies which the magician would use for his personal work, i.e. they require the elemental fluids for physical work, the electric or the magnetic fluid, as well as the Akasha Principle. The beings mostly draw the substance and the energy from the atmosphere of the magician. Therefore, a magician must always bear in mind that every evocation is always at his expense. For this reason he will not perform an evocation to satisfy the curiosity of others. However, he will carry out an evocation to help other human beings, or he will do it to increase his powers over the beings and elements and to gather more experience.

When a magician summons a being, he does not cite a sorcerer's formulas or similar nonsense. Since the magician is in communion with God during the entire evocation, i.e. in an exalted state, he transfers himself with his consciousness into the sphere of the being he has chosen.

Then he calls the being by its name and he asks it to come into his vicinity, i.e. to appear to him. The being perceives the magician and reacts immediately to his call and comes into his vicinity. A true magician will rarely ever threaten a being in order to make it obedient. This only occurs in the case of obstinate demons, to whom the magician expresses the power of his bond with God. A being, regardless of its rank, would hardly ever dare to oppose a Divinity, i.e. someone who has a true bond with God, because the Divinity is the power who created the being and must therefore be respected.

For a magician, the axiom applies that the stars influence but they do not coerce; it is at his discretion to choose the time for the evocation in accordance with astrological guidelines, provided the magician is conversant with the basics of astrology. Therefore he also has the ability to establish the appropriate and favorable planetary and spherical time for the beings.

The different kinds of invocations described in the grimoires are not intended for a magician, as they are only for sorcerers. Therefore, the instructions contained in them are worthless to a magician, and he deals with them accordingly. A magician knows the true path of initiation, and he knows exactly how to carry out an evocation properly; therefore, he knows in advance that his work will be successful.

Upon the conclusion of his magical evocation, it is the task of the magician to return the being to its plane, in other words to give the being license to depart. The magician accompanies the being with his consciousness, which provides him the inner satisfaction and certainty that the summoned being will return to the sphere from whence it was called and from whence it came. All the magical aids which the magician used are returned to their place of safekeeping, as are all the accumulated powers or energies he dissolves by means of his will and his imagination, which concludes the evocation.

Chapter 20
The Practice Of Magical Evocation

A magician would certainly welcome it if I gave an example of a typical evocation. The reader will not find in any book heretofore published a description of an evocation in accordance with the universal laws which is as thorough and detailed as the one which follows. As far as the presentation, procedure etc., of the evocation is concerned, it is left to the magician's discretion to make minor changes or improvements which are in each case in accordance with the magician's individual circumstances and also the location where he chooses to perform the evocation. It would be ideal if the magician had a suitable room at his disposal for this noble purpose, one to which no one else has access except the magician himself. In this particular case, he must do the unavoidable cleaning of the room himself and not entrust it to another person. A room such as this is in the truest sense of the word a kind of temple. Should a magician have this opportunity, he can take all the laws of analogy into consideration and arrange everything in his room in such a manner as, for example, everything was arranged in the temples of the ancient magicians. These ancient temples had an altar on the east side. In accordance with his maturity and religious beliefs, the magician can express his Divinity symbolically on the altar. Or he can place a magic mirror in the center of the altar in the manner of the oldest initiates or magi and on each side he can place a candelabrum with seven arms and a censer in the center of the two candelabras. The ancient temples had four columns which were usually adorned with various symbolic figures, each pillar representing an element. The walls were adorned with pictures which portrayed the various deities of the four elements. Only those initiates who belonged to the highest circles in society could afford these kinds of temples for their magical operations. Unfortunately, there are only a few today who are sufficiently financially independent to afford such magnificent appointments for their magical workroom.

This information only refers to the most important magical utensils and accommodations, and it allows every magician, without exception, whether rich or poor, to carry out true magical evocations, even when no special room is available. A magician is not dependent on a particular room or place, for he can summon a being in any room, be it the kitchen, attic or basement, as long as these places are free of interference during the evocation. Should these locations offer no possibilities for interference-free evocations, then he must find a secluded place outdoors, where he is certain that he is not watched by anyone, and may consequently work undisturbed. When it comes to the description of an evocation, these circumstances do not necessarily have to be taken into consideration, because every magician must know best how and where he can carry out his operations. For easier understanding I have chosen the Venusian intelligence, *Hagiel*, as an example. The same procedure applies when it comes to other beings and intelligences, only the magician must always take into consideration the laws of analogy of the individual sphere as regards color light-accumulation.

Before a magician commences with the actual evocation, he must work out a plan in advance in every detail, and he must also have precise prior knowledge of the plane or sphere from which he intends to summon an entity and what he will demand from this entity. In the second part of this book, which deals with the hierarchy of the beings, the magician will find a large number of positive beings from the individual spheres. This gives him a large selection, so he can choose a particular being that can help him realize his wish. Bear in mind that the beings and intelligences mentioned in this book are not by any means all that there are; in every sphere or plane there are thousands of such beings and intelligences. However, the intelligences mentioned here should suffice for the practice of evocation.

Let us suppose that a magician has chosen the Venusian intelligence *Hagiel* for his evocation, and that he will ask her for good luck and success in one of his undertakings wherein he requires the friendship or sympathy of a particular person. *Hagiel* fits this purpose perfectly well, because all matters concerning friendship, love, success and good fortune are her responsibility.

However, before the magician begins his evocation he must bathe or at least clean his body, because no one should carry out an evocation with a pure being — especially a high and good intelligence — while he himself is in an untidy and unclean condition. An evocation not only requires a clean spirit and a clean soul, but also a clean body. Should it be impossible to bathe or shower or to wash the entire body, then the magician must at the very least wash his hands very carefully. Everyone can do this much, and it must not be disregarded under any circumstances. As he washes himself, the magician must concentrate on the idea that all unfavorable corporeal and astral influences drain away with the water.

The magician, having thus prepared himself, takes all his magical instruments from the place of safekeeping and places them on a clean cloth. It is better to use a brand new cloth, which is kept at the place of safekeeping and intended only for the purpose of keeping the instruments free from dust.

If, for example, we summon *Hagiel* into our living room, we must be certain that we will not be disturbed during the entire evocation. In order to avoid being watched by curiosity seekers, draw the drapes in front of the window so that no one has the opportunity to watch.

The next step is to change clothes, i.e. to dress magically. First put on the silk stockings. Should it be a cold day, one may wear silk underwear and then put on the slippers or house shoes. The evocation begins with the dressing. You can only entertain thoughts that correspond with your immediate activities. Therefore, focus in on the thought that by putting on the silk clothes you are insulated against all unfavorable influences which the universe or the invisible world could inflict upon you. While dressing, you must be absolutely certain that your body does not pick up any influences from any being, regardless of whether the being is good or not. Then put on your silk robe and, while you dress, remain in a meditative state of mind of being completely insulated and totally protected. Then put on your magic belt and allow yourself to be completely permeated by the feeling that you are master of the elements and the master of all powers. Finally put on the Magus headband or, if you prefer, the magic headdress with the feeling that you are in communion with God and that the Divinity in the body rather than the magician performs the entire operation. You must unite in your innermost with the Divine Principle, so much so that you perceive yourself directly as a Divinity.

Only when you have prepared yourself in this manner are you able to proceed to the next step of the operation. Ignite the magic lamp; and in this particular case the magic lamp must emanate green light into the room. Place the magic lamp in such a location that you can draw the magic circle around the lamp or hang the lamp in the center of the room. This does not mean that you have to hang the lamp in the *exact* center of the room, although this has the advantage of keeping the entire room evenly illuminated.

The next task is to set up and impregnate the magic mirror; perhaps you may even prefer to work with two magic mirrors. In this example I shall give you instructions on how to make use of two magic mirrors. The first mirror will bring about the materialization of *Hagiel* on the physical plane, whereas the purpose of the second mirror is to keep undesirable influences away.

While you are completely conscious of the fact that not you but the Divinity within you carries out this procedure, imagine a huge ocean of light in a wonderful emerald green color. With the aid of the light energy-accumulation in the mirror, you must condense this ocean of light imaginatively from the entire universe to such a degree that the entire surface of the mirror is engulfed by this color. The luminosity of the condensed green light-accumulation must be bright enough to extend over the entire room in which you work. During this operation you must imagine that this light-accumulation is an actual energy matrix, a fluid that is almost visible to the physical eye. At the very least you must have the constant perception that you move about the room in a green light-oscillation. In this manner the room is now magically prepared for the being to be evoked, and there are no more obstacles for the being to perceive its sphere. During the accumulation process, concentrate on the fact that the accumulation automatically condenses or materializes the summoned being to the degree that it is perceptible with your physical eyes and audible to your physical ears. The stronger the imagination, the firmer the belief, will and conviction, the more *Hagiel* will materialize and the more faithful will be its appearance. When you impregnate the room, remember to add the wish that the accumulated planetary light-energy remains effective in the mirror and in the room until you dissolve it again with your imagination.

In *Initiation into Hermetics* you will find similar practices described in the chapter on room impregnation, and you will find what has now been confirmed, that all the exercises and magical operations of the first book have their particular purpose. You will also realize that in the course of your future magical operations you will not be able to do without a single practice or exercise that is contained in the first book. Should you not have practically carried out the exercises contained therein, you will be unable to establish a conscious contact with a being outside of yourself, because you will not be able to materialize the being.

Now proceed to impregnate the second mirror by loading it with the Akasha Principle. Onto the mirror surface, which has been imaginatively treated with a fluid condenser, place the wish that not one single disruptive being, not one single undesirable power or the like, will force its way into your evocation chamber. This then concludes the second step of the evocation, and the room in which you work is now appropriately prepared. You also have another possibility: you can, if you wish, use the mirror which was designated to ward off undesirable influences and impregnate it with the wish that the desired being appear in that mirror. The impregnation must have the light-accumulation in the particular planetary color, in this case green. Now take a piece of blotting paper and cut it in such a way that it has the shape of a heptagon.[14] Then draw the seal of *Hagiel* with green Indian ink, or better yet with a green pencil, in the center of the blotting paper. (See the drawing of *Hagiel's* seal on this page.) Now trace the heptagonal seal either with your magic wand or

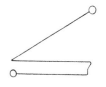

[14] Every planetary sphere requires a different shape. The blotting paper must have the following design: for the Saturnian sphere, a triangle; the Jupiter sphere, a square; for the Martian sphere, a pentagon; the Sun sphere, a hexagon; for the Venusian sphere, a heptagon; the Mercurian sphere, an octagon; and for the Moon sphere, a nonagon. For the zone girdling the earth (or the earth zone) and for all the other spheres, the shape of a circle is used to draw the seal.

with your finger and concentrate *Hagiel's* attributes — such as good fortune, love, friendship etc. — into this seal. Before the operation, moisten the blotting paper with a fluid condenser and let it dry. Furthermore, concentrate on the idea that this intelligence is in contact with the sign (seal), and that it reacts to the seal at all times, and that it is always willing to carry out the will of the magician, i.e. your will. Always be conscious of the fact that not you, but the Divinity, draws the particular sign and that the intelligence renders absolute obedience to the Divinity. From the beginning, failure is impossible when you are in this meditative state of mind. The seal is finished, and now you will prepare the magic circle and the magic triangle.

Place the magic circle on the floor next to the triangle. Now, in a meditative state of mind trace once more all the lines of the circle with the magic wand or with the right hand or with a finger of the right hand. Meditate that they represent the eternity, the microcosm and the macrocosm, and therefore symbolically express the universe on a small and large scale. When evoking the intelligence, you must stand in the center of the circle which, for you, represents the world on both a small scale and on a large scale. Your meditative state of mind must be so strong, so focused, that there is no room for any other thought.

Follow the same procedure when tracing the triangle which symbolizes the three-dimensional world, i.e. the spiritual (mental), astral and physical world. While in this meditative state of mind, you must also take into consideration that the intelligence that you summon into the triangle must appear not only mentally, but also astrally and physically. When tracing the magic triangle, your imagination is just as important and necessary as it is when tracing the magic circle. During this procedure the magician determines the shape and the sphere of activity of the intelligence which he summons. Should he neglect to do this, then *Hagiel* will only appear mentally, namely she will only be present mentally. She will not manifest or appear physically, and therefore she cannot be effective as far as her influence is concerned. Once all these preparations have been completed, place the triangle in front of the magic circle and place the prepared seal in the center of the magic triangle. Some magicians enhance the three-dimensional effect of the summoned being by placing a spirit lamp[15] into each corner of the triangle and igniting each lamp. The fuel that is used for these spirit lamps is an extract of chamomile with an alcohol base, in other words a fluid condenser which the magician has prepared in advance with the wish-imagination of materializing in the three-dimensional world. These little lamps are equipped with small wicks and they resemble Bunsen burners. When they burn, the power of the imagination which is concentrated into the fuel begins to permeate the room through the gradual evaporation of the fuel, and it promotes the materialization of the summoned being. However, these spirit lamps are not absolutely necessary, but for the novice in evocative magic they are a great aid, because when it comes to this kind of work a beginner requires more memory aids than an experienced magician. Besides placing these spirit lamps in the corners of the magic triangle, the novice can also place them along the inside line of the magic circle equidistant from each other. The number of lamps required is in accordance with the number that is analogous to the particular planet.

In this case we are dealing with an intelligence of the Venusian sphere, and the Venusian sphere is analogous to the number seven. I shall give the reader the number which is analogous to every planet in our solar system, and in this case it refers also to the number of lamps which are to be placed on the inside of the magic circle:

For the	Earth zone	10 lamps
	Moon zone	9 lamps
	Mercurian zone	8 lamps
	Venusian zone	7 lamps
	Sun zone	6 lamps
	Mars zone	5 lamps
	Jupiter zone	4 lamps
	Saturn zone	3 lamps

The magician also has another opportunity: he can symbolize the elements in the circle, in which particular case he only has to place four lamps inside the magic circle. The magician who stands in the center of

---

[15] A spirit lamp is a lamp that burns alcohol or some other liquid fuel. – ED.

the magic circle is the representative of the Akasha Principle and as such he represents the fifth element. When the magician places the little lamps in the magic circle, he must at all times take the four compass directions into consideration and place one lamp to the east, one to the west, one to the south and one to the north. It is at the discretion of the magician to either express the planetary number or to symbolically represent the elements through the lamps.

There is yet another possibility: the magician can draw three circles. In the second circle he places four lamps as the symbol of the universe, and in the outer circle, the third, he places the number of lamps which correspond to the planetary number of the being that is to be evoked. However, placing the lamps into the magic circle somewhat complicates the preparatory work for the evocation. But whomever has the opportunity to avail himself of these lamps should not fail to do so, because the more memory aids the magician has in the beginning, the better.

The next magical aid that has to be put in its proper place is the censer.[16] The magician places the censer either between the magic circle and the magic triangle, or else directly into the magic triangle. Then he places either burning charcoal into the censer, or liquid fuel with a wick, or a candle. Above the heat or flame there should be a small copper sheet, which is of course heated by the flame. The incense must be placed upon the copper sheet, and the incense itself must be compatible with the sphere of the being. Since we are dealing with an intelligence of Venus, the incense that is to be used is ground cinnamon bark. A small quantity of incense should be used, so that only a faint waft of cinnamon fragrance permeates the room. Instead of the cinnamon powder, you can also place on the copper sheet a few drops of cinnamon tincture, available in health food stores; in other parts of the world you might find it in drugstores and apothecaries. You can also prepare the cinnamon tincture yourself as follows: take one-third cinnamon and two-thirds spirit of wine and let it steep for eight days. Then filter the substance and the cinnamon tincture is ready for use. Should the magician decide not to use a censer during a magical operation, he can moisten blotting paper with a few drops of

---

[16] Censers or incense burners are commercially available. – ED.

cinnamon tincture. In any case, the cinnamon fragrance creates a temple atmosphere which appeals to an intelligence such as *Hagiel*, and it also favorably influences the materialization of this intelligence in the physical world. The fumigation is not as important as many books claim it to be; again, all of these things are aids. A being can never be condensed without materializing the light-energy substance, irrespective of how much incense powder the magician uses.

Generally, when a room is fumigated too much it has the disadvantage that the magician will experience irritation in his throat and cough on account of the strong odor. This is certainly not desirable or pleasant. It must be mentioned that a true magician will never make use of any harmful poisonous drugs and mixtures of narcotic substances. When a magician is dealing with a being that does not originate from any of the seven planetary spheres and he does not know the exact analogy in regards to the kind of incense he should burn, he can use a universal fluid condenser. This rule is usually applied to beings that belong to the zone girdling the earth. The fluid condenser must be impregnated accordingly, and the light-energy accumulation has to be carried out at the same time that the fluid condenser is loaded with the wish for success.

The following is a table of the various kinds of incense for the particular planetary spheres. However, I should mention that the burning of incense should only serve the beginner as an aid for materialization and is not absolutely necessary.

1. *The Zone Girdling the Earth:*
The powder of sage (*Salvia officinalis*) and elder pith (*Sambucus nigra*) must be mixed by volume in equal parts.

2. *Moon Sphere:*
Aloe powder can be used by itself as the only incense, or it can be enhanced by mixing equal parts of aloe, white poppies, storax [17] and benzoin. Add to this just a pinch of natural camphor powder.

---

[17] An aromatic resin which is obtained from snowbells; it is also known as styrax. – ED.

3. *Mercurian Sphere:*

Mastic[18] can be used by itself as the only incense, or it can be enhanced by mixing equal parts of mastic, frankincense, carnation petals, aniseed, wood from the juniper shrub or small tree (*Juniperus communis*), chamomile flower and valerian roots. All these ingredients must be mixed in powder form.

4. *Venusian Sphere:*

Cinnamon powder can be used by itself as the only incense or cassia flowers (*cassia flores*) in powdered form. Or an enhanced mixture can be prepared in equal parts by volume from the following ingredients in powder form: cinnamon, rose petals, coriander seeds, wild thyme flowers (*Thymus serpyllum*) and lily flowers.

5. *Sun Sphere*:

Sandalwood powder can be used by itself as the only incense. Or an enhanced mixture can be prepared from the following ingredients in equal parts by volume: sandalwood powder, myrrh, aloe wood powder,[19] frankincense, saffron, carnation petals, bay leaves (laurel leaves).

6. *Martian Sphere:*

Pulverized onion seeds can be used as the only incense. Or an enhanced mixture can be prepared in equal parts by volume, as follows: onion seeds, stinging nettle leaves, mustard seeds, hemp seeds, rue leaves and peppermint leaves.

7. *Jupiter Sphere:*

Pulverized saffron can be used as the only incense. Or an enhanced mixture can be prepared in equal parts by volume: saffron, linseeds, the roots

---

[18] Resin from the mastic tree. – ED.

[19] Since the aloe vera plant does not contain any wood, this can only be the aloe wood mentioned in the Bible. This is known in Latin as *Lignum Aloes*. It is the resinous wood of *Aquilaria agallocha*, a large tree that grows in the Malayan Peninsula. However, the aloe powder mentioned under 2, Moon sphere, can only be the commonly known aloe vera. – ED.

of the blue Iris (*Iris germanica*), peony blossoms, betony leaves and birch leaves. All these herbs have to be pulverized.

8. *Saturnian Sphere:*

Black poppy seeds in pulverized form can be used as the only incense. Or an enhanced mixture can be prepared in equal parts by volume and in powdered form: black poppy seeds, willow leaves, rue leaves, fern, caraway seeds and fennel seeds.

For all the other spheres a universal mixture of pulverized herbs can be prepared in equal parts by volume: frankincense, myrrh, storax, benzoin and aloe. When incense is burned during an evocation, the amount used is no more than what fits on the tip of a knife. The amount used when burning a single herb or a mixture of pulverized herbs remains the same. It is not necessary to fumigate the workroom of the magician to such an extent that the room becomes filled with smoke. The purpose is served when the fragrance of the herbs pervades the room.

This completes another preparatory step of the operation, and now the actual evocation begins. In this case we are dealing with *Hagiel*, a positive planetary intelligence; therefore you can attach your magic sword to your magic belt or secure it behind the belt on your left side. Should you have a dagger among your magical instruments, you can secure the dagger behind your magic belt as well. Very rarely do you require a sword or a dagger for a positive being, regardless of its sphere of origin. However, if dealing with a demonic being you must hold the sword or dagger in your right hand as a symbol of victory and you must hold the magic wand in your left hand. Having the sword tucked behind the magic belt indicates that in the present case the being does not have to be coerced to comply with your will. When it comes to obstinate spiritual beings, the magician cannot do without his magic sword or magic dagger. As a sign of victory, the magician uses his flaming sword to command negative beings in order to render them to absolute obedience and make them comply with his will. There is not one single demonic entity that will not be submissive to a true magician through his magic sword. All the magician need do is point his magic sword in the direction where he wishes the summoned negative being to appear — its rank represents no obstacle at all — and the being will immediately obey the order of the magician. All demons fear a magic sword or dagger, because every being possesses an instinct for self-preservation, and when the magician is in communion with God a magic sword, symbolically expressed, will tear a demon to pieces.

Take the magic wand into your right hand. Step into the center of the magic circle. Concentrate on the fact that you are the center, i.e. God Himself, Lord over all spheres, and concentrate that with your omni-consciousness you are at that very moment in the Venusian sphere. Having arrived in the Venusian sphere as the Divine Principle, call the intelligence *Hagiel* in your mind. Do so as if her name echoes through the entire Venusian sphere. You must be completely convinced that uttering the name penetrates the entire sphere and that *Hagiel* hears you and acknowledges you as her God. Remain in this tensive state for a few moments, whereupon you will immediately perceive in your spirit that *Hagiel* answers you therein. Since you are in the Venusian sphere with your omni-consciousness, you will initially perceive *Hagiel's* voice as if it comes from the innermost depth of your own spirit. As soon as you perceive her voice and you are certain that your spirit sees the being, return to your soul. But you must maintain your God-consciousness, i.e. the certainty that you are God, and upon your return you must feel in your physical body that you are connected with your soul again. Now whisper *Hagiel's* name and repeat it in that manner several times. You will immediately perceive that *Hagiel* is in her astral atmosphere, namely that she is in your room. As you have proceeded to this point in your evocation and *Hagiel* is now in your room — actually she is above the seal — now call her in a low undertone, or you may even call out loud, telling her that she is to appear to you in physical form. Never forget: when you pass over from the astral world into the physical world, you must be certain within your person and ascertain all three forms of your existence. You must feel that as a spirit you are connected with your astral body. You must also perceive that you are with your spirit and your astral body together at the same time in your physical body. This verification helps the being to follow the magician's train of thought and to proceed from its sphere to the sphere that the magician has prepared for the being where the evocation is carried out. Therefore the being appears mentally and astrally and, depending on the magician's ability to materialize it, also assumes a physically condensed body.

You can now see and hear *Hagiel* in the magic triangle. Or, if you have appropriately prepared the magic mirror for the appearance of this intelligence, she will appear in the magic mirror in her symbolic depiction in accordance with the attributes of the Venusian sphere, so that you can now establish a conscious contact with her. *Hagiel* appears as a queen with a stunningly beautiful countenance. Her eyes are clear and she also has a most beautifully shaped body. She is dressed in a green gold-embroidered dress and her head is adorned with a royal crown. Her voice is so lovely that it is beyond description, and every person who would see *Hagiel* in that state would see in her the true embodiment of beauty. Now is the time to express your demands to the intelligence. Should it be your intention at this point to establish contact with *Hagiel* more frequently, then do not forget, even though this is your first meeting with her, to come to an agreement with her as to how to readily contact this high, beautiful intelligence. Should you be interested, you can also gain access to her servants. Her servants are usually placed at the magician's disposal in female form. Even the servants of this Venusian queen are ravishing beauties, as the magician will see for himself.

You can gain the most diverse experiences during this kind of evocation. It would be impossible to mention them all here. It is the magician's prerogative to gather as many experiences as he sees fit. I can give a few guidelines from my personal experiences as to how a magician, as a true initiate, should proceed when it comes to the evocation of spiritual beings.

Once you have come to an agreement with *Hagiel* and she has promised to fulfil your wishes, you can be certain that she will honor her promises. All that remains now is to give her license to depart. In a very individual manner, you express your gratitude to her. For example, you express your delight that *Hagiel* acknowledges you as a perfect magician and that she is willing to obey you, and then you ask the intelligence to return to her own sphere. Then you transfer yourself with your omni-consciousness into the Venusian sphere and, with the imagination, you concentrate that *Hagiel* will return from the limited sphere in your room to her home sphere. Immediately after completing this meditative procedure, return from your omni-consciousness to your normal consciousness as a magician, which then concludes the evocation. After *Hagiel's* departure, you will experience an exhilarating feeling in the room where you carried out the evocation; a blissfulness will permeate you for quite a while, and you will find yourself in an exalted state, as if you were under the control of happiness

Should it please you, you may remain in the magic circle for a while longer, and you may reflect upon the entire experience that you had with *Hagiel*, and try to impress upon your mind every little detail. Then proceed to finally conclude the evocation. Through the imagination, dissolve the light-accumulation into the universe, remove the seal from the triangle, and put it away for safekeeping. You can step out of the magic circle now without any danger to yourself, and then extinguish the little lamps, etc. You must return all the magical instruments and aids to their place of safekeeping. If *Hagiel* has entrusted you with some special teaching which you were not allowed to record but had to commit to memory, then you must respect her wish. Otherwise, record the entire procedure of the evocation in your diary, because this will give you the necessary control and it will also serve as a reference for your work. Now you can follow the same procedure which you employed with *Hagiel* when summoning a being from any other sphere. In time you will become a master in this particular aspect of magic as well, and you will also be able to gather magical experiences in great abundance. This concludes the description of the practice of a magical evocation.

Part II
Hierarchy

Part II
Hierarchy

In this part of the book I shall describe only those beings and intelligences with which I have been in personal contact, either evocatively or through mental travel in the various planes and spheres. It is absolutely impossible to describe all the beings of the entire hierarchy, from the beings of the elements to the beings of the accessible Saturnian zone and even beyond to the extra-planetary beings. This does not mean that the practicing magician must strictly adhere to the hierarchy described in this book and contact only those beings mentioned here. He can also endeavor to contact beings through other reliable literature in order to get them under his control and to eventually realize his wishes.

The entire magical literature consists of many books which contain different beings, their signs, seals, etc., and it is at the discretion of the magician to make use of them. I have deliberately refrained from describing demons of any rank and sphere in order to prevent any misuse. However, on the basis of his development and on account of the precise instructions given in this book, a true magician will have the ability to invoke and control demons. Many ancient and modern books on the subject of magic contain information about demons of the various spheres, their attributes, seals, and so on. In accordance with the hierarchy contained in this book, the magician can classify every being, whether positive or negative, into its appropriate zone or sphere. The beings listed in this book are known to only a few initiates, simply because these initiates have been in contact with these beings and intelligences. Therefore, the magician may, if he so wishes, make use of the hierarchical table of beings and intelligences contained in this book for his magical operations. When the magician contacts any of these beings on his mental and astral travels, he can immediately determine from which sphere the being originates. In these cases the esoteric synthesis of astrology and the Kabbalah with its analogies will serve the magician well. For example, a magician who is well-versed in the Kabbalah will immediately be able to determine the correct name of a being in accordance with its attributes etc., without being misled by the being and even though it might prefer to be summoned by a name other than its real name. From this, the magician will gather that the name of the being indicates its fundamental attributes.

The seal of an individual being, which graphically depicts its individual fundamental attributes, is used in evocative magic to summon the being into the magic triangle. The seal can be destroyed after the evocation. In such cases the seal is drawn with the corresponding planetary color of the being on blotting paper that has been moistened with a fluid condenser. Afterwards the seal is destroyed depending upon the element to which the seal is subject. If they are beings of the Fire and Air principles, their seals are burned, whereas if they are beings of the Water principle their seal is torn into small pieces and thrown into flowing water, and the seals of the beings of the Earth principle are buried.

Furthermore, there is another possibility: the seals of the beings can also be made into the form of a talisman. In this particular case the signs are engraved onto the metal which corresponds with the sphere of the being. This engraved metal talisman is then placed into the magic triangle at the time of the evocation when contact with the being is first established. The summoned being must then acknowledge the seal and in this case it must bring about the contact with the seal on its own, i.e. with its appropriate sphere. In this case, the magician does not destroy the metal seal and, in agreement with the being, it can be kept for future evocations. Whenever the magician wishes to contact the being, in order to see it in his magic mirror or if he wishes to prompt the being to fulfil a wish, he merely has to take the seal in his hand. However, the details of the evocation depend upon the personal agreement that the magician has made with the particular being. Many years ago I myself worked in this manner. By taking into my hand the seal upon which the character of the being was engraved, I magically drew the sign of the seal in the air, i.e. three-dimensionally, and by so doing the sign was transferred directly into the Akasha Principle. Contact with the being was established immediately and in the manner I wished. Of course, this merely serves as an example, for the magician can make his own arrangements in regards to how to establish contact with the being that he has under his control.

If a magician wishes to be in constant contact with a particular sphere or being, all he needs to do is to carry the seal constantly on his person; he can wear the seal as a pendant, a ring or in another manner. However, it is not recommended that one should wear a seal for too long or wear an engraved amulet throughout one's entire life, regardless from which sphere the being originates. In time the magician would become too dependent on the particular being, and hence lose his equilibrium, his magical authority. As soon as he has a being under his control, a trained magician, without any great effort, can make such a seal in the form of a talisman in which he engraves the character of the being chosen, inclusive of the being's particular sign. Whereupon he loads the seal in a magical manner with the attributes of the being without having to establish contact with the being, in other words without going through the entire procedure of an evocation. The loading has to be carried out in the manner described in *Initiation into Hermetics* in Step IX in the chapter "The Loading of Talismans, Amulets and Precious Stones." Bear in mind: only if the magician is master over the particular being, i.e. if he has previously had this being under his control, under his will, can he carry out this magical practice. If he does not have this being under his control and nevertheless carries out the aforementioned practice by loading the talisman, he automatically comes immediately into contact with attributes of the being and with its sphere, regardless of whether he wishes to do so or not. Therefore, the magical loading of a seal in the form of a talisman should never be undertaken unless the magician has become absolute master over the being or intelligence through a previous magical evocation.

I shall now introduce in the proper order the hierarchy of the spiritual beings, to help the burgeoning magician. For this purpose I shall name a few beings and intelligences from every sphere. As I have mentioned, in accordance with our concepts, every sphere is inhabited by millions of beings which are endowed with various attributes in accordance with their rank, and they are entrusted with various spheres of influence. The beings and intelligences with which I had personal contact are arranged in accordance with the hierarchy into chapters. Even though I have had dealings with countless other beings of many different spheres, the ones which are to follow may serve the magician as the basis for his magical evocations. It is of course at the magician's discretion, by transferring his consciousness into the various spheres, to establish his own individual hierarchy of beings with which he comes into contact.

Chapter 1
The Beings Of The Four Elements

The Beings of the Fire Element:

Fig. 1: *Pyrhum* – In the kingdom of the elements *Pyrhum* is a powerful fire spirit. He occupies the rank of a king and potentate. A large number of subordinate fire spirits are under his control and are constantly at his disposal. A magician who has this fire spirit under his control will be entrusted with special methods from which he will achieve sweeping successes in all three kingdoms with the help of the Fire element. *Pyrhum* will also place at the disposal of the magician servant spirits which are endowed with his powers and therefore bring about the same effects as if *Pyrhum* carried them out himself. You can learn from *Pyrhum* everything that can be achieved with magic through the pure element of Fire. *Pyrhum* can bring about the desired effect even when it concerns causing influences through the Fire element. Any magician who personally contacts this fire spirit will discover his versatility for himself. The first time this fire spirit is evoked, the sign of his seal must be drawn in red on a piece of blotting paper. Once the magician has this fire spirit under his control, instead of the blotting paper a small iron plate can be engraved with his seal. A talisman that is made in this manner must have the shape of a pentagon, and this applies to all signs or engravings pertaining to the beings of the fire principle.

Fig. 2: *Aphtiph* – is also a fire spirit. He occupies the same rank as *Pyrhum* and he can bring about the same effects. The only difference between the two is that *Aphtiph* is not as active as *Pyrhum* and consequently he is easier to control. On the other hand, he has a greater fondness for human beings. He can give the magician various magical instructions regarding the Fire element, for example how excellent effects can be achieved through the Fire element with the aid of various effective rituals. ⎦ magician find it desirable, *Aphtiph* initiates the magicia᷉ methods into the consummate magic of the Fire element. He ⎦ places his subordinate beings at the disposal of the magician, and he ⌣ fers on them the same powers that he possesses. For the first evocation his seal must be drawn in red.

Fig. 3: *Orudu* – also of the fire sphere, is a severely feared being of high rank. Through his subordinates, *Orudu* causes volcanic eruptions, directly and indirectly, and he initiates all occurrences that are connected with severe and large fires. Not only can *Orudu* cause these events, he can also control them or set them at rest. Whoever gets *Orudu* under his control and befriends him can achieve great things through the Fire element with his instructions, provided that his activities are not in violation of the laws of divine harmony. *Orudu* can also place subordinate fire spirits at the disposal of the magician, as can the two previous fire spirits. Many magicians have achieved many magical feats with the Fire element through the spirits that were assigned to them by *Orudu*. For the first evocation, *Orudu's* seal must be drawn in yellow.

Fig. 4: *Itumo* – His sign is also to be drawn in yellow. He is also a male fire spirit, and he likes to be and move about in the vicinity of our earth's surface. Through his subordinate spirits he causes thunderstorms, but preferably downpours. If the magician has this fire spirit under his control, it will teach him how to cause various kinds of thunderstorms through his subordinate fire spirits or, should these thunderstorms be already in progress, how they can be stopped. Everything that occurs due to lightning and thunder is caused by *Itumo* and his beings. I have often influenced thunderstorms successfully with the help of this spirit and his subordinates.

Fig. 5: *Coroman* – The color of his sign must be drawn in red. *Coroman* occupies the rank of a grand principal. He has legions of beings which perform various tasks in the Fire element. *Coroman* has the Fire element under his control in all three kingdoms — the human, animal and plant r vegetable kingdoms — and he can be effective through these three kingdoms. He places at the disposal of the magician reliable subordinates who assist him in every aspect through the Fire element, regardless of whether he works with these subordinate servant spirits in a ritualistic manner or whether he asserts his influence through sympathetic magic. *Coroman* can teach the magician many magical practices, i.e. healing ailments which can and should be treated through the Fire element.

Fig. 6: *Tapheth* – The color of his sign must be drawn in red. *Tapheth* is like the previous being, for he too is well disposed towards human beings. He is in the position to assist the magician in various alchemical procedures and to protect him through his element of Fire. He allows the magician to succeed in various kinds of magical procedures by using the Fire element. Besides that, he instructs the magician how to distinguish the various stages and to recognize the individual processes in alchemical procedures. *Tapheth* also places positive subordinate beings at the disposal of the magician, with whom the magician can work successfully with the Fire element in many respects.

Fig. 7: *Oriman* – The color of his sign must be drawn in blue. *Oriman* is a mighty fire spirit. He has the ability to assist the magician with the Fire element in many magical practices. His fundamental attribute is pyrotechnics. Hence he possesses the ability to initiate the magician in many aspects of pyrotechnical artistry, which the magician may then call forth himself by using ritualistic magic or he can have it done by the subordinate spirits at his disposal. *Oriman* and his subordinate spirits like to oversee the work in blacksmith shops, particularly at the forging furnace, and they have a fondness for places where work is done with fire, be that in a manual or technical manner. But above all the magician receives from *Oriman* and his subordinates the most interesting information about all things that pertain to pyrotechnics.

Fig. 8: *Amtophul* – The color of his sign must be drawn in blue. *Amtophul* is, in rank and power, on the same level as the previous fire spirits. This fire spirit instructs the magician how to be effective in the kingdom of the

Fire element. *Amtophul* teaches him to establish and assert his magical authority to bring every being of the Fire element under his control. *Amtophul* is an excellent initiator of the "magic of fire." This fire spirit instructs the magician how to protect himself from the Fire element, so much so that the magician becomes to a certain extent invulnerable to fire. For example, the magician can take red-hot coals into his hands without suffering any burns. *Amtophul* loves to disclose to the magician many other magical skills which can be realized through the Fire element. Even if the magician has *Amtophul* completely under his control, he is still a very dangerous fire spirit.

Besides the fire spirits I have mentioned, there are many more of the same position with which I have been in personal contact in the past and which I could list here. However, these eight examples should suffice.

The Beings of the Air Element:

I shall also list eight principals of the Air element with which I was once personally in contact, along with their seals:[20]

Fig. 25: *Parahim,* Fig. 26: *Apilki,* Fig. 27: *Erkeya,* Fig. 28: *Dalep,* Fig. 29: *Capisi,* Fig. 30: *Drisophi,* Fig. 31: *Glisi,* Fig. 32: *Cargoste.*

I shall refrain from a closer description of these intelligences for the simple reason that, except for their shyness, they are not at all well-disposed towards human beings. It takes great effort to control them, and only a very competent magician will be able to succeed in bringing them completely under his control. Whatever the beings of the Air element taught me was eventually imparted to me by every principal of the zone girdling the earth. In the following chapter, the second chapter of the hierarchy, I shall inform the reader about the zone girdling the earth and

---

[20] The beings of the Air element are numbered 25 to 32 because there are no descriptions. It is very difficult for the aspiring magician to get them under his control. That is why they appear at the very end of the beings of the elements listed at the back of this book. – ED.

its beings. Every magician has the opportunity to discover for himself through his own practice whether my statements are correct.

The Beings of the Water Element:
The description of eight beings of the Water element now follows.

Fig. 9: *Amasol* – The color of the seal for the first evocation is red. *Amasol* or his subordinate spirits have the task of calling forth the storms on the oceans or setting them at rest, depending on what Divine Providence has ordered. *Amasol* also teaches the magician how to control the magnetic power of water magically and Kabbalistically. *Amasol* also places excellent subordinate water spirits at the disposal of the magician, which help him realize his wishes through the Water element.

Fig. 10: *Ardiphne* – The color of his sign is red. *Ardiphne* is a good initiator and teaches the magician, in order to be always successful, how to influence, i.e. properly carry out, ritual magic on human beings and animals through the Water element. When the object which is to be influenced somehow comes in contact with the element of Water, be it through rain, getting wet or washing oneself, drinking of liquids etc., then *Ardiphne* or his subordinates will help to accelerate the influence through which the wishes of the magician are realized.

Fig. 11: *Isaphil* – The color of her sign is silvery-white. *Isaphil* is an extraordinarily beautiful female potentate in the kingdom of the Water element. Even the most talented poet would have great difficulty in describing her beauty with words. *Isaphil* has many subordinates which are generally known as undines and mermaids. *Isaphil* knows many magical secrets that pertain to working with the Water element, and she has the ability to give the magician many insights, and she can entrust him with the practice. The magician must constantly be on the alert when working with *Isaphil* and the next female potentate, *Amue,* that he does not lose his head over them. Both are masters at enthralling human beings with their ravishing beauty, thus seizing them under their control. *Isaphil* will gladly put her subordinate beings at the disposal of the magician.

Fig. 12: *Amue* – The color of her sign is silvery-white. This female potentate has a large number of subordinate water beings under her control. Should the magician stay in contact with this female potentate, *Amue* will instruct him how to gain control over fish and all other water animals. If the magician concerns himself in the physical world with fish farming, fishing etc., he will receive from *Amue* valuable advice and instructions, on the basis of which he will be able to completely control everything that swims and creeps in the water. *Amue* also places subordinate beings at the disposal of the magician for the realization of his wishes.

Fig. 13: *Aposto* – The color of his sign is red. *Aposto* is a male being in the kingdom of the Water element. He rules over all creeks and rivers, small or large. *Aposto* gives the magician information as to what can be found at the bottom of creeks and rivers and where semi-precious and precious gemstones can be found in these waters. *Aposto* is completely familiar with the water principle. If the magician requires any subordinate water spirits, *Aposto* will gladly put them at his disposal. These subordinates have saved many a swimmer from drowning and have also saved many lives in all kinds of water sports. These water spirits can tell the magician where the corpse of a drowned victim is located.

Fig. 14: *Ermot* – The color of his sign is red. *Ermot* has almost the same attributes as *Aposto*. *Ermot* familiarizes the magician with the magic of the Water element and teaches him how to produce magic volts through the Water element for particular purposes. *Ermot* gladly places his subordinate servants at the disposal of the magician. *Ermot's* fundamental attribute lies in calling forth mutual love and affection among human beings through the Water element. *Ermot* especially exercises this influence on women.

Fig. 15: *Osipeh* – The color of her sign is blue. *Osipeh* is an extraordinarily beautiful female water spirit. Not only does she completely rule over this element, she also completely rules the magic of the Water element. With great fondness she initiates the magician into the rhythm of the Water element through the magic of sound. She is outstanding when it comes to song and dance, and that is why her subordinate water spirits perform the most beautiful dances, accompanied by the loveliest songs. If the magician does not succumb to the seductive temptations of this female potentate and brings her under his control, she will place countless subordinate beings at his disposal. However, I know from my own experience that she herself would rather serve the magician who controls her.

Fig. 16: *Istiphul* – The color of her sign is blue. *Istiphul* is the last being of the Water element whom I shall describe. *Istiphul* is a female water spirit. Besides the magic of water, with which she can familiarize the magician, she also has the ability to show him pictures from the past, present and future on the surface of water or any other liquid. She is the master of various transformations which can be achieved through the Water element. Among other things, if it is the magician's wish, she can teach him how to rouse love in a friend or an enemy through the element of Water, either on his own through magical practices or with the help of her subordinate water spirits. *Istiphul* has been the downfall of many magicians because she has succeeded in enthralling them on account of her great beauty and her great skills in erotic love, thereby stopping the magician from making any further progress. Due to the fact that a magician came into contact with *Istiphul,* he lost interest in any further development and very important contacts. Therefore, every magician should reiterate to himself: I shall control and rule over a being, but I shall never succumb to any being regardless of its position or from which sphere it comes.

The aforementioned beings are obviously not the only beings in the Water element. The magician can, in accordance with his own wishes, contact any other beings of the Water element of the same rank.

The Beings of the Earth Element:
Fig. 17: *Mentifil* – For the first evocation the color of the sign must be black. *Mentifil* is a mighty king of the gnomes in the subterranean kingdom who is endowed with many powers and attributes. This potentate can inform the magician about all the existing healing herbs and teach him how to prepare the herbs to make healing remedies for any existing disease that has befallen mankind and animals. He can also inform the

magician as to the effects of these herbs. In addition, *Mentifil* is a master in alchemical procedures and he will entrust the magician as to how the *prima materia* can be transformed into the "Stone of the Sages,"[21] and how the *lapis philosophorum* can be produced. *Mentifil* has a large number of gnomes at his disposal as subordinates who assist him in his labors and activities in the kingdom of the earth. Once a magician has gained control over this earth spirit, he gains a friend and can learn much from this mighty potentate and thereby enrich his knowledge with many a secret.

Fig. 18: *Ordaphe* – The color of his sign is black. *Ordaphe* is likewise a mighty king of gnomes. This earth spirit exerts great influence on all metals that are underground. If the magician wishes, *Ordaphe* will show him his kingdom and draw his attention to all the treasures that are underground in the form of ore. *Ordaphe* also has a large number of subordinate gnomes under his jurisdiction which fulfil tasks that are assigned to them underground. Some of them protect the ore while others labor to maintain and refine it. *Ordaphe* gladly places gnomes at the disposal of the magician to assist him in his work with the Earth element. The magician must be very careful never to ask this being for anything material. He must also never use these servant spirits for greedy or selfish purposes, because he would be in constant danger and it would be very difficult to escape the sphere and power of this king of gnomes.

Fig. 19: *Orova* – The color of his sign is black. *Orova* is the next great potentate in the kingdom of the gnomes. Besides the customary sphere of influence to which every earth spirit is entitled, *Orova's* particular task is the protection of all stones and precious stones that are underground. *Orova* possesses the ability to transform pebbles into precious stones and he can also give the magician points of reference as to how stones can be charged or loaded for specific purposes through the Earth element or on the basis of other particular methods. The occult significance of all precious stones is well known to *Orova* and the magician can find out all the information about talismans, lucky stones etc., from this earth spirit. If

---

[21] Also known as the Philosopher's Stone or *lapis philosophorum*. – ED.

the magician wishes, this mighty potentate of gnomes can place many subordinate gnomes of his kingdom at the magician's disposal. The magician is forewarned not to succumb to the sparkling appearance of *Orova*. He can allow himself to be taught by these earth spirits but he should never demand anything material from them, because they love to seduce the magician into accepting gifts, and by so doing the magician becomes dependent upon them.

Fig. 20: *Idurah* – The color of his sign is black. *Idurah* is another mighty potentate in the kingdom of gnomes, entrusted with the crystallization in the earth principle. His greatest sphere of activity is underground, where crystalline products are located, as for example various salts. The magician receives from *Idurah* the information about the location of rock salts and other crystalline compounds, and he is taught by this king of gnomes how these salts come into being. Furthermore, he receives information about their chemical and Hermetic analogies, and also learns through the Earth element about the occult usage of various salts for magical purposes. *Idurah* knows many secret methods of obtaining various kinds of salts from plants and minerals, and he entrusts these methods willingly to the magician and divulges their practical use in alchemy, the healing arts etc. The magician can obtain a great deal of knowledge from *Idurah,* knowledge that mere orthodox sources, such as our present-day educational institutions, could never provide.

Fig. 21: *Musar* – The color of his sign is brown. *Musar* is one of the mighty kings of gnomes and he is also a specialist in earth magic. He teaches the magician how the electromagnetic currents are effective in the interior of our earth and how the magician can practically control and utilize them. Furthermore, *Musar* familiarizes the magician with the magic of nature, which he is able to call forth through the plus and the minus of the earth, i.e. the electric and the magnetic fluids. Through this king the magician discovers how these two radiations which, through chemical dissolution, influence life on and under the earth, come into being from a Hermetic point of view. *Musar* is one of the most respected beings in the kingdom of the Earth element. In accordance with our concepts he can be considered a true earth magician.

Fig. 22: *Necas* – The color of his sign is brown. *Necas* also ranks among the gnomes as a potentate. He will give the magician an explanation about the Hermetic process of vegetation and its occult significance. From *Necas* the magician learns how trees, plants and all other growth are maintained and nourished by subterranean streams and energies. Furthermore, the magician will find out from *Necas* how he can foster and control the life of vegetation through elemental magic.

Fig. 23: *Erami* – The color of his sign is black. *Erami* is considered to be a mighty gnome magician. If a magician who controls *Erami* makes the request, this earth spirit will teach him complete sympathetic magic as well as the preparation of an earth-mirror and the preparation of various fluid condensers. Besides that, he will initiate the magician into the practical use of the Earth element. The magician will also find out from *Erami* how to protect himself from a variety of dangers through the Earth element. *Erami* can entrust the magician with many secrets in regards to magical knowledge in the kingdom of the elements. And this earth spirit will gladly place his servants at the disposal of the magician.

Fig. 24: *Andimo* – The color of his sign is black. *Andimo*, like *Erami,* is well disposed towards human beings. *Andimo* knows exactly what takes place underground in caves, grottos, subterranean waters, coal mines, etc. It is *Andimo's* special task to protect and to stand by all human beings who are working underground. He is a great friend of all miners. A magician who is in his good graces will always be under *Andimo's* protection while he is underground, regardless of where the magician might be. Since *Andimo* is well-versed in alchemy, he may assist the magician in word and deed on this subject as well. From my own experience with this earth spirit, I should like to forewarn magicians that *Andimo* loves to lead them astray by physically projecting the burning stone, the living sulfur, himself or through his subordinate earth spirits. If the magician takes this stone into his hands without any precautions after the projection, he will suffer severe burns. *Andimo* loves to place the stone either at the feet of a magician or before the magic circle. The magician should *never* touch the stone and he must order *Andimo* to remove it. However, if the magician touches the burning sulfur that *Andimo* has transmuted out of the earth principle (i.e. the stone was already alchemically prepared) with parchment paper containing *Andimo's* seal and which has been specially magically prepared in advance for this purpose by the magician, then the parchment paper will catch fire and the sulfuric stone will immediately be transmuted into the genuine alchemical red projection powder, the well known Red Lion. This powder is completely harmless and can be gathered with a glass spoon and stored in a glass jar that seals well. This projection powder has a projection capacity of 1:10,000 and it is the purest form of the Stone of the Sages. Having this powder in his possession might tempt the magician to use it to make gold or to prolong his own life. Should the magician fall victim to such temptation, his alchemical work would turn into a formal pact with the particular being. Therefore, the magician is herewith forewarned in good time not to commit such an impulsive act. He should never make use of these kinds of alchemical practices, even when he is of the opinion that he has the necessary maturity and experience in everything as far as magical knowledge is concerned. In spite of that, this can very easily entice him to take an ill-considered step. During my contact with *Andimo* I myself experienced these events personally, at which time I ordered *Andimo* to take the powder back to his kingdom, whereupon the powder disappeared within moments with a hissing sound.

The aforementioned eight beings of the Earth element should be sufficient to serve the magician as examples. Every magician can gather individual experiences through his own practical work.

Nota Bene: I must emphasize this once again — and this applies to all magicians — it is of the utmost importance that during the first evocation the magician not address or speak to the being first, regardless to which element it belongs.

Furthermore, it must be mentioned that every being appears in a different sort of way. I have refrained from describing the individual beings as to color, height, shape and mode of speaking, because it is of little importance for the practical working magician. It could occur, on account of an exact description of a being, that the magician could bring his powers of imagination into play during the evocation and, instead of evoking a being, he might inadvertently create an elemental which takes on the form of the being. In order to avoid this I have refrained from describing a being's outer appearance in every detail. A magician who honestly does his work will not indulge in any hallucinations and he will not create any phantoms and the like. If he is magically well prepared, he will always get the true entity under his control and he will see, hear and feel it like all other genuine magicians. It is solely the practice which will enable the magician to attain mastery in everything.

Chapter 2
Some Of The Original Intelligences
Of The Zone Girdling The Earth

As soon as a magician who practices ritual magic has become complete master over the beings of the elements, he can continue with his magical work and proceed to work to the next sphere. The next sphere is the zone girdling the earth, the spiritual-astral sphere of our planet. In this zone exist many beings which the magician can contact in order to enrich his knowledge and increase his powers. From this sphere I shall mention those beings with which I was in contact long ago. Of course, it is at the discretion of the magician through mental and astral travel to contact other beings in this sphere.

Fig. 1: *Aschmunadai* – is a mighty initiate in the zone girdling the earth who occupies the rank of an absolute potentate. His universal seal in Section 2, Figure 1 of the Illustrations of Seals in the back of this book is very complicated. However, it graphically represents all the fundamental attributes with which this high intelligence is endowed, and this applies to the zone girdling the earth and to our world. For the first evocation his seal must be drawn in blue, red, green and yellow, and the magician must place this seal in the magic triangle. Once the magician has established contact with *Aschmunadai* he will receive an abbreviated version of his seal (see under Section 2, Illustrations of Seals, Figure 8). Subsequently the magician can summon this intelligence with the help of this seal at any time. However, the magician can only make use of this seal if *Aschmunadai* approves it.

Aschmunadai can familiarize the magician with all the laws which are in force in the mental and astral spheres of the zone girdling the earth, and he can make it possible for the magician to avail himself of these laws. The magician can control the entire zone girdling the earth with *Aschmunadai's* help, and he can gain a tremendous amount of knowledge. Since *Aschmunadai* possesses a large number of servants for the zone girdling the earth and also for our physical world, he can place them at the magician's disposal to willingly fulfil his wishes if he so chooses.

Fig. 2: *Aladiah* and Fig. 3: *Kolorom* — These entities are *Aschmunadai's* representatives and closest subordinates. For the first evocation, their seals have to be drawn in black. *Aladiah* is outstanding when it comes to controlling the elements in the zone girdling the earth. To provide proof of that I point to the next entity, *Gibora*.

Fig. 4: *Gibora* – During my onetime contact with *Aladiah* I received from him both the name and seal of this entity to control thunderstorms and storms. When the magician utters *Gibora's* name and draws the sign in the air with his magic hand, then *Aladiah* stops thunderstorms, storms and severe winds on his behalf. This sign is only magically effective after the magician has first made contact with *Aschmunadai* and his two representatives.

Fig. 5: *Siilla* – The color of his sign is green. *Siilla* is another principal of the zone girdling the earth. He has the ability to explain to the magician all the symbols so that the magician properly understands the symbolic language of forms. Once the magician masters the symbolic language of solid forms, he also becomes well-versed with the analogous connections of every form with the universal laws and therefore with the Akasha Principle.

Fig. 6: *Lilitha* – The color of her sign is red. *Lilitha* is a female arch-intelligence of the zone girdling the earth. She has a complete understanding of all magical practices, as does *Aschmunadai*; this applies to the zone girdling the earth as well as our planet.

Fig. 7: *Asamarc* – The colors of his sign are red and blue. *Asamarc*, as an arch-intelligence of the zone girdling the earth, controls the precise lawfulness, i.e. the laws of analogy of the zone girdling the earth and the physical world, and he can teach the magician accordingly. As a high intelligence he can instruct him as to the highest knowledge of the zone girdling the earth and he can teach the magician how this knowledge can be practically applied as well.

Fig. 8: *Aschmunadai* – His abbreviated seal.

Fig. 9: *Emuel* – The colors of his sign are red, blue and black. *Emuel* can explain to the magician the synthesis of plus and minus in reference to propagation, i.e. the prime secret of life.

Fig. 10: *Ubiveh* – The colors of his sign are red and blue. *Ubiveh* instructs the magician on how the influences of the Moon sphere effect the zone girdling the earth and our earth in a mental, astral and physical respect.

Fig. 11: *Asael* – The colors of his sign are red, blue and green. *Asael* instructs the magician on the electric and magnetic vibrations of the zone girdling the earth, and he also teaches the magician to understand and control the influence of these vibrations on our physical world. From this intelligence the magician learns about the true electric and magnetic fluids in the mental and physical worlds and how to apply them properly. In particular, *Asael* has precise knowledge of how to produce electromagnetic volts for special purposes, and he can provide the necessary instructions to the magician in this regard.

Fig. 12: *Gojel* – The colors of his sign are red, black and green. *Gojel* is a specialist regarding the chemical components of all created things. The magician learns from this intelligence many facts in regards to the various chemical combinations, compounds, energies etc., and he can learn their practical utilization in so far as magical knowledge is concerned.

Fig. 13: *Armiel* – The colors of his sign are red, blue and black. *Armiel* is well-versed in all alchemical processes. This intelligence can reveal to the magician the secret of the transmutation of metals. For example, he can give the magician information on the requirements of the preparation and production of the Stone of the Sages through the dry process.

Fig. 14: *Amuthim* – The colors of this sign are red, blue and green. *Amuthim* teaches the magician how any kind of form can be changed into another form through a magical method. This means that *Amuthim* reveals the secret of the dematerialization and materialization of objects to the magician.

Fig. 15: *Coel* – The colors of his sign are red and blue. *Coel* acquaints the magician with the laws of analogy as they pertain to the animal kingdom, and he teaches the magician how to magically influence animals on the basis of the laws of analogy.

Fig. 16: *Yod-Heh-Vau-Heh*[22] – The colors of this sign are red, blue and green. Here the magician will find the symbolic representation which the electric and magnetic influence has in respect to its effect in the zone girdling the earth. Every being in the zone girdling the earth can explain to the magician the symbolic form these influences take in order to express themselves in the three-dimensional world. However, if the magician

---

[22] The German spelling of this is "Jod-He-Vau-He." – ED.

meditates thoroughly on this sign, he will find the explanation for these symbolic analogies by himself.

Fig. 17: *Aeoiu* – The colors of this sign are red, blue and green. *Aeoiu* teaches the magician who has transferred himself to the earth-girdling zone how he can draw energy three-dimensionally out of other spheres from the electric and magnetic currents into the zone girdling the earth and from there into the physical world. This intelligence has the knowledge of how to load any object three-dimensionally with the above-mentioned energies, and it will teach the magician how to do this.

Fig. 18: *Juoea* – The colors of this sign are red, blue and violet. *Juoea* instructs the magician how to control, understand and see into any being's consciousness and subconsciousness.

Fig. 19: *Nahum* – The colors of his sign are red, blue and violet. *Nahum* entrusts the magician with a very particular magical practice with which the magician can put any being of either gender, male or female, human or animal, to sleep. *Nahum* has great expertise in hypnosis. *Nahum* or his subordinates instruct the magician how to call forth dreams and visions in any human being of the male gender, at his discretion.

Fig. 20: *Immicat* – The colors of her sign are red and green. In the zone girdling the earth, *Immicat* is the female counterpart to *Nahum*, who is considered to be the lord and master of dream-life. From her the magician discovers the method of how, at his own discretion, he can put a human being into a refreshing, dreamless sleep. Or if the magician so wishes, he can have this state of sleep brought about directly through *Immicat* herself or through her subordinates. *Immicat* is the lord and master of sleep. The magician can learn from *Immicat* everything that is connected with sleep. In the case of anesthesia or deep unconsciousness or a coma, this intelligence offers the magician the protection that he will always awaken from these and similar circumstances without any harm.

Fig. 21: *Osrail* – The colors of his sign are red and violet. *Osrail* is a mighty and much feared intelligence of the zone girdling the earth, for he is considered to be the "Angel of Death" of this sphere. All things connected with death in the earth-girdling zone as well as on our physical world are influenced or affected by this intelligence. It is not advisable to evoke this intelligence, and only one who is very experienced would dare to do so. However, should the magician succeed in getting *Osrail* under his complete control, then he will have complete power over the life and death of every person. The magician should never make use of this ability, otherwise he will severely burden himself, cosmically and karmically. If someone were to misuse *Osrail's* sign, this intelligence could lead him to his downfall. In this case the magician must exercise extreme caution, and the only reason I mention it is to inform the magician about *Osrail* and also to warn him about this intelligence.

Fig. 22: *Ados* – The colors of his sign are red, blue, green, violet and black. *Ados* is the guardian of many magical treasures. He teaches the magician how to practice magic with the aid of the Earth element. He also teaches the magician how to practically utilize the electromagnetic currents of the physical earth in a magical manner.

Fig. 23: *Sata-Pessajah* – The colors of his sign are red, violet, and yellow. *Sata-Pessajah* makes the magician cognizant of how the Akasha Principle expresses itself in all beings of the zone girdling the earth and how he can transfer himself from this sphere into the Akasha Principle, i.e. the causal principle. *Sata-Pessajah* is a mighty and powerful intelligence who can give the magician several possibilities and instructions regarding how to protect himself from all dangers through the Akasha Principle when he transfers his mental and astral bodies into the zone girdling the earth. Also, *Sata-Pessajah* initiates the magician into the secret of how to make his mental and astral bodies invisible in the zone girdling the earth to the extent that he cannot be seen by any being, regardless from which sphere the being originates. This intelligence can also reveal many more secrets to the magician.

Fig. 24: *Laosa* – The colors of her sign are red, blue and green. *Laosa* is a female intelligence of the zone girdling the earth. She instructs the magician how he can freely and without danger move about in the various subdivisions of degrees of density. Besides that, *Laosa* introduces the magician to a very special kind of magical practice with which he can transfer his mental and astral bodies into the zone girdling the earth whenever he wishes. *Laosa* is considered to be an excellent initiator in the magical practice of mental and astral travel.

Chapter 3
The 360 Principals Of
The Zone Girdling The Earth

The principals whom I shall now describe in more detail keep all the activities of the earth-girdling zone in constant harmony. Each principal is a high intelligence endowed with all the abilities which any being of this sphere might possess. For example, a magician can ascertain information from any one of these principals about matters of the past, present and future of our physical world, and each principal can also be effective on our physical world through the Akasha Principle. Besides that, each principle has specific attributes, i.e. he is entrusted with particular tasks. The magician does not have to contact all the principals of the zone girdling the earth. Whenever he engages in the practice of evocation, he only needs to determine which intelligence seems to be the one that is most important for his purpose. When it comes to the evocation of beings from the zone girdling the earth, the magician can simplify his work somewhat by utilizing Kabbalistic astrology at the first evocation. Beginning at sunrise, another principal is in control every four minutes. Commencing at sunrise, the first four minutes are reserved for the principal who exerts the greatest influence upon our earth. The following four minutes are ruled by the second principal, the third principal rules the next four minutes, and so forth. Since a four-minute time period is allotted to every principal, that is the time when that particular principal can be evoked most easily, because at that time a close contact exists between the particular principal and our physical world. However, an experienced magician does not have to rely on evoking the intelligence at the particular Kabbalistic time, since he is in the position to evoke any being from any zone or sphere at any time.

In the case of these intelligences I shall also refrain from giving a detailed description of the form in which they appear. In the course of his practice, every being that a true magician summons will appear to him in the form which is determined by its character traits. The sequence of the seals is in accordance with the signs of the zodiac and their degrees, as well as the influences of the elements. As I have already mentioned, I shall only mention a few main attributes when it comes to the individual intelligences, because each being and each intelligence in every sphere is endowed with the usual magical abilities. Besides, every magician may ask the intelligence at any time how it may be of service to him. Should an intelligence not be able to fulfil the wishes of the magician simply because its sphere of influence is a different one, then it can name the intelligence which is capable of fulfilling the magician's wishes.

The 30 Principals Of The First Sign Of The Zodiac: Aries

The seals of these principals must be drawn in red.

Fig. 25: *Morech* – (1° Aries) This intelligence is quite active and impulsive and distinguishes itself through extraordinary acuity. As he is highly erudite, not only can he instruct the magician in general knowledge, but above all he can also disclose to him excellent methods with which he can favorably influence his memory and increase his intuitive abilities. Besides that, *Morech* can influentially assist the magician with inventions of every kind. *Morech* controls the Fire element, through which he can achieve tremendous effects. *Morech* can answer all questions on the subject of electricity, be they electro-technical or electro-physical. Furthermore, he can give the magician information in regards to astral or mental electricity, which concerns the electric fluid and how it can be applied in magical operations.

Fig. 26: *Malacha* – (2° Aries) *Malacha* has the same abilities as *Morech* and is able to cause the same effects. In addition to that, this intelligence teaches the magician how to move about or behave in the kingdom of the salamanders and how he can employ or work with the energies or powers of fire in the various planes. Furthermore, the magician can learn from *Malacha* by which manner he can achieve particular states of trance through the Fire element. If it is the magician's wish, *Malacha* himself will load volts of the elements for him for specific purposes and then transfer them into the Akasha Principle of the zone girdling the earth. These volts will then call forth effects on the physical world. If the magician finds it desirable, *Malacha* will gladly place at his disposal suitable *spiritus familiaris* which are highly active magically and which have high magical abilities. I should like to mention that I know from my own experience that *Malacha* can give the magician excellent advice in alchemy, i.e. he can provide the magician with the *prima materia* for the preparation of the grand elixir for the dry process. When the magician comes in contact with *Malacha,* this intelligence also entrusts him with many other things.

Fig. 27: *Ecdulon* – (3° Aries) *Ecdulon* can initiate the magician into love-magic. At the magician's request, *Ecdulon* exchanges animosity for friendship and secures the good graces of very important people in high places for the magician. This intelligence has the ability to load magic mirrors with the fluid of the particular element for specific purposes, for example a magic mirror which is loaded by this intelligence allows the magician to see the kingdom of the salamanders and many more things along those lines. Since this principal is well-versed in all magical rituals, he is therefore qualified to give the magician various specific hints in evocative magic.

Fig. 28: *Lurchi* – (4° Aries) *Lurchi* can be most helpful in all affairs of the heart. *Lurchi* can secure the magician's livelihood and, if it is deemed necessary, he then allows the magician to become wealthy by either showing him ways and means to achieve this or by achieving it directly through his subordinates.

Fig. 29: *Aspadit* – (5° Aries) *Aspadit* is a very pleasant intelligence, and, if the magician so desires, this intelligence will arrange that the magician has good luck in games, gambling, competitions, contests, betting etc. Manual skills in one's profession, in the arts, etc. can also be achieved with *Aspadit's* help.

Fig. 30: *Nascela* – (6° Aries) This intelligence helps the magician on the road to literary talent, or the magician is given methods with which he can develop this talent easily and quickly. And of course this intelligence can be very helpful in literature and the arts.

Fig. 31: *Opollogon* – (7° Aries) This principal is a guardian of magical secrets and he can entrust the magician with many magical practices, rituals etc., for his personal use, besides which he can give the magician information on how to contact the beings of the Moon sphere easily. Once contact with *Opollogon* has been established, the magician, with the help of *Opollogon* or his subordinates, can travel throughout the Moon sphere and establish contact with the beings there in a very specific manner. *Opollogon* teaches the magician how to practice Moon magic in the spirit in the Moon sphere, and how to accomplish various effects directly in the Moon sphere, or he can have the beings of that sphere bring about effects on our physical world.

Fig. 32: *Ramara* – (8° Aries) *Ramara* is an outstanding master of magic. As such he can teach the magician how to acquire special magical abilities through appropriate methods, predominantly ritual and magical formulas, and then make use of them accordingly.

Fig. 33: *Anamil* – (9° Aries) This intelligence has control over the electromagnetic fluid. *Anamil* teaches the magician how to load electromagnetic volts for particular purposes. Should the magician desire it, *Anamil* will form these volts himself and transfer them into the Akasha Principle and release the effects either in the mental, astral or physical spheres. In the zone girdling the earth, there is not one problem which *Anamil* cannot solve. The magician can ask this intelligence any question and he will receive the answer momentarily through inspiration.

Fig. 34: *Tabori* – (10° Aries) This intelligence gives the magician insight into the profound secrets of the Water element and its analogies. And pertaining to that, *Tabori* points out all magical practices and methods and how the magician can carry out various effects on himself and on other people through the magnetic fluid of water. Should the magician make the request, *Tabori* will bring about the effect himself or through his subordinates. The magician also receives special instructions from *Tabori*, for example, how to contact the beings of the Water element without any effort on his part and how he can associate with them without exposing himself to danger. Upon *Tabori's* command, the magician will have at his disposal the most beautiful undines as servants. The magician will find out from this intelligence how storm spirits can be calmed, how thunderstorms can be stopped and how a raging ocean can be calmed.

Fig. 35: *Igigi* – (11° Aries) This principal teaches the magician how to gain power over human beings and animals. He also teaches the magician how to dynamically charge magical formulas so that they have an especially strong effect.

Fig. 36: *Bialode* – (12° Aries) From this intelligence the magician learns how to obtain respect as a magical authority. He also learns how to use the powers of the earth zone whenever he requires them, and, furthermore, the method of changing base metals into precious ones. A magician who has an especially great disposition in respect to magic can make this intelligence carry out the transmutation of metals for him. *Bialode* also acquaints the magician with sun-magic, i.e. the magician learns how to consciously utilize the powers of the Sun on a magical and physical basis in the mental, astral and physical planes. Furthermore, the magician learns how to protect himself from the negative influences of the Sun sphere while on mental travels.

Fig. 37: *Opilon* – (13° Aries) *Opilon* himself can help the magician to succeed in all his undertakings, or this can be accomplished through *Opilon's* servant spirits. This intelligence can instruct the magician on any branch of the sciences of our physical world and he can also bestow this knowledge upon the magician.

Fig. 38: *Jrachro* – (14° Aries) This intelligence itself can also be of assistance to the magician in all his undertakings on the physical world or else through its subordinates. If the magician so wishes, *Jrachro* has the ability to make him eloquent and quick-witted and can also well teach him how to call forth this ability within himself and others through the Akasha Principle.

Fig. 39: *Golog* – (15° Aries) This principal is well-versed in all branches of our earthly sciences and there is actually no problem which he cannot solve. *Golog* is regarded as a great philosopher and he makes the synthesis of philosophy understandable to the magician through intuition and inspiration.

Fig. 40: *Argilo* – (16° Aries) This principal gives the magician advice and support on the mental, astral and physical planes in matters of friendship and affairs of the heart. The magician can realize all his wishes in this respect through this principal.

Fig. 41: *Barnel* – (17° Aries) *Barnel,* like *Argilo,* is well-versed in the art of love or matters of the heart and has expertise in excellent practices with which the favor or good graces of friend and foe of both genders can be obtained. *Barnel* gives the magician specific instructions and methods in sympathetic magic. This principal places good beings from his own region at the disposal of the magician, and he also makes it possible for the magician to establish contact with individual beings of the air, which otherwise have a certain shyness of the earth, making any contact with them very difficult. *Barnel* is also well-versed in music and, if the magician wishes, *Barnel* will inspire him with compositions of music, provided his interest is such.

Fig. 42: *Sernpolo* – (18° Aries) With the help of this intelligence the magician can rather quickly develop his talent for languages. *Sernpolo* helps to improve the magician's status in life and gives him methods and directions with which he can practically utilize the magnetic powers in accordance within his sphere of activity.

Fig. 43: *Hyris* – (19° Aries) *Hyris* is a master of water magic. The magician learns from this principal how to utilize the powers or energies of water in regards to the elements and the magnetic fluid, and how to be effective with these powers. *Hyris* can disclose to the magician many ways of influencing the physical plane through the element of Water. Besides that, he can entrust the magician with specific instructions and secrets from the kingdom of the undines.

Fig. 44: *Hahadu* – (20° Aries) Not only is *Hahadu* well-versed in water magic, he can also give the magician various instructions, on account of his particular attributes, on how to prepare liquid fluid condensers, in particular how to load the magnetic fluid. *Hahadu* is quite well liked in the kingdom of the undines, i.e. in the element of Water. Should it be the magician's wish, this principal can send him as many male and female servants from the kingdom of the Water element as he requires for the fulfillment of his wishes.

Fig. 45: *Oromonas* – (21° Aries) *Oromonas* acquaints the magician with the various laws, powers and effects of the zone girdling the earth. The magician learns from *Oromonas* how to set the individual powers into motion with the aid of various methods and instructions. *Oromonas* is a very generous intelligence and well disposed toward human beings, and he is always willing to realize the magician's wishes as long as they are within the bounds of his possibilities.

Fig. 46: *Bekaro* – (22° Aries) By this intelligence, the magician is granted the knowledge and wisdom which applies to the zone girdling the earth. There are only a few such beings of this sphere that have this ability. *Bekaro* places great emphasis on justice and harmony and therefore he can help the magician in the physical world in every respect wherever he has to deal with justice, whether that be in legal matters or in other situations of life. *Bekaro* is much feared by storm spirits and salamanders, because he is in a position to entrust the magician with particular formulas, which, when employed in the fire region of the zone girdling the earth, call forth severe electrical and elemental effects. This can make even the most obstinate salamander spirit immediately submissive, regardless of its rank. When *Bekaro* places any being from the kingdom of the salamanders as a servant for the magician, this being stands faithfully at the magician's side with its high intelligence, great intellectual activity and with great understanding.

Fig. 47: *Belifares* – (23° Aries) This principal is, with the exception of the two previous ones, superior to the others in wisdom, intelligence and keenness of mind. The magician can learn from him how to employ the laws of the zone girdling the earth on the physical plane through the Akasha Principle. *Belifares* is only too willing to help the magician in every respect.

Fig. 48: *Nadele* – (24° Aries) *Nadele* is well-versed in the healing arts, in particular with magnetism, and he reveals to the magician methods through which even the most severe ailments can be cured either with magnetism or with the appropriate remedies. *Nadele* is not only a physician of the physical body, he can also teach the magician how to heal himself and others through the Akasha Principle in every respect and in every situation of life. This principal is well liked in the kingdom of the gnomes, and when a magician comes into contact with the kingdom of the gnomes through *Nadele's* mediation, even the kings of the gnomes place themselves at his disposal.

Fig. 49: *Yromus* – (25° Aries) *Yromus* is also a master of magical knowledge, namely he is a master of alchemy and spagyric. The magician learns from *Yromus* how to process and prepare various herbs and roots in a spagyric and alchemical manner and how to make them exceedingly dynamic through the electromagnetic fluid and a particular kind of volting. If the magician expresses the wish, then he receives instructions from *Yromus* in accordance with which he can change causes for himself and others in the Akasha Principle so that they exert a less unfavorable influence upon the mental, astral and at times even upon the physical plane. Besides that, *Yromus* teaches the magician how to change the destiny of a person and how to perform magical operations without them being imprinted in the Akasha Principle, so that they do not cause counter-effects. *Yromus* is also well liked in the kingdom of the gnomes and all gnomes, especially those of the upper classes, approach this principal with the greatest awe.

Fig. 50: *Hadcu* – (26° Aries) *Hadcu* is a master of mental and astral magic. He teaches the magician how to practically employ extra-planetary powers in the mental, astral and physical world for various purposes.

Fig. 51: *Balachman* – (27° Aries) *Balachman* is an excellent initiator of synthetic[23] astrology and reveals to the magician the profoundest secrets of the astrological sciences. The magician learns through this initiator the astrological influences upon the mental and astral world. Furthermore, the magician learns about the reciprocal oscillations and vibrations of the various spheres in regards to the mental, astral and physical planes. Also, knowledge in regards to cosmic effects upon the mineral, plant and animal kingdoms is communicated to the magician either directly or through intuition and inspiration.

---

[23] Bardon uses the word "synthetic" here in the same sense that we might refer to a "synthetic fabric," i.e. he is referring to a system of astrology designed and developed by the human intellect and consciousness rather than by Divine Providence. – ED.

Fig. 52: *Jugula* – (28° Aries) *Jugula* instructs the magician in the art of talismanology. The magician learns from this principal how to correctly solve even the most complicated symbol from the synthetic point of view. Furthermore, *Jugula* instructs the magician as to how he can correctly express, through a corresponding symbol, every power and every being belonging to the zone girdling the earth together with its attributes, or how the magician can graphically depict the power or spirit-being properly. At the same time, *Jugula* initiates the magician into the secrets of how these symbols become magically effective through various methods.

Fig. 53: *Secabmi* – (29° Aries) *Secabmi* brings about various effects on the mental, astral and physical planes through the magnetic fluid. This principal is a master in the art of pleasant fragrances and can instruct the magician how not only healing remedies but also pleasant fragrances can be spagyrically prepared from various plants.

Fig. 54: *Calacha* –(30° Aries) *Calacha* is the last principal of this sign of the zodiac. The magician learns from this principal how to treat various ailments through the element of Water. *Calacha* is a master of hydrotherapy and gladly gives the magician advice and support on this subject. Any magician whose interest is in the area of naturopathy finds in *Calacha* an excellent initiator who can entrust him through intuition and inspiration with many secrets which to this very day have not been unveiled.

The 30 Principals Of The Second Sign
Of The Zodiac: Taurus

The seals of these principals must all be drawn in green.

Fig. 55: *Serap* – (1° Taurus) *Serap* is the first principal of this sign of the zodiac. He informs the magician about sympathetic magic that is realized through the Fire element. I know from personal experience that this principal teaches the magician practices which mostly consist of how to make use of fluid condensers after they have been applied to blotting paper which is exposed to the burning process. *Serap* gladly gives special instructions and methods as well as various magical practices for establishing friendships, to call forth feelings of love, increase the procreative capacity, etc. On this subject matter the magician can learn plenty from this principal.

Fig. 56: *Molabeda* – (2° Taurus) Should it be the magician's wish to come into contact with this principal, then he will be taught how various kinds of natural phenomena that border on the miraculous are brought about through the electric fluid in connection with the Fire element. *Molabeda* is a faithful guardian of the most profound secret sexual mysteries, which he reveals only to a mature and ethically highly developed magician.

Fig. 57: *Manmes* – (3° Taurus) *Manmes* is well-versed in the magic of botany. The magician learns from this principal about the various kinds of plants from the Hermetic point of view, and he will gain an insight in the art of how the greatest variety of effects can be achieved with plants by employing magic. *Manmes* draws the magician's attention to a variety of plants that are excellent for burning as incense and which may serve the magician well as an aid in various operations.

Fig. 58: *Faluna* – (4° Taurus) This intelligence is extremely favorably inclined toward human beings and helps the magician to live in prosperity if he so wishes. *Faluna* gives him various kinds of instructions on how to prepare remedies from plants which preserve his body, yes, which may even rejuvenate his body and protect him from disharmonious influences such as ailments, etc. and thereby make him more resistant. *Faluna* is an excellent teacher on how to prepare spagyric remedies which are produced from plant substances.

Fig. 59: *Nasi* – (5° Taurus) *Nasi* or his subordinates can give the magician advice on how to make his life more pleasant and joyful through various improvements. The magician can learn from *Nasi* how to increase his income, and he or his subordinates can also help the magician attain a better lifestyle. *Nasi* is considered a consummate master in providing joy and earthly happiness.

Fig. 60: *Conioli* – (6° Taurus) This principal is an excellent mathematician as far as the knowledge of numbers is concerned. This principal initiates the magician into Astro-Kabbalah. *Conioli* knows how to express every power, every ability, every realization etc., mathematically in numbers and, vice versa, he can explain to the magician every number in the form of influences and attributes. Besides that, *Conioli* teaches the magician how he can practically make use of the acquired knowledge.

Fig. 61: *Carubot* – (7° Taurus) Should the magician also be active as a writer, then this principal can be of assistance to him through intuition and inspiration in so far that he supplies him with outlines, suggestions, events or incidents for literary treatment in a well chosen style. Magicians whose subject matter is fairytales, legends, mythology etc., will find a fabulous initiator in *Carubot*.

Fig. 62: *Jajaregi* – (8° Taurus) *Jajaregi* is considered to be a great initiator for authors of occult literature, because he possesses the excellent ability to inspire the magician to describe occult powers, effects, laws etc., in the form of novels. Many magicians who have published occult novels may have been inspired by this intelligence without their knowledge. On the other hand, *Jajaregi* can explain personally or through his servants or by means of intuition all occult novels, events etc., to the magician in accordance with the universal laws and the laws of cause and effect in the mental, astral and physical planes.

Fig. 63: *Orienell* – (9° Taurus) *Orienell* gives information about occult aids, auxiliary methods etc., which contribute to the development of various spiritual, astral and physical abilities. *Orienell* also discloses to the magician how he can acquire certain abilities. These aids are for the larger part rituals, formulas and gestures, which I remember from my own past practical experiences when I was still in contact with this principal. Should the magician remain in contact with *Orienell* for a longer period of time, then in a separate book he can record all magic auxiliary methods that he receives intuitively from this principal.

Fig. 64: *Concario* – (10° Taurus) *Concario* is a good master and teacher of Moon magic. He points out to the magician the various influences of the Moon, among which are the 28 Moon stations and how they have an effect on the zone girdling the earth as well as on our physical world in a mental, astral and physical respect and how they can be utilized in practice. *Concario* explains to the magician the synthesis of the astrological Moon magic.

Fig. 65: *Dosom* – (11° Taurus) *Dosom* is a very good initiator in the field of occultism, especially hypnosis, suggestion, and magnetism as they apply to the healing arts, etc. The magician learns from this principal to apply hypnosis correctly in respect to the spirit, soul and physical body. If the magician makes use of *Dosom's* servants, they will carry out all the work and effects in this connection, upon the magician's wish. The abilities and powers should never be used for ignoble purposes, otherwise the magician will encounter *Dosom's* counterpart, the negative genius.

Nota Bene: In order to guard against any misuse with intelligences and beings, I have refrained in this book from listing and describing those principals and intelligences of the zone girdling the earth which represent the negative attributes. However, there are as many negative principals as there are principals with positive attributes.

Fig. 66: *Galago* – (12° Taurus) *Galago* instructs the magician on how he can secure for himself honor, esteem, dignity, friendship and love etc., in a magical manner by impregnating his aura, his magical space, by means of the electric fluid and the Fire element.

Fig. 67: *Paguldez* – (13° Taurus) *Paguldez* is an excellent initiator in all forms of nature magic. When the magician contacts this principal, he will learn how to set into motion various powers through natural means, how to create various causes and, as the result of that, effects that border almost on the supernatural. This principal will entrust, upon the magician's specific request, the manner in which various phenomena in nature can be produced. For your information, I would like to mention that *Paguldez's* counterpart, the negative genius, is the guardian of the secrets of various sorcery projects of nature magic.

Fig. 68: *Pafessa* – (14° Taurus) *Pafessa* assists the magician in his profession and gives him the proper inspiration on how to improve his professional position. For example, if the magician is employed in a commercial enterprise, then this principal's subordinates will assist him to increase his clientele, etc. *Pafessa* is very accommodating and gladly helps the magician on the physical plane in every respect. This principal enjoys great respect in the kingdom of the gnomes and they gladly serve the magician at *Pafessa's* request.

Fig. 69: *Jromoni* – (15° Taurus) *Jromoni* is an excellent initiator, and as such he can inform the magician how he can come into money easily and quickly through winnings, entering into bets, speculations etc., provided Divine Providence permits it. *Jromoni* also knows where hidden treasures can be found and, if he thinks it appropriate, he will disclose the exact location to the magician. This principal is well aware whether the help he offers to the magician is karmically permissible or not. If *Jromoni* is not supposed to fulfil the magician's wishes, he will tell the magician during the first evocation, and he will help the magician only as much as Divine Providence permits but without burdening the karma of the magician. The magician may rest assured that now and then prosperity, wealth, and abundance of money can be great obstacles on the path of perfection.

Fig. 70: *Tardoe* – (16° Taurus) *Tardoe* possesses the power to awaken various talents in the magician such as artistic or literary talents etc., through appropriate practices and rituals. Should the magician have a disposition for any such talents, he will develop them quickly.

Fig. 71: *Ubarim* – (17° Taurus) *Ubarim* initiates the magician as to how various love remedies can be used to ignite love and friendship, and he can give the magician many methods and directions for this purpose. Furthermore, the magician receives from him detailed instructions on how to produce love and friendship amulets. Should it be the magician's wish, then *Ubarim* himself or his servants will load the talismans and amulets for these purposes.

Fig. 72: *Magelucha* – (18° Taurus) *Magelucha* gives the magician various kinds of directions as to how he should magically employ the air and Water elements in the mental, astral and physical planes and how to utilize these two powers for various purposes. *Magelucha* is a master of these two elements and his practices — which he reveals only to a true magician who has been called upon to attain that status — are extremely valuable. A magician can learn much from this principal in regards to fluids and their utilization for various purposes.

Fig. 73: *Chadail* – (19° Taurus) *Chadail* is a faithful guardian of agriculture. Generally, not only does he inspire magicians on earth, but also all those who are engaged in agronomy, agro-chemistry and agricultural improvements. Should the magician be a farmer, this principal will disclose to him how to improve his soil with normal or occult methods so that the growing process of his crops is accelerated. He will also learn how he can improve the quality and increase the yield of his crops by exposing chemical products to various kinds of radiation. *Chadail* also points out to the magician various working methods and gives him directions as to how to produce an improved and better growth pattern of natural products through the electromagnetic fluid or with the help of the elements or Kabbalistically. With *Chadail's* help or that of his servants, the magician will be successful in an almost phenomenal manner in cultivating the soil.

Fig. 74: *Charagi* – (20° Taurus) This principal is a fabulous inspirer of technical inventions for forestry and agriculture. When the magician contacts *Charagi,* he gains much knowledge on the aforementioned matter from this intelligence or by its servants.

Fig. 75: *Hagos* – (21° Taurus) *Hagos* is a master when it comes to polarization magic and the electrical fluid. This principal gives the magician instructions on how to achieve fast plant growth through polarization magic in connection with the electrical fluid. For example, *Hagos* instructs him how to proceed when a seed that has just been planted grows so quickly that it becomes a tree-bearing fruit within one hour.

Fakirs who have the ability to actually grow a tree from a seed within one hour accomplish this feat on the basis of their knowledge of polarization magic and the electrical fluid. In India this miracle is known as the true mango tree miracle. However, for the magician it is not a secret as to how this is done. In *Initiation into Hermetics* I gave a description as to how this phenomenon is accomplished, namely on the basis of the electromagnetic fluid, therefore on the basis of polarization magic. The reason that I mention this here is because the possibility exists that the magician can achieve the same phenomenon through *Hagos* or his servants.

Fig. 76: *Hyla* – (22° Taurus) Through his influence, *Hyla* can assist the magician to the point that, through a high level of intuition and inspiration, he allows the magician to acquire a clear mind, good powers of judgement, quick-wittedness and prudence in every respect. This principal or his servants can be of service to the magician in various matters of concern. For example, he can assist the magician during examinations in any field of physical science.

Fig. 77: *Camarion* – (23° Taurus) From this principal the magician learns about the magical relationships of individual foods on the whole in respect to the health and harmony of the physical body. *Camarion* gives the magician instructions as to how to choose the proper foods in accordance with the occult laws of analogy, be they fruit or prepared meals with a variety of ingredients. Through intuition and inspiration, *Camarion* imparts to the magician how food and meals (combinations of different foods) are to be loaded, either with the electric or magnetic fluid. Furthermore, the magician is also taught what element the food is to be loaded with in order to exert an effect on the mental, astral or physical body. *Camarion* is also an excellent inspirer in diet and asceticism and in diseases of all kinds, i.e. disharmonies of the body, soul and spirit, and he is always prepared to give advice and support.

Fig. 78: *Camalo* – (24° Taurus) In addition to other attributes and spheres of activity, *Camalo* is very familiar with the secrets of mineral compounds and their occult utilization, which he strictly protects. Above all, he teaches the magician about the various metals and how they correspond to the spheres, the powers, the individual beings etc., and how these powers can be magically utilized in the mental, astral and physical world. Should the magician deem it desirable, he will receive from *Camalo* a number of recipes for solid fluid condensers. Furthermore, the magician will also receive the true *electro magicum*, which can be used for various purposes, as for example to produce a magic wand, mirror etc. And of course the magician learns in which manner these fluid condensers are to be loaded for magical use in the zone girdling the earth and on the physical world for a variety of purposes.

Fig. 79: *Baalto* – (25° Taurus) *Baalto* gives the magician information on the construction of mines. On our planet, he supervises the gnomes in the underworld and he knows all about the subterranean waters and ores. This principal can give the magician information about volcanoes and the exact time of their eruption. Furthermore, *Baalto* can give instructions and methods as to the magical manner in which the currents which are under the surface of the earth can be utilized for a variety of purposes. Should the magician deem it desirable, *Baalto* will teach him the art of using the divining rod and how to correctly use the sidereal pendulum to ascertain the location of electromagnetic currents and many other things in this respect.

Fig. 80: *Amalomi* – (26° Taurus) This high initiator is considered to be the cosmic language teacher. The magician learns from *Amalomi* how to use the Kabbalah, the cosmic language, in the physical world. *Amalomi* initiates the magician into many different formulas and tantras and at the same time teaches him to dynamically charge them in order to produce effects through the Akasha Principle in the mental, astral and physical worlds. [24]

Fig. 81: *Gagison* – (27° Taurus) In the zone girdling the earth, this principal is considered to be a universal philosopher. He allows the magician, through intuition, to understand and gain insight into all religious systems in their true lawfulness. That applies to all such systems which have existed on this earth thus far and which exist now. A magician who enjoys a friendly relationship with this principal can learn a great deal and, with his help, will understand any religious system which he wishes to investigate from the Hermetic point of view and will find the universal laws within each system he investigates. At the same time he will realize to what extent the universal laws were concealed or veiled, or why they were mutilated for other possible reasons. However, from a philosophical point of view he may correct them for his own personal use, and he will learn from the religious philosophy how to separate the chaff from the wheat. Should the magician contact *Gagison* on a more frequent basis, he will find out that from time immemorial all religious systems have pursued the universal laws like Ariadne's thread and that they are represented in every religious system, however in one more than another.

Fig. 82: *Carahami* – (28° Taurus) This principal could rightfully be considered the teacher of cosmic universal physics. He teaches the magician to understand and control the cosmic powers, their analogies and their lawfulness in nature. *Carahami* can reveal to the magician many metaphysical and metapsychical secrets in regards to nature. These are phenomena which become known to the magician through the knowledge of the cosmic powers in their cause and effect. On account of this knowledge, these natural phenomena no longer cause any doubt within him. Not only will he be able to find, from a Hermetic point of view, the correct explanation for all phenomena in nature, he will also be able to bring

---

[24] N.B. – In *The Key to the True Kabbalah* I have listed some formulas, working methods etc., which this principal allowed me to publish.

them about himself in accordance with his maturity. However, a true magician would never dare cause any chaos through a magical operation of this kind, for he would burden himself severely with karma.

Fig. 83: *Calamos* – (29° Taurus) *Calamos* has the ability to entrust the magician with excellent methods of grafting plants on our physical world. However, this principal is particularly fond of the ocean and the life therein, and he can give the magician specific magical methods. With the aid of these methods the magician can control everything that lives underwater. *Calamos* also confides magical words to the magician that calm stormy seas, and teaches him how to protect himself on an ocean voyage. Should it occur that an entire ship with crew and passengers were to sink, the magician who is in contact with *Calamos* would always succeed in saving himself. If the magician expresses such a wish, *Calamos* will place beings of the element of the ocean at his disposal, or *Calamos* will give the magician instructions how he can contact these oceanic beings. This principal of the zone girdling the earth is held in very high esteem by undines who spend most of their time on lonely beaches. That also includes all the subterranean beings of the water. Whenever they encounter this principal, they approach him with the greatest respect and immediately fulfil all his wishes and orders.

Fig. 84: *Sapasani* – (30° Taurus) *Sapasani,* like *Calamos,* is an excellent master in the magic of water. All beings that live under the water and the beings of the elements obey this principal. His specific knowledge is based on exploiting sea salt for magical purposes and alchemical operations. *Sapasani* will give the magician instruction on how to contact water beings in a sympathetic manner by using a small dosage of sea salt, and how he can utilize the powers of the elemental beings in the ocean for various purposes. This principal of the earth-girdling zone will also teach the magician many other practices, besides the aforementioned.

The 30 Principals Of The Third Sign Of The Zodiac: Gemini

The seals of these principals must all be drawn in brown.

Fig. 85: *Proxones* – (1° Gemini) The magician receives from this principal exact information on all questions about the electrical fluid in reference to the mental, astral and physical planes. *Proxones* is the master of the electrical fluid, including electricity. At the same time he is the guardian of inventions, and as long as these inventions are based on electricity he keeps them in proper equilibrium. All human beings engaged in inventions in the field of electricity are accordingly inspired by *Proxones*. To a discreet magician, *Proxones* will disclose future inventions which will not be invented for many years to come, and at times he will even disclose those which will not be invented for centuries. Of course, a magician who has been given this knowledge cannot disclose it to the public. However, the magician learns from *Proxones* how far and in which period of time technology will progress in the field of electricity, in which respect he can acquire the greatest knowledge. Should *Proxones* permit it, the magician may then make use of certain secrets for his personal use, but under no circumstances should this knowledge result in chaos in the order of the world.

Fig. 86: *Yparcha* – (2° Gemini) *Yparcha,* like the previous principal, is entrusted with the protection of all technological inventions. *Yparcha* can inform the magician — under the seal of complete secrecy, of course — how far the world will progress in fifty, a hundred or more years in the field of technological inventions. Should the magician himself be working on an invention, then he has the best inspirer in *Yparcha,* who will provide him with good ideas intuitively.

Fig. 87: *Obedomah* – (3° Gemini) This intelligence instructs the magician in all branches of chemistry, biology etc., in respect to metaphysics and metapsychics. As such the magician can receive from *Obedomah* recipes for the treatment of the various ailments which, on the basis of their chemical or biological analogous connections, have an entirely different sphere of activity and sphere of indication than the merely chemical attributes of every single substance. This principal can also instruct the magician in homeopathy from the metaphysical point of view, and he can give the magician wondrous information in this particular field. In addition, *Obedomah* familiarizes the magician with the possible uses of chemical radiation in regards to the various analogous laws of nature and of human beings in the microcosm and in the macrocosm.

Fig. 88: *Padidi* – (4° Gemini) *Padidi* is considered to be the inspirer for those who occupy themselves on our physical world with the art of painting. Should the magician occupy himself with this art, then this intelligence has the ability to instruct him through intuition or inspiration to create compositions that will boggle his mind. The magician learns through *Padidi* how to express real beauty — of course, that will always be in accordance with the magician's state of maturity. It is a great art to project beauty outwardly in any kind of manner that corresponds with the analogous laws of the microcosm and macrocosm. However, that can only be developed through an inborn genius. When a magician is in contact with *Padidi*, then this rare art will be bestowed upon him, besides which *Padidi* will also confide many secrets about the composition of particular color combinations.

Fig. 89: *Peralit* – (5° Gemini) This principal is a great master when it comes to the knowledge of life and death. From this principal the magician can find out at what time a child should be procreated on this earth in order to have particular abilities. *Peralit* teaches the magician how to procreate a child consciously in the magical manner, and he gives the magician special instructions for the child's prenatal education. On this basis the magician can impress upon the child before it is born, i.e. the fruit in the mother's womb, specific attributes, abilities and talents. The magician also learns from *Peralit* what kind of being from the zone girdling the earth enters into the child that he has procreated and what kind of destiny and karma it will have. The magician will also be told by this intelligence how he can help his child during the course of its life and the kind of position he has to take vis à vis his child, not only as its father, procreator, but probably also as a teacher, and so forth. Since *Peralit* is an authority on the subject of the sex mysteries, this gives him the ability to make them easily understandable to the magician.

Fig. 90: *Isnirki* – (6° Gemini) *Isnirki* gives the magician instructions and methods with which he will understand the mental and astral form of any animal on our earth, be they land animals, water animals or animals of the air, and thereby make them more accessible to the magician's intellect. The magician learns from this principal the ability to transfer his consciousness into the mental and astral form of any animal and therefore understand it from these two states of consciousness, thereby influencing it whenever he deems it necessary. Through this ability the magician may also see and know the destiny of any animal. With *Isnirki's* help, the magician can transfer himself into the sphere of the animal species into which every animal departs after its death on this earth and where he can make contact with these animals if he so wishes. For magicians who are animal lovers, a great deal can be learned from *Isnirki* in this respect.

Fig. 91: *Morilon* – (7° Gemini) This intelligence is a fabulous initiator and master of symbolism. *Morilon* teaches the magician by way of specific methods how to acquire the abilities to express the astral and mental analogies of any external form on this physical world through an analogous symbol in accordance with the laws of the microcosm and macrocosm. At the same time, the magician learns from *Morilon* how to acquire the abilities to express every law and every attribute, regardless of the sphere, through an external form. Once the magician is in possession of this ability, he can be considered an interpreter of dreams, because he will then be able to interpret every dream correctly. After having acquired the abilities of the symbolic analogies, the magician learns to completely understand every being intellectually wherever it appears to him, regardless of the sphere. Once the magician has acquired these abilities, never will a being be able to deceive him, because it must always take on the form that is in accordance with its attributes.

Fig. 92: *Golema* – (8° Gemini) *Golema* is considered to be an outstanding occult philosopher. This principal knows all the laws of our world as well as all the laws of the zone girdling the earth. Should the magician contact *Golema,* he can teach the magician how he can gain the ability to translate the most difficult problems into our physical language, i.e. into the language of the intellect, in such a way that they are easily understood. Only a magician who works as an occult author, teacher or advisor knows how difficult it is to express occult and philosophical matters in words that can be understood by an uninitiated person. That is why the magician finds in *Golema* the best inspirer to help him, through intuition or inspiration, to express the most difficult problems in such a way that any misunderstanding is impossible. Any magician who lacks intellectual comprehension and who, in addition, has a bad memory can, through *Golema's* methods or through his direct help, acquire excellent intellectual comprehension and a good memory.

Fig. 93: *Timiran* – (9° Gemini) This principal is an outstanding authority in the laws of harmony, not only of the zone girdling the earth but also of the microcosm and macrocosm. He can explain the harmony on our physical world and the zone girdling the earth to the magician in an understandable manner from the Hermetic point of view. *Timiran* will explain the true significance of introspection and the manner in which magical equilibrium is employed. Once the magician has completely understood the magical secrets of introspection, he can, with this acquired knowledge and abilities, establish complete harmony within himself, and he can do this within other human beings as well. Wherever he wishes, the magician can also establish harmony and equilibration in any situation where chaotic and disharmonious influences exist. Very few magicians posses this ability; however, *Timiran* can be of great assistance in this respect.

Fig. 94: *Golemi* – (10° Gemini) Like the previous principal, this one is an outstanding authority on all the laws of analogy, not only in the physical world and the zone girdling the earth but also in all other spheres. The magician learns to correctly judge every being of every plane and sphere with *Golemi's* intuitive or inspirational support. The magician also gains the experience of knowing the exact degree of efficiency of every being which was granted to it by Divine Providence, so that no being can boast that it understands or knows something which in reality it does not. Furthermore, the magician learns from *Golemi* how to identify and classify every being correctly by its external appearance in accordance with its color, tone, form etc.

Fig. 95: *Darachin* – (11° Gemini) From this principal the magician learns to understand any human being's intellect in every nuance, and also how to influence it, i.e. the mind of every person is an open book to such a magician. *Darachin* will give the magician, if he so wishes, appropriate instructions and methods by which he can develop the ability to perceive the intellectual abilities of any person and be active in the consciousness of that person. These abilities make the magician complete master over another person's mind. The magician can, if he deems it appropriate, increase or diminish the intellectual abilities of another person. For example, the magician has it at his discretion to bring back anyone's memories from the past, or he can influence the mind of a person to such an extent that these memories completely vanish from the mind of the particular person. However, *Darachin* will only reveal specific methods and instructions for developing the necessary abilities to an ethically highly developed magician. When a magician is endowed with these abilities, it means that if he so wishes he can know everything that the other person knows.

Fig. 96: *Bagoloni* – (12° Gemini) *Bagoloni* has a special fondness for mental telepathy or thought transference. He is an outstanding master on this subject. The magician receives from this principal the appropriate methods and instructions which help him attain these abilities. A magician who follows the specific instructions of this principal acquires the ability to transmit any picture or image to another person over the farthest distances either visually, acoustically or through the consciousness. At the same time, the magician acquires the ability to call forth particular character traits in the astral body of another human being who is not familiar with magical knowledge.

Fig. 97: *Paschy* – (13° Gemini) This principal can help the magician to attain diplomatic successes. Should the magician be a diplomat, then *Paschy* can put his diplomatic career on a secure footing; for example, he can reveal to the magician strictly guarded secrets known only to a few diplomats. In very difficult diplomatic affairs, *Paschy* can inspire a magician who is in contact with him to be successful in his undertakings. This intelligence can rightfully be considered the principal of the diplomats.

Fig. 98: *Amami* – (14° Gemini) *Amami* will assist the magician in finding the proper philosophical literature or help him to obtain books and written material. However, as a rule it is not necessary for the magician to find any books on the subject of philosophy and spiritual knowledge, because anything he wants or needs to have can be obtained from this being. However, it happens that a magician may be a great friend or collector of scientific books, and therefore it is more a matter of personal preference rather than obtaining the knowledge contained therein. Should a magician have this fondness, then there is nothing which should stop him from asking *Amami* for this favor, which he will certainly honor.

Fig. 99: *Pigios* – (15° Gemini) Should the magician be a writer, he will find in this principal a faithful friend and advisor who will help him at any time with inspiration. This principal's specific preference is to support poets through inspiration and to help them in their choice of words and form of expression. *Pigios* rightfully occupies the position as the principal of all poets and writers.

Fig. 100: *Cepacha* – (16° Gemini) *Cepacha* has a great fondness for beauty, harmony and external splendor. Should it be the magician's wish, this principal is prepared to initiate him into the various mysteries of beauty care, and he will show him ways to beautify his physical body and make it more attractive. Magicians who possess a sense of beauty and place a particular value on their external appearance will find an excellent inspirer in this principal.

Fig. 101: *Urgivoh* – (17° Gemini) *Urgivoh* gives the magician advice and support to gain the favor and good graces of important people in high places. *Urgivoh* gives the magician instructions on how to become popular with men and women alike, depending upon his requirements. If the magician follows the instructions exactly, without acting upon his individual attitude or point of view, he will be successful in this endeavor.

Fig. 102: *Amagestol* – (18° Gemini) *Amagestol* initiates the magician into all secrets concerning love, into the lawfulness, cause and effect of love, regardless of whether it is the lowest animalistic love or the highest cosmic love. *Amagestol* is the guardian genius of all those who love each other on earth.

Fig. 103: *Debam* – (19° Gemini) *Debam* is a master of magic, namely in the field of gesticulation and individual ritualism. Should the magician require a ritual for an individual purpose, this principal will give him the best possible advice. The magician learns from *Debam* how to make full use of any power from any sphere with appropriate gesticulations and how to set particular powers in motion on all three planes with appropriate gesticulations.

Fig. 104: *Kolani* – (20° Gemini) *Kolani* is considered to be the initiator of occult dances, namely those which have the purpose either to set in motion very specific power or to connect with this power. This principal can also intuitively impart certain dance styles that awaken various extraordinary abilities in a human being. Should the magician wish to put himself into spiritual ecstasy through occult dances, then *Kolani* will advise him accordingly.

Fig. 105: *Mimosah* – (21° Gemini) All human beings who are engaged in the philosophy or science of law (jurisprudence) are under the protection and supervision of this intelligence of the zone girdling the earth. If this principal is called upon regarding a legal matter where a judicial decision was made and an unjust sentence was passed, then *Mimosah* or his subordinates will help the magician. Therefore this principal can rightfully be considered to be the guardian of all human rights. All judges, lawyers, etc., who are engaged in jurisprudence can turn to this intelligence, provided they are magicians.

Fig. 106: *Eneki* – (22° Gemini) This principal can initiate the magician into the various ways of the art of prophecy. In this respect, *Eneki* confers upon the magician perspicacity and a high level of intuition. When a magician comes in contact with this intelligence he learns every kind of prophecy, for example chiromancy or palmistry, graphology etc., and he learns them to perfection.

Fig. 107: *Corilon* – (23° Gemini) This principal is considered to be the guardian of all artists that work in public, be they be singers, stage artists, actors, virtuosos, etc. If he is called upon, he helps them in so far as letting the artist carry out his work or art through inspiration to the satisfaction of all concerned. *Corilon* endears professional artists to their public and at the same time makes certain that they are financially successful, too. Should the magician himself be a stage artist, or if he wants to give someone else advice and support, all he has to do is turn to this principal with the fullest confidence and his wishes will be fulfilled at any time.

Fig. 108: *Ygarimi* – (24° Gemini) *Ygarimi* has been appointed to explain to the magician all the causes of the mental, astral and physical planes, which are recorded in the Akasha Principle. If a magician has a good relationship with this principal he can learn how causes that are provoked through thoughts, feelings, character traits and physical activities can be distinguished from each other in the Akasha Principle and also how destiny can be read from these causes in the Akasha Principle on the mental, astral and physical planes. It should be mentioned that under these conditions this information is completely reliable. Once the magician has reached such a level that he can make these distinctions, then he is in the position to recognize obstacles which will occur in the mental, astral and physical world in advance. Having this information, the magician will find ways to lessen the effects of these obstacles and at times he might even be able to make them completely ineffective.

Fig. 109: *Jamaih* – (25° Gemini) From the magician's point of view, this principal could be considered to be a historian of religions. He can inform the magician about all religions which have existed on our earth until now and which still exist, not only from the esoteric but also from the exoteric point of view. This intelligence can also acquaint the magician with the secret esoteric knowledge of the oldest religious sects.

Fig. 110: *Bilifo* – (26° Gemini) This principal is entrusted with the custodianship of all magical and mystical circles of people, and also other associations and sects, and he is to be considered as their rightful protector. *Bilifo* makes the decision as to the coming into being, the existence and the demise of lodges and associations. A discreet magician can find out from this principal all the details regarding magical and mystical lodges and all their secrets without becoming a member of any lodge or similar association, brotherhoods, etc. The information and knowledge that is gained in this manner can only be employed for one's own use.

Fig. 111: *Mafalach* – (27° Gemini) *Mafalach* helps the magician to solve difficult problems in an indirect manner by leading the magician to the appropriate books, manuscripts etc. This occurs either through *Mafalach* himself or through his subordinates. If, for example, the magician works alone, i.e. without the guidance of a teacher and initiator, then this principal can be of help to him. He can arrange to introduce him to a person in whom the magician will find his true master. The quality of the teacher depends upon the quality and maturity of the seeker.

Fig. 112: *Kaflesi* – (28° Gemini) *Kaflesi* initiates the magician in the secret correspondences of the various laws of analogy of the microcosm and the macrocosm. This principal teaches the magician all the laws of analogy of the body, soul and spirit in regards to the universe and how he can correctly employ these laws in the practice of magic.

Fig. 113: *Sibolas* – (29° Gemini) On the other hand, *Sibolas* instructs the magician in the reverse order by explaining to him in detail and in the proper context all the exoteric things, i.e. the worldly things with the help of the true laws of analogy. He also teaches the magician the manner in which he can draw the attention of the higher powers to himself through external things and occurrences and at times even set them into motion. The magician can learn much from this principal, especially in regards to the magic of nature.

Fig. 114: *Seneol* – (30° Gemini) The last principal of the zodiacal sign of Gemini is a protector of all human beings who pursue or are engaged in water sports. This intelligence can be of great help to the magician in achieving extraordinary athletic abilities through appropriate methods and instructions. For example, establishing record times in the various swimming events as well as establishing records in long distance swimming and underwater endurance. *Seneol* can also be of assistance to the magician by saving people from drowning. If someone is considered missing, i.e. presumed drowned, either *Seneol* or his subordinates will disclose to the magician the exact location of the corpse. If the magician has a good relationship with this principal, he will never drown, because *Seneol* will take care that the magician be rescued in one way or another should this event occur.

The 30 Principals Of The Fourth Sign Of The Zodiac: Cancer

The seals of these principals must be drawn in a silvery-white color.

Fig. 115: *Nablum* – (1° Cancer) *Nablum* gladly gives the magician information about the various degrees or levels of heat that are to be applied when working alchemically and spagyrically; this information is provided to the magician in the form of intuition and inspiration. However, since the degrees of heat are not the only consideration in the preparation of plants and metals — besides which there are other fluids which must be considered, for example light, color, tone (sound), vibration, etc. — the magician can obtain this information from this principal as well. *Nablum* is well-versed in all alchemical and spagyrical operations and the magician can learn much from him in this regard through inspiration.

Fig. 116: *Nudatoni* – (2° Cancer) A magician who is in contact with this principal can find out the details about volcanic eruptions on our earth as well as earthquakes which are connected with them. *Nudatoni* can inform the magician in advance when a volcano will begin to spew lava. *Nudatoni* himself or his servants can accompany the magician if he so wishes to the subterranean world through mental and astral travel and show him hot springs, stalactite caves and stalactite formations, hidden treasures and, on the whole, everything that can be found underground. This intelligence is also an excellent initiator in the field of pyrotechnics, namely when it comes to working with the electric and magnetic fluids. He also instructs the magician how to magically achieve various pyrotechnical miracles with these two fluids.

Fig. 117: *Jachil* – (3° Cancer) This principal knows all erotic secrets, into which he can initiate the magician. *Jachil* is willing to give the magician the recipes for many magical potions with which he can either arouse love or diminish it. Furthermore, this principal can give the magician informa-tion as to how he can magically make himself popular and sought after by the opposite sex, how he can make himself attractive and how he can make himself appear erotic. If the magician wishes, this intelligence can disclose the most secretive arts of erotic magic.

Fig. 118: *Helali* – (4° Cancer) This principal is an excellent initiator when it comes to sympathetic or mummial magic. He gives the magician infor-mation as to how he can achieve various effects with the help of the ele-ments through mummial magic. Furthermore, he explains to the magician the influence that the electric and magnetic fluids have on nature. *Helali* introduces the magician to very particular and, up to now, completely unknown methods of operation in the field of mummial magic. On the basis of specific magical mummial instructions by *Helali* himself or his servants, the magician can achieve so much, things which he never would have deemed possible.

Fig. 119: *Emfalion* – (5° Cancer) *Emfalion* gives the magician advice on how to attain a strong and healthy physique, handsome and attractive facial features, fascinating eyes and youthful vigor and preserve it all until a ripe old age. The magician receives from *Emfalion* the appropriate instructions on how to prepare these remedies with which he can impregnate his body so that it will not be subject to the decline of life. When a magician has a good relationship with this intelligence, he will have the appearance of a young man even when he has already reached a ripe old age, or at least he will have the appearance of a middle-aged person. The magician will also be thoroughly instructed on the preparation of magical potions from a variety of plants for specific magical operations.

Fig. 120: *Pliroki* – (6° Cancer) *Pliroki* explains to the magician the actual purpose of the so-called "messages through the air" which are well known to most people in the Orient. *Pliroki* has at his disposal appropriate methods with which the magician, if he so wishes, can acquire the ability to send messages even over far distances, not only to initiates, but also to completely uninitiated people. *Pliroki* will disclose these methods to the magician at his request. The magician learns about this phenomenon with the help of the electromagnetic fluid and the Air element on the mental, astral and at times even on the physical plane. He either learns how to achieve that by himself or with the help of beings, spirits etc. The magician will also achieve other similar phenomena with *Pliroki's* instructions.

Fig. 121: *Losimon* – (7° Cancer) *Losimon* gives the magician information about the original mysteries and the original systems of religion of the oldest nations of our earth. He also gives the magician information in regards to the magical phenomena these ancient people were capable of creating, especially the high priests. *Losimon* is quite conversant with the manner and circumstances under which the phenomena of the days of yore can be called forth today. At the magician's request, this principal will initiate him in these methods in order that he may achieve such phenomena. This principal can also reveal the secret of the levitation phenomenon to the magician, for example, how it can be brought about, either with the help of beings or on the basis of specific powers and abilities which the magician has acquired by controlling the electromagnetic fluid and with whose help he can regulate and overcome the gravitational force of the earth. These specific powers and abilities permit the magician to withdraw the gravitational force from the earth, through which he can make himself and others as light as a feather. For example, he can walk on water without sinking or rise with his physical body into the air. It is also a foregone conclusion that he will become capable of achieving this feat with any object he might choose.

Fig. 122: *Kiliki* – (8° Cancer) *Kiliki* initiates the magician into the mysteries of rhythm and vibration. At the same time he teaches him how both rhythm and vibration can be employed magically in all spheres and planes. *Kiliki* is deemed to be the master of life, since life is really no more than rhythm and vibration.

Fig. 123: *Oramos* – (9° Cancer) *Oramos* can give excellent information about occult abilities, namely clairvoyance, clairaudience, clairsentience, psychometry etc. He can give the magician specific instructions for the manufacture of magic mirrors and how they are loaded with particular influences etc., or he can teach the magician how to load a magic mirror Kabbalistically. Should the magician be a consummate clairvoyant, he can learn from *Oramos* how to expand on his already acquired abilities in this respect. This principal also gives the magician advice as to how he can acquire servant spirits for various purposes and how he must deal with them. *Oramos* also gives the magician exact information for controlling these spirits for magical operations. If the magician has a good relationship with this intelligence, he can receive even more valuable advice.

Fig. 124: *Tarato* – (10° Cancer) The magician learns from this principal how to influence the weather through the magic of water, the electric and magnetic fluids, through magical rituals, through the cosmic language, and more. Whosoever has a good relationship with this principal can make it rain or stop raining at his discretion, and he can also direct lightning and have it strike in a particular direction, or cause it to hail; in short, he can do and evoke everything connected with the weather.

Fig. 125: *Horomor* – (11° Cancer) This principal knows all the high magical mysteries, i.e. the mysteries of initiation of the zone girdling the earth and of our physical world. Not only does he teach the magician these mysteries intellectually but he also knows how to awaken the magician's intuition and inspiration through his emanation to such an extent that the magician will actually have complete command over all the mysteries of wisdom from a universal point of view. This principal could be deemed to be the conveyor of magical enlightenment.

Fig. 126: *Tmako* – (12° Cancer) In the zone girdling the earth, *Tmako* initiates the magician into all the transmutation secrets of powers, effects etc., and on our physical world he initiates the magician into the transmutation secrets of plants, minerals and metals. This principal can be considered the guardian of true alchemy.

Fig. 127: *Nimalon* – (13° Cancer) Every magician who deals with invisible beings and intelligences and who possibly is conversant with the Kabbalistic teachings must have frequently experienced the difficulty of translating the cosmic language and the language of the beings into an intellectual language. *Nimalon* can assist the magician by giving him appropriate methods to acquire the ability to explain, express, describe and interpret the cosmic language and the language of the beings and intelligences. Therefore, *Nimalon* is a fabulous initiator of all intellectual languages when it comes to the form of expression, i.e. finding the correct words to express oneself properly so that everyone understands what is being said.

Fig. 128: *Camalo* – (14° Cancer) This principal is well informed about the greatest secrets of magical knowledge. He can reveal ways to the magician and also familiarize him with specific methods with which to achieve invisibility. The magician can make himself invisible with *Camalo's* help, i.e. he can enter all spheres mentally, astrally and if necessary physically, without being perceived or detected by anyone there. The ability to make oneself invisible wherever the need arises is a very special ability and only very few magicians have perfected it.

Fig. 129: *Nimtrix* – (15° Cancer) Through the appropriate methods this high initiator of magic will teach the magician how to dematerialize and materialize any object to a destination of his choosing. Should the magician request it, he can have a dematerialization and materialization carried out by beings which *Nimtrix* places at his disposal.

Fig. 130: *Kalote* – (16° Cancer) *Kalote* is a phenomenal authority and master of cosmic laws. At the same time he can give the magician information about the divine virtues. He instructs the magician on this subject matter and informs him how the divine virtues become effective as far as cause and effect are concerned in consideration of the lawfulness in the microcosm and macrocosm.

Fig. 131: *Ysquiron* – (17° Cancer) *Ysquiron* makes the magician aware how far-reaching Divine Love, Mercy and all the parallel Divine virtues in all spheres and planes are in regards to righteousness (justice), harmony and lawfulness and to what extent all of them are effective, i.e. the influence they exert. The magician learns from *Ysquiron* how to distinguish these theurgic secrets. A magician who is contact with this principal not only knows about all karmic effects and consequences in all spheres, but very high Kabbalistic secrets of the Divine Emanation are also revealed to him.

Fig. 132: *Sikesti* – (18° Cancer) *Sikesti* teaches the magician about the most profound analogies and secrets of evolution in the microcosm and macrocosm. The magician learns from *Sikesti*, even though it is from the perspective of this intelligence, the act of creation of all existence and the manner in which Divine Providence intended it to be.

Fig. 133: *Abagrion* – (19° Cancer) *Abagrion* is a master of formula magic. A magician who is in contact with this principal will learn how to make use of the various magical formulas and at the same time learn about their magical efficacy in the mental, astral and physical planes. *Abagrion* can give the magician many formulas to protect him from negative and undesirable influences from the various spheres.

Fig. 134: *Kibigili* – (20° Cancer) The magician learns from this principal the ability to carry out evocations of subordinate beings with his mental body in the zone girdling the earth and how to protect himself from various dangers, insidiousness etc. It is of course considerably more difficult to carry out an evocation in the zone girdling the earth only with the mental body, because the magician lacks any kind of mnemonic aid. The magician will receive from *Kibigili* detailed information about everything that can be achieved with these kinds of evocations.

Fig. 135: *Arakuson* – (21° Cancer) *Arakuson* teaches the magician about the cause, the purpose and the effect or consequence of various laws. Besides that, he can lead the magician to profound wisdom. Like many of the principals of the zone girdling the earth, *Arakuson* can be deemed a high priest of magic.

Fig. 136: *Maggio* – (22° Cancer) The magician learns from this principal how to set in motion laws and therefore powers directly from the zone girdling the earth, those that realize themselves on the mental, astral and physical planes. *Maggio* allows the magician to penetrate deeply into the Divine Emanation, i.e. into Divine Providence's workshop.

Fig. 137: *Dirilisin* – (23° Cancer) *Dirilisin* is an initiator and master of space magic. The magician learns from him to become master over time and space, not only on our physical world and in the zone girdling the earth, but also in all the other spheres of the macrocosm. Only a mature magician truly understands the real significance of being a master over time and space in all spheres. The magician receives detailed information from *Dirilisin* as to how he can make full use of this ability magically.

Fig. 138: *Akahimo* – (24° Cancer) For the purpose of emanation, the magician learns from this principal to understand and control the various degrees of vibration of Divine virtues, attributes and powers that originate from the Akasha Principle of the zone girdling the earth. The significance of this ability cannot be expressed in mere words. Only an experienced magician who also practices this high knowledge has an understanding of this subject matter.

Fig. 139: *Aragor* – (25° Cancer) *Aragor* gives the magician the opportunity to look into the workshop of Divine Providence by employing appropriate methods and purification processes and recognizing and experiencing the reciprocal interrelations between the Akasha Principle and the divine light of the first emanation of Divine Providence. It is obvious that this opportunity bestows upon the magician the highest enlightenment in the zone girdling the earth.

Fig. 140: *Granona* – (26° Cancer) *Granona* gives the magician the means by which he can call forth various visions. These visions can occur in a trance, whilst asleep, or in a futuristic dream or vision that are called forth through the magic mirror. With the help of these visions the magician reaches the cosmic connection in the region of the inner-planetary spheres. In this manner the magician can recognize, through *Granona,* the causes and effects in the planetary spheres which are reproduced either in pure form or symbolically.

Fig. 141: *Zagol* – (27° Cancer) *Zagol* teaches the magician cosmic spheric magic. If the magician transfers himself with his mental body into a sphere (for example the zone girdling the earth) where he can practice ceremonial magic, from that sphere he can evoke beings from other spheres just as well as if he were to evoke beings from other spheres onto our physical plane. The laws which have to be considered for such operations can be obtained from *Zagol.*

Fig. 142: *Mennolika* – (28° Cancer) *Mennolika* is a master of the Kabbalah, i.e. the divine Theurgy. The magician is taught how to use the divine names Kabbalistically by this principal for the various spheres. Furthermore, he learns from *Mennolika* the Kabbalistic point of view regarding the various virtues of the Divine Emanation, their cause and effect in the individual planetary spheres.

Fig. 143: *Forfasan* – (29° Cancer) *Forfasan* draws the magician's attention to the various systems of wisdom and shows him his own individual path, which he will travel as soon as he has reached a certain level of maturity. In the zone girdling the earth, this principal is considered the guardian and the key of wisdom.

Fig. 144: *Charonthona* – (30° Cancer) *Charonthona* teaches the magician various magical practices with the Akasha Principle. On the basis of specific methods, *Charonthona* shows the magician how various magical operations have their causes and also their effects directly in the Akasha Principle. *Charonthona* is an outstanding authority on the laws of cause and effect, i.e. karma.

The 30 Principals Of The Fifth Sign Of The Zodiac: Leo

All the seals of these principals must be drawn in a golden-bronze or golden-yellowish color.

Fig. 145: *Kosem* – (1° Leo) *Kosem* instructs the magician about the fire principle of the zone girdling the earth and its influence on our physical world. The magician also learns from this principal how to magically employ the principles of light, fire and above all the principles of the electric fluid for the spirit, soul and physical body.

Fig. 146: *Methaera* – (2° Leo) *Methaera* teaches the magician how to put to proper use the powers or energies of the Sun and the electric fluid on the physical world with the appropriate practices, and at times even by utilizing magical aids, as for example fluid condensers, sun-ether radiation devices etc. This principal also draws to the attention of the magician the reciprocal actions of the electric and magnetic fluids, their harmony and how this harmony can be utilized for various magical operations.

Fig. 147: *Jvar* – (3° Leo) *Jvar* gives the magician information about the origin of passions and their embodiment in the soul. In connection with this information, the magician also learns the profound and secret purpose of all passions, how they serve as a means to an end and how they should contribute to the strengthening of the will and other magical powers. The magician also learns from *Jvar* how passions can be controlled and transmuted into their opposite positive attributes through magical aids and other instruction. The practices recommended by this intelligence can be employed by the magician for those students who are on the path of magical development and who have certain passions which they cannot control.

Fig. 148: *Mahra* – (4° Leo) *Mahra* instructs the magician in the magic of the elements with which he can practically utilize the electromagnetic fluid in nature. *Mahra* is a master of the magic of the elements, namely nature magic.

Fig. 149: *Paruch* – (5° Leo) *Paruch* teaches the magician about the tetrapolar magnet in the physical world, which in its relationship to nature is analogous to the physical body of a human being. At the same time *Paruch* instructs the magician how these powers can be used in practice in regards to the universal laws.

Fig. 150: *Aslotama* – (6° Leo) *Aslotama* is well informed about the germinative power of all seeds in nature as well as in human beings. This intelligence knows all the mysteries of the germinative powers and discloses to the magician how he can make use of them in practice. Besides that, the magician can learn how the electric fluid in its reciprocal action to the magnetic fluid calls forth life and thereby brings about growth.

Fig. 151: *Kagaros* – (7° Leo) *Kagaros* draws the magician's attention to the relationships of the air principle, which in nature occupies the position of a mediator. At the same time *Kagaros* teaches the magician about the interrelationship between nature and the human body to the astral body and to the spirit.

Fig. 152: *Romasara* – (8° Leo) *Romasara* reveals secrets of the air principle to the magician from the magical point of view. *Romasara* is an outstanding initiator in the art of breathing, i.e. pranayama. He teaches the magician how this art is to be practiced correctly. The magician can also receive from *Romasara* the *abhisheka*, i.e. initiation, into the true knowledge of the magic of breathing, which is not the accumulation of air, but the accumulation of power or energy in the true sense of the word.

Fig. 153: *Anemalon* – (9° Leo) *Anemalon* is a good initiator on all mystical paths, particularly on that of love and holiness. *Anemalon* explains to the magician the difference between the path to holiness and the path to perfection.

Fig. 154: *Tabbata* – (10° Leo) The magician learns from this intelligence how to make his body resistant to fire in a magical manner through the transmutation of the elements, even to the point of invulnerability. Besides that the magician learns how to change water into ice in an alchemical Kabbalistic manner.

Fig. 155: *Ahahbon* – (11° Leo) *Ahahbon*, as an initiator, has at his disposal many kinds of methods to produce the various states of ecstasies, trances and consciousness. The magician learns from *Ahahbon* to school the consciousness to such an extent that he will be able to accurately transfer the impressions that he gains from any sphere into the physical world.

Fig. 156: *Akanejonaho* – (12° Leo) *Akanejonaho* is a master of Divine Theurgy and Kabbalistic mysticism. *Akanejonaho* teaches the magician how to correctly make use of the divine virtues analogous to the laws of creation for the purpose of spiritualization.

Fig. 157: *Horog* – (13° Leo) *Horog* can show the magician the path to perfection exactly in accordance with the laws of creation, and he helps the magician solve the most difficult and mysterious problems.

Fig. 158: *Texai* – (14° Leo) The magician learns from this principal to fully and correctly understand the synthesis of all religious systems and philosophies. Besides that, the magician will learn to translate the symbolic representation of philosophical systems into an intellectual language.

Fig. 159: *Herich* – (15° Leo) *Herich* teaches the magician about the relationships between the mental, astral and physical worlds and therefore the reciprocal action of the mental, astral and physical fluids in the physical body and in Nature. Furthermore, *Herich* teaches the magician how disharmonies come into being through these fluids and how these harmonies can be reestablished. In this respect this intelligence can elucidate all disharmonies to the magician. Besides that, the magician will be given various methods with which influences upon the mental, astral and physical materia can be carried out.

Fig. 160: *Ychniag* – (16° Leo) *Ychniag* entrusts the magician with methods whereby he has access to omniscience and the highest Divine Intuition. Furthermore, the magician can enlighten his intellect through these divine virtues.

Fig. 161: *Odac* – (17° Leo) *Odac* is an initiator of cosmic love magic. He gives the magician theurgic magical love methods with instructions on how to make use of them in the mental, astral and physical worlds.

Fig. 162: *Mechebbera* – (18° Leo) *Mechebbera* teaches the magician the occult anatomy of human beings, in particular about their relationships. He also gives the magician theurgic magical healing methods.

Fig. 163: *Paschan* – (19° Leo) *Paschan* is an initiator, and he will initiate the magician into talismanic magic. The magician leans from *Paschan* how to make talismans and how to load them accordingly to heal various ailments or to bind a being to the talisman.

Fig. 164: *Corocona* – (20° Leo) *Corocona* familiarizes the magician with the preparation of alchemical remedies prepared from metals. The magician learns from this intelligence how to prepare the true alchemical gold tincture and how to administer it for various ailments. The magician is also instructed as to the dosage to be administered when it comes to alchemical remedies.

Fig. 165: *Rimog* – (21° Leo) *Rimog* gives the magician instruction with which to awaken within himself the talent of prophecy. At the magician's request, *Rimog* himself will awaken the ability of prophecy within him or he will have it done by his subordinates. *Rimog* is deemed to be the prophet of the zone girdling the earth. His prophecies are not limited to this zone and also include our physical world.

Fig. 166: *Abbetira* – (22° Leo) *Abbetira* shows the magician ways to attain worldly riches, power, and be held in high esteem. Besides that, *Abbetira* or his servants help the magician attain the favor or good graces of very important people in high positions.

Fig. 167: *Eralicarison* – (23° Leo) *Eralicarison* administers *abhisheka,* i.e. true initiation, into all religious systems, in particular all the various kinds of yoga. He also helps the magician to understand the most difficult Tantric texts.

Fig. 168: *Golopa* – (24° Leo) *Golopa* teaches the magician to read mental, astral and physical occurrences in the Akasha. Furthermore, he allows the magician to gain knowledge on how causes of the mental, astral and physical kind, that come out of the Akasha Principle, set off effects. For example, *Golopa* can show the magician exactly how causes that he has created through his thoughts will turn into effects during his present life or in another incarnation. The same applies to astral and physical causes.

Fig. 169: *Jgakys* – (25° Leo) *Jgakys* places methods at the disposal of the magician with which he can refine his consciousness for spheric impression without the separation of the mental body.

Fig. 170: *Pagalusta* – (26° Leo) *Pagalusta* instructs the magician how he can manage to bring about mediumistic phenomena, either by himself or with the help of mediums. This intelligence gives the magician exact instructions on how objects can be transported over vast distances by dematerialization and materialization.

Fig. 171: *Ichdison* – (27° Leo) *Ichdison* initiates the magician into the particular method with which he can realize every wish through magical powers on the physical plane or whatever concerns the physical plane.

Fig. 172: *Takarosa* – (28° Leo) *Takarosa* gives the magician magical formulas. By using these formulas in the mental, astral and physical worlds he can call forth effects through the elements or through the beings of the elements. The magician can also receive from this intelligence Kabbalistic formulas through which he can easily make the beings of the air and water principles compliant.

Fig. 173: *Andrachor* – (29° Leo) *Andrachor* is considered to be the master of the magic of water. He entrusts the magician with many secret practices through which to achieve wonderful phenomena through the Water element, phenomena concerning which he would otherwise not have the faintest idea, for example healing very difficult ailments, and so on.

Fig. 174: *Carona* – (30° Leo) *Carona* will reveal to the magician means of protection which will make him immune to or protect him from thunderstorms, hurricanes, etc. Besides that, this intelligence draws the attention of the magician to Kabbalistic practices to calm the most stormy ocean, stop or cause thunderstorms, calm or evoke hurricanes etc.

The 30 Principals Of The Sixth Sign
Of The Zodiac: Virgo

All the seals of these principals must be drawn in brown.

Fig. 175: *Peresch* – (1° Virgo) *Peresch* supervises all political events on our physical world. *Peresch* permits mankind to give rise to certain ideas and he allows certain social attitudes to prevail. Furthermore, he decides the duration of a political power, whether through diplomatic channels or through war, and he permits successes and failures of political trends as Divine Providence has commanded and in consideration of humankind's spiritual development. This principal can help the magician attain the highest political career, and he can bestow upon the magician the ability to become an outstanding political speaker and enthrall an audience. Aside from that, he can arm the magician with an unparalleled endurance and tenacity so that he can realize all his wishes in this respect.

Fig. 176: *Bruahi* – (2° Virgo) *Bruahi* is the guardian of all inventions in the Akasha Principle, in that these inventions do not prematurely become a reality. In accordance with prevailing demands, he inspires individuals to certain inventions and allows these inventions to become a reality on the physical plane. On the other hand, this principal also prevents those of great talent and abilities from realizing inventions which are not supposed to be invented for the next hundred or even five hundred years. This principal, under the seal of secrecy, will show a magician who gains his good graces all kinds of inventions in the Akasha Principle. In a hundred, or at times even in a thousand years from now, mankind will marvel at these inventions.

Fig. 177: *Moschel* – (3° Virgo) *Moschel* rules over all the arts on our earth. His subordinates are in charge of and administrate the individual branches of the arts. A magician will, at his request, be given any artistic talent which he deems desirable, whether through the appropriate methods or directly by transference from this principal or those of his subordinates who are in charge of that particular branch of the arts. *Moschel* will also be instrumental in the magician's artistic rise to fame.

Fig. 178: *Raschea* – (4° Virgo) This principal is considered to be the king of flowers, because all the flowers on our earth are under his guardianship. The magician learns from *Raschea* to understand the language of flowers, i.e. the symbolic significance of the individual species of flowers as they relate to human beings and to the universal laws. The color, form and number of petals reveal to the magician the analogies that correspond with the universal laws. From this he can gather what represents true beauty in the world of flowers. By immersing himself more deeply into this knowledge, the magician learns to understand every flower from the esoteric point of view and also to grasp the attributes of individual flowers from every aspect and use them for magical purposes.

Fig. 179: *Girmil* – (5° Virgo) This principal is a representative of love, harmony and beauty and at the same time he is their guardian. The magician learns from him to see love in everything we look at. The magician will see harmony in love and disharmony in hate, which enables him to comprehend the precise laws of sympathy and antipathy. Only on the basis of this knowledge will the magician realize what genuine beauty is and that beauty is actually the correct expression for harmony. This principal helps the magician to perceive beauty properly.

Fig. 180: *Zagriona* – (6° Virgo) All teaching professions, in the broadest sense of the word, are in the sphere of influence of this principal. All teachers, writers, editors and journalists are under the protection of this intelligence. Should the magician require any advice pertaining to this subject matter or related matters, or if he needs specific protection or strives for success, then *Zagriona* or his beings will gladly be of assistance.

Fig. 181: *Ygilon* – (7° Virgo) *Ygilon* is considered to be the arch-initiator of language and writing (script). At the behest of Divine Providence he made the necessary arrangements so that human beings, since their creation, have been able to express thoughts, concepts, ideas, etc., first through signs, then through articulated words, and later on through coherent sentences which finally became a language. Thereupon, this principal produced through his subordinates the effect that this language was expressed externally in symbolic form in various manners, through which the cornerstone was laid for script (writing) as the means of communications, which occurred in the form of symbols. However, it took a long time of development until the language in the form of symbols reached the level of today. For the magician who is occupied with deciphering ancient writings or hieroglyphs which have not been deciphered to this day, this principal can make it easy for him to do so. There are no writings on earth that cannot be deciphered by the magician with the help of this intelligence and its subordinates. The magician can also learn the true magic of runes from *Ygilon*.

Fig. 182: *Alpaso* – (8° Virgo) From time immemorial this principal has been the protector and guardian of all the poor and oppressed. He controls in the Akasha the destinies of all slaves, beggars, gypsies, the homeless etc. He also controls the destiny of all victims of persecution, especially those who have suffered an injustice. He also helps those human beings that have been thrown off the normal path of life by drugs or narcotics of all kinds, provided they are not to meet with some misfortune according to their destiny. These human beings then get off lightly, and here the proverb applies that: "Drunks have two guardian angels," or: "Drunkards live a charmed life."

Fig. 183: *Kirek* – (9° Virgo) *Kirek* is considered to be an outstanding initiator of alchemical magic. The magician receives from him a variety of methods by which he can solidify the matrix between the astral body and the spirit. Furthermore, in order to achieve astral immortality he can make his astral body immune to dissolution by the astral elements. Should the magician request it, this principal will give him the methods whereby he can achieve the same effect with the physical body, through which he can prolong his life on earth as long as he wishes. Should the magician work in accordance with the methods he receives from this intelligence, then age has no influence on his physical body nor does he fall victim to any ailment; he remains tenacious, strong and resistant to any external influence. A physical body that has been taken care of in this manner cannot be harmed in any way, and even stab wounds or cuts cannot be inflicted on such a body, and not even the most severe heat will affect it.

Fig. 184: *Buriuh* – (10° Virgo) *Buriuh* is an excellent initiator of alchemical secrets. He entrusts the magician with methods through which he can attain various powers and abilities with the help of suitable alchemical remedies. This intelligence reveals to the magician the manner by which the various alchemical love potions and incenses for burning, magic ointments, oils for exteriorization and other mediumistic experiments are prepared. Besides that, *Buriuh* or his subordinates will help the magician to load or impregnate alchemical remedies or substances.

Fig. 185: *Yraganon* – (11° Virgo) Should the magician express the wish that he would like to achieve success, honor, wealth and be held in high esteem in business, this principal can be of great assistance to the magician through his subordinates. He can also help the magician attain a high level of skill in his profession or trade. All craftsmen or tradesmen who work with metal, in particular iron or steel, enjoy the specific protection of this principal. These professions include technicians, technical engineers, designing engineers, metalworkers, locksmiths, millwrights, mechanics, blacksmiths, etc. Should a magician work in any of these occupations, he can achieve a great deal with the help of this principal.

Fig. 186: *Argaro* – (12° Virgo) *Argaro* is a guardian of all relics, shrines, temples, churches, pictures and statues of saints, etc. Furthermore, he is the guardian of all religions in the world, from ancient times to the present. A magician who contacts this principal will be informed in what manner divine ideas, divinities etc., are represented by symbols, temples, statues and pictures of saints, and so forth. And on the other hand, *Argaro* teaches the magician how these pictures, statues and monuments as personified divinities represent their true analogies of divine ideas and concepts. *Argaro* enlightens the magician as to the rituals that are carried out with personified divinities and he reveals their secret meaning.

Fig. 187: *Algebol* – (13° Virgo) *Algebol* knows and guides all traditional rites, rituals and ceremonies of all religious systems. This principal is the master of rituals. He familiarizes the magician with all ceremonies, rituals and customs that a religion or sect may have had in the past or still has now; he also reveals their secret meanings. Through this he gives the magician the opportunity to learn the true magical value of the power or dynamics of a ritual or ceremony.

Fig. 188: *Karasa* – (14° Virgo) *Karasa* is the patron of all the physicians in the world. Medicine men in ancient times revered this principal of the zone girdling the earth with great awe and they brought him sacrifices. Even in present times physicians, in particular surgeons, are inspired by this intelligence. *Karasa* sees to it that some ailing person is made well by some physician. The entire chemical-pharmaceutical industry is under the jurisdiction of this principal. A magician who seeks personal advice from him will receive a precise diagnosis and at the same time the method to restore his physical health.

Fig. 189: *Akirgi* – (15° Virgo) The magician can call upon this principal in every kind of business matter and *Akirgi* ensures the magician great success in every case. *Akirgi* is particularly fond of everything that has to do with paper and textiles. But his influence also extents to the processing of animal hides and leather. Therefore, not only can the magician depend on his support in business matters, but he will also receive specific recipes from this principal on how to process animal hides, leather etc. The magician will also receive many methods and procedures for processing paper and the substances which are required to impregnate paper; these processes and impregnation substances are not presently known to the public.

Fig. 190: *Basanola* – (16° Virgo) Since this principal supervises vegetation, he can be considered the patron of forestry and agriculture. This principal is multifaceted in these aspects, and when a magician comes into contact with him he can learn much from him. Besides methods and guidance on the basis of which vegetation will thrive and grow well, *Basanola* will give the magician specific instructions as to how he can promote and impede growth in a magical-Kabbalistic manner.

Fig. 191: *Rotor* – (17° Virgo) *Rotor* is a master of fantasy. All folk legends, fairytales and stories are under his jurisdiction. This principal inspires all those poets and authors whose field of endeavor is to write or record legends, myths, fairytales and stories. *Rotor* bestows upon them an excellent fantasy, which he allows these writers and poets to transform into appropriate words. This principal loves to veil true occurrences and magical secrets in the form of a fairytale, so that every magician who summons him will be informed as to what every fairytale contains from a Hermetic point of view.

Fig. 192: *Tigrapho* – (18° Virgo) *Tigrapho* is a master of architecture and the art of building. From time immemorial he has inspired human beings as to how they should dwell. On earth *Tigrapho* is the patron of all master builders and architects, and he supports them through inspiration when they design buildings. This also applies to street and highway construction, river basins, waterworks and so forth. Should this be the magician's profession, then *Tigrapho* can be of great help to him through intuition.

Fig. 193: *Cobel* – (19° Virgo) *Cobel* can initiate the magician into the art of magical fragrances. The magician learns from *Cobel* how to blend harmonious and disharmonious fragrances, for example fragrances that give rise to love and sympathy or those that produce arbitrary dreams. Furthermore, this principal will teach the magician how to blend fragrances that increase the ability to concentrate, fragrances for meditation, and incense for various magical experiments etc. The magician can also find out details from this principal in regards to fragrances that are very effective in aromatherapy, i.e. the treatment of ailments through fragrances.

Fig. 194: *Hipogo* – (20° Virgo) This intelligence's sphere of influence or jurisdiction encompasses everything in connection with water as it concerns human beings. For example, swimming, underwater diving, or movement on the water, from the most simple raft to the most modern nautical crafts or ocean vessels. *Hipogo* is the inspirer of shipbuilding, submarines and everything that moves through human hands on the surface of the water or under it. Should the magician be interested in this subject matter, *Hipogo* will show him all technological inventions that have to do with locomotion on the water as it concerns mankind, even into the farthest future.

Fig. 195: *Iserag* – (21° Virgo) *Iserag* is considered to be the bearer of good fortune for humankind. He brings good fortune in gambling, in petitions, in the stock market, speculations and enterprises of all kinds. Should this principal be fond of the magician, he will grant his every wish in the physical world, and this principal will make certain that the magician is successful in everything he undertakes. Besides that, he entrusts to the magician methods that will make him happy and content in every respect.

Fig. 196: *Breffeo* – (22° Virgo) *Breffeo* can be considered the guardian of material laws and justice. Whenever the magician is within his rights, this principal makes certain that every matter in this respect is decided in the magician's favor. *Breffeo* himself or his subordinates punish all those who do an injustice to the magician or who harbor the intention of so doing. Perhaps the magician might not even have any knowledge of this. This occurs when the magician has had or still has a good relationship with this principal. In this case, anyone who pursues or persecutes the magician will be struck by *Breffeo's* servants in a most malicious manner.

Fig. 197: *Elipinon* – (23° Virgo) The magician will be instructed and trained in all mantic arts on the basis of the laws of analogy, whether it is reading cards, Tarot, the *I Ching*, chiromancy or palmistry, horoscopes, etc. *Elipinon* gives the magician the opportunity to reach the level of prophecy through the mantic arts, and he helps the magician become a great master in this field of endeavor. All human beings on earth who practice the mantic arts are subject to this principal of the zone girdling the earth.

Fig. 198: *Naniroa* – (24° Virgo) *Naniroa* protects the property of every human being. When this principal is fond of a magician, he protects the magician's property through his subordinates from all catastrophes, such as fire, thunderstorms, lightning, flooding, burglary, theft, and so on. The magician also receives from *Naniroa* the methods whereby a thief will return stolen property, or at the very least be influenced to such a degree that he will give himself away. There are also other magical practices which pertain to the recovery of lost or stolen property which this principal will reveal to the magician.

Fig. 199: *Olaski* – (25° Virgo) *Olaski* is the arch-initiator of all vehicles and modes of transportation on land, from the most simple cart to the most advanced automobile. Should the magician in this field of endeavor wish to know or make technological improvements or invent something entirely new, then in this principal he has the best master and assistant. If the magician has a good relationship with this principal, he can be assured that he is completely safe while he is in any vehicle that travels on land. When I was in contact with this intelligence, I could see in the Akasha Principle vehicles of the distant future which are not powered by motors that run on fossil fuel or atomic energy. These future vehicles are powered by a completely different kind of motive power. They will be completely noiseless and odorless and will move along at incredible speed. It is, however, strictly forbidden to reveal any details about these future inventions. The future will prove that these inventions were not a figment of my imagination and that I truly saw them in the Akasha Principle and that every new invention has been recorded there long ago.

Fig. 200: *Hyrmiua* – (26° Virgo) *Hyrmiua* is a mighty protector of human consciousness on our earth. The extent of the sphere of influence or jurisdiction of this principal is almost impossible for the average person to comprehend. For example, he prevents the consciousness of the average human being from going beyond the limits of the material world. However, he allows a magician to expand his consciousness, of course always in accordance with his magical maturity. In other words, this principal monitors the maturity and development of every human being.

This principal also decides if someone who suffers from disturbances of consciousness, i.e. a mentally ill person, should recover and regain his or her normal state of mind. Whenever this intelligence approves a cure, a psychiatrist will be successful in bringing about a complete recovery. *Hyrmiua* also monitors all individuals that commit suicide — in the event that their suicide was not caused by karma — so that they will not regain complete consciousness in the astral world until the time of their earthly existence has passed. Only when this time has expired will this person awaken from his twilight sleep and regain his complete astral consciousness. Much more could be said about this principal, but this brief description should suffice. A magician who contacts this principal can never step out of line mentally, and he gains the power to read and influence the consciousness of every human being, for example to bring back memories or erase such pictures completely from his memory. The magician also learns how to carry out a transference of consciousness on a magical basis, which in the Orient is called *abhisheka* or *ankhur*.

Fig. 201: *Sumuram* – (27° Virgo) *Sumuram* is considered to be the ruler of all the animals that move about in the air. From the smallest of flies to the royal eagle, all are under his protection. To a magician who is in contact with him, this principal will reveal all secrets that pertain to flying animals. Should the magician request it, then *Sumuram* will give him the methods and instructions through which he will gain the power to control every air-borne animal. Through the appropriate words, the magician will then be able to coerce the most gluttonous eagle or vulture down from their dizzying heights to sit without fear on the magician's shoulder. This enables the magician to tame any bird to the extent that children can play even with birds of prey, and so that they will not harm even the smallest animal. The magician will be able to perform many other magical operations in the animal world which, to the average human being, will seem very difficult to believe.

Fig. 202: *Astolitu* – (28° Virgo) *Astolitu* is a very special custodian of many magical keys and secrets. In our present period of development he conducts and directs the entire field of aviation on our world, inclusive of all the inventions pertaining to this endeavor. The magician can receive from *Astolitu* many inspirations in this respect. *Astolitu* will reveal (though only to magicians of the highest rank) the secrets of gravitation, and he will instruct them about the practical use of the force of gravity. Long before our present-day civilizations, several thousand years ago, our globe was inhabited by highly civilized nations who, in comparison to us, were far superior in the technology of aviation. The secrets of gravitation were the common property of all the people in those days. They reached tremendous heights without the propulsion of a motor and without using gases. They moved about in spheres high enough to reach speeds of the rotation of our earth without any mechanical devices, and they effortlessly transported the heaviest loads from location to location. When these civilizations became extinct, *Astolitu*, the principal of the zone girdling the earth, revoked these keys and took them back and he will safeguard them strictly until such time as humankind has reached the necessary maturity and level of development for these mysterious inventions. However, in the Akasha Principle nothing is ever lost, and it will be recorded there for all eternity. Only magicians of the highest rank will be able to read everything in the Akasha Principle which must remain concealed to the everyday world.

Fig. 203: *Notiser* – (29° Virgo) Under the protection of this principal of the zone girdling the earth are the intellect and the knowledge of every human being in the physical world. He guides every human being's ability of perception in accordance with that person's maturity, and bestows upon him the amount of knowledge that is equivalent to his present level of development. This principal is deemed to be the master of knowledge, because on earth it is his influence that hones the intellect and makes the memory more receptive, regardless of the field of knowledge in which a person is engaged. The magician receives instructions from this principal, and should he follow these instructions he will expand his mental powers, hone his intellect and strengthen his memory. *Notiser* will willingly give the magician information about any field of knowledge. This principal provides all branches of learning with the amount of knowledge which humankind can comprehend at its present level of development.

Fig. 204: *Regerio* – (30° Virgo) The last principal of Virgo in the earth-girdling zone is named *Regerio*. He is the custodian of many mysteries of wisdom, and he makes certain that true wisdom is, in effect, only made available to those who are actually mature. Despite that, if it should happen that an immature and incompetent person should gain illegal access to some magical secrets, then this custodian of the mysteries of wisdom would close the gates of wisdom to that person by obscuring his mind with disbelief, distrust, doubt, self-conceit and a one-sided point of view. The true secrets would remain occult and veiled, even if the revealing writings were to be stored in thousands of drawers of the immature. A magician who is in contact with *Regerio* will learn from this principal by means of intuition the difference between knowledge and wisdom.

The 30 Principals Of The Seventh Sign Of The Zodiac: Libra

All seals must be drawn in green when evoking these principals for the first time.

Fig. 205: *Thirana* – (1° Libra) This principal is in control of the sexual sphere of humankind. He has the propagation of the human race under his jurisdiction. *Thirana* has at his disposal many directions and methods to teach the magician how to magically impregnate his own semen with various attributes before sexual intercourse, in order to pass these attributes on to the child that is conceived in this manner. From this principal the magician receives instruction which gives him complete knowledge about magical prenatal education, on the basis of which he can incorporate particular attributes, abilities, and talents in the baby while it is still in the mother's womb.

Fig. 206: *Apollyon* – (2° Libra) From the beginning of time, this principal has inspired human beings in accordance with their maturity when they are engaged in processing metals. Therefore, *Apollyon* is the arch-initiator of all who are engaged in the processing of metals, whether they be foundry workers, metal casters, blacksmiths, locksmiths, millwrights, or mechanics. Not only is *Apollyon* the arch-initiator of all ideas and concepts in this field of endeavor, he is also their faithful custodian.

Fig. 207: *Peekah* – (3° Libra) In primeval times, this principal taught primitive nations through inspiration that animal flesh is not as palatable when eaten raw as when it is roasted or cooked. He inspired certain individuals as to how they could differentiate one kind of meat from another by taste, and he taught them through intuition how to prepare many different kinds of meat dishes. In order to prepare these various meat dishes they began to domesticate animals and breed them, so that, over the course of time and development, farming and the breeding of animals came into being. It was *Peekah* who gave mankind all these good inspirations, as he still does to this day. The smoking, curing and conservation of meat are also part of his domain. At the magician's request this principal initiates him into the art of cooking, and he will give the magician many recipes for the preparation of meat dishes which are to this day still unknown.

Fig. 208: *Nogah* – (4° Libra) The ability of a man and woman to procreate, as well as their fertility, are under the jurisdiction of this principal. Through his vibrations he controls the sexual sphere of both man and woman and allows life to flourish in the semen, i.e. he gives the semen its vital ability to thrive. The magician can find out from *Nogah* how to maintain his sexual energy even to a ripe old age. Furthermore, this principal can instruct the magician how impotence in a man or woman can be eliminated. The magician can receive many more answers and solutions to many problems on this matter.

Fig. 209: *Tolet* – (5° Libra) This principal monitors the manner in which people nourish themselves, and he teaches them which foods are necessary for maintaining one's life and how to be healthy. He also teaches what foods are harmful. *Tolet* is the initiator of all dietary rules. The magician learns from this principal the analogies of the electric and magnetic or the electromagnetic fluids in regards to the various kinds of foods and how they have to be taken into consideration during ailments. This principal also points out to the magician the various foods which can be ingested as stimulants to call forth particular states of mind.

Fig. 210: *Parmasa* – (6° Libra) *Parmasa* is a master of cheerfulness. He allows human beings to laugh from the bottom of theirs hearts and to enjoy themselves. Under his jurisdiction are funny ideas, pleasantries, jokes, anecdotes, comedies and other kinds of amusements. He or his subordinates inspire human beings to tell, write or perform comical ideas and events that have occurred. The magician can receive from this principal or his subordinates the funniest ideas with which he can entertain people at social gatherings or among friends. Should the magician come into contact with this principal he will find out for himself that *Parmasa* is always cheerful.

Fig. 211: *Gesegos* – (7° Libra) This principal's jurisdiction is wood, and everything connected therewith. He is the patron of all individuals whose occupations are connected with wood and with the processing of wood, as for example woodcutters, lumberjacks, carpenters, cabinet makers, joiners, wood turners, wood carvers, model constructors, pattern makers etc. Should the magician's interest be in this field of endeavor, then this principal can teach him a great deal, especially things which are unknown to this very day. For example, he will learn how to impregnate wood against all influences of the elements, and about substances and preparations which lend even the softest of wood a hardness and resistance which can only be compared to steel. This principal can familiarize the magician with this and many other new and interesting inventions regarding the preparation and uses of wood.

Fig. 212: *Soteri* – (8° Libra) *Soteri* is the arch-initiator of all musical instruments that humankind has ever used, inclusive of the most modern instruments of our present times. *Soteri* inspires all composers. This principal will teach a magician who has a talent for or an interest in music how to adapt any musical composition to the appropriate element. On the other hand, *Soteri* will teach the magician whatever he intends to express through music in a harmonious manner, i.e. whatever the magician intends to express in the proper sense through music in accordance with the universal laws. This principal deserves to be called the musician of the zone girdling the earth.

Fig. 213: *Batamabub* – (9° Libra) From time immemorial up to the present, the clothing and headgear of mankind have been under the jurisdiction of this principal. He influences the clothing and headgear and he controls and guides their development in accordance with the climate, the weather influences, the maturity of humankind, their characteristics and points of view. *Batamabub* inspires all fashion and whatever is in fashion, through which rank, position, religion etc., are expressed. Furthermore, he inspires human beings as to the type of materials that should be used in the manufacture of clothing and headgear. All fashion designers, window dressers, tailors, dressmakers, and milliners are under his protection. Should it be of interest to the magician, this principal will present to him in the Akasha the various fashions of all nations, from primeval times to the present. Furthermore, the magician will also be able to view fashions of the distant future.

Fig. 214: *Omana* – (10° Libra) The jurisdiction of this principal encompasses everything that has to do with the hair of human beings. He inspires all the various kinds of beards and hairstyles. All barbers and hairstylists, male and female alike, are constantly under his influence. This principal controls all inventions that pertain to beard and hair growth, from simple combs to the most modern hair curlers, from a simple pair of scissors to razorblades to electric shavers. A magician who is in contact with this principal can find out the kind of preparations that promote hair growth, remove unwanted hair, etc. He can also point out to the magician the various kinds of hair dyes. At the time when I was personally in contact with this principal, he showed me in the Akasha Principle the manner in which hair was to be dyed in the future. When that time has arrived, chemical preparations will no be longer in use, because for the larger part these preparations are harmful to the scalp. Instead, in the future hair will be dyed with a radiation device without causing any negative detrimental consequences to the hair or the scalp. However, I am not allowed to say anything further about this device; the future will confirm my prediction.

Fig. 215: *Lagiros* – (11° Libra) This principal or his subordinates can assist the magician in obtaining the good graces of people in high positions, and having petitions approved and granted by them. This principal can make a person in a high position well-disposed toward the magician and can create favorable situations for him, and so on.

Fig. 216: *Afrei* – (12° Libra) This principal is an initiator and master of love magic at a high level. He teaches the magician by energizing divine attributes, especially divine love and mercy, to accomplish many miracles in the mental, astral and physical worlds.

Fig. 217: *Rigolon* – (13° Libra) Since time immemorial, *Rigolon* is considered to be the initiator of all the various kinds of courtship. He or his subordinates inspire human beings to all kinds of courtship. If a magician wishes to acquire the art of courtship, if he wishes to be well liked everywhere, and if he wishes to be considered good company or a good companion, then this principal can help him in every respect. He can also give him advice on how to obtain the affection of a particular person, how he can secure the favor of people, and more.

Fig. 218: *Riqita* – (14° Libra) *Riqita* is a master of song. Should the magician request it, this principal can bestow upon him a melodious voice that has a fascinating and charming effect on his audience. Consequently, this principal is considered the patron of all singers, regardless of whether they are professional or if they merely sing on certain social occasions. *Riqita* shows the magician ways to care for one's voice.

Fig. 219: *Tapum* – (15° Libra) This principal is an outstanding artist; his calling is to teach the magician a sense of art. He is the arch-initiator of all that which has to do with beautification and embellishment, for example, decorations at public festivals, store decorations, etc. At the same time *Tapum* is also the arch-initiator of any type of advertising. Whenever the magician is in need of his help, this principal is prepared to cooperate at any time.

Fig. 220: *Nachero* – (16° Libra) *Nachero* monitors the health and life span of all animals on earth. At the same time he guides their instincts. That is why he gives human beings ideas in regards to all healing methods and remedies for the various ailments that afflict animals. All zoologists, veterinarians and veterinary surgeons, as well as animal tamers, are under his protection. Whenever animals suffer from an ailment, *Nachero* helps the magician to find various remedies and healing methods. This principal can also reveal to the magician many magical practices which can be employed for animals, for example, so that animals which produce milk give more milk and how they can be protected from certain influences, and so forth.

Fig. 221: *Arator* – (17° Libra) This principal is the arch-initiator of all intoxicating drinks or potions. Since time immemorial he has taught human beings through intuition how to produce the various intoxicating drinks, such as wine, mead, beer, liqueur, etc. which call forth a cheerful mood in humans, so that they can bear their worries somewhat more easily. However, this principal should not be mistaken for the counter-genius of this sphere who controls the notorious alcoholics. All human beings who are employed in the manufacture and trade of alcoholic beverages are under *Arator's* protection. The magician can obtain excellent recipes from this principal on how to produce wine, beer and liqueurs, and he can also obtain advice on how to improve alcoholic beverages through various methods. *Arator* will also give the magician magical recipes and instructions as to how he, for example, can turn water into wine through the influence of combining the elements. Furthermore, the magician is told how to protect himself successfully against the alcohol that is contained in these beverages, so much so that even if he imbibes large amounts of alcohol he will remain sober.

Fig. 222: *Malata* – (18° Libra) *Malata* informs the magician about the secrets of the blood as it concerns human beings and animals. Not only does he inform the magician about the different blood groups, the four blood types, and the Rh factors which are known to the medical science of today, but also many other facts in regards to medicine, chemistry, physiology, psychology, genetics etc. Besides that, he initiates the magician into secrets of the blood from a magical and alchemical point of view. If this knowledge were committed to paper it would encompass many volumes.

Fig. 223: *Arioth* – (19° Libra) *Arioth* is the protector of all pregnant women on earth. This principal has inspired human beings to employ the various birthing methods, from the most primitive to the most modern achievements in gynecology. Hence, he is the patron of all gynecologists, midwives, obstetricians, etc. *Arioth* points out to the magician the various magical and sympathetic remedies and methods that ensure a painless delivery.

Fig. 224: *Agikus* – (20° Libra) Electro-chemistry has much that has not been discovered yet, but will be discovered in the course of time and in the distant future. This principal can unveil and entrust to the magician many secrets in this field. *Agikus* is the arch-inspirer of the galvanic current. Through his intuitive inspiration man has invented batteries, accumulators, the dissolution of metals through electric currents, catalysis etc. Electro-homeopathy is also under the jurisdiction of this principal. In his sphere of influence *Agikus* allowed me to look clairvoyantly into the future, where, for example, I saw tiny amounts of chemical compounds transmuted into large electric discharges with tremendous voltage and amperage. This knowledge will greatly benefit humankind technologically and domestically. If details were disclosed in regards to this, it would seem too fantastic; rather than be the object of ridicule, it is indeed better to keep silent. Once humankind becomes more mature and more developed, some individuals will be inspired accordingly by this principal to new discoveries and new inventions.

Fig. 225: *Cheikaseph* – (21° Libra) On earth, *Cheikaseph* is the arch-initiator of mathematics. From simple addition to the most difficult mathematical methods and mathematical problems with astronomical figures, the fundamental ideas of numbers, measurements and weights in relationship to matter, all of this is under the jurisdiction of this principal. The magician can learn, for example, how to express an idea mathematically with numbers. On the other hand, he can find out how he can intellectually acquire knowledge about quality and quantity. *Cheikaseph* also initiates the magician into the Kabbalistic tetrapolar key of the four fundamental mathematical methods: addition, subtraction, multiplication and division as they apply to the magical and Kabbalistic knowledge and to the elements in the microcosm and macrocosm. *Cheikaseph* is a very powerful principal and the magician can gain a tremendous amount of knowledge from him.

Fig. 226: *Ornion* – (22° Libra) *Ornion* is considered to be the initiator of physiology. He not only teaches the magician the subject of common physiology, he also allows the magician to view this subject from a Hermetic point of view. *Ornion* acquaints the magician with all these teachings, on the basis of which he can recognize the character traits of every person by his external features. For the information of the reader, I shall list a few talents which this principal can awaken in the magician: the art of reading one's face (physiognomy), the art of reading one's forehead (metoposcopy), finger and nail diagnostics, eye diagnosis (iridology), and so forth.

Fig. 227: *Gariniranus* – (23° Libra) *Gariniranus* is an initiator of physics. All the research that has been accomplished to this very day on this subject has occurred through the intuitive inspiration of this principal. Not only can the magician find out from this principal about achievements in physics in the distant future, he can also be initiated in all phases of metaphysics and instructed as to their practical utilization. This principal can initiate the magician into astrophysics.

Fig. 228: *Istaroth* – (24° Libra) *Istaroth* is the guardian of fidelity. He keeps a husband and wife together in faithfulness. Should the magician request it, he can, with the help of this principal or his subordinates, influence any person, male or female, to such an extent that any infidelity is impossible. The magician will also be able to uncover any unfaithfulness through this principal and prevent it at the outset. *Istaroth* can change the magician's worst enemy into his best friend and secure the love, friendship and sympathy of any person for him.

Fig. 229: *Haiamon* – (25° Libra) *Haiamon* teaches the magician about the transmutation of sexual powers. He entrusts him with various practices in this respect which are completely unknown to this day. *Haiamon* is well-versed in the most secret mysteries in this field of endeavor. The magician can learn much from this principal, for example, how sexual power can be increased and decreased and how it can be transmuted for various magical practices into the elementary primary substance. This principal can give the magician information about new hormone combinations and com-pounds which are unknown at this point in time, as well as many other things.

Fig. 230: *Canali* – (26° Libra) From time immemorial, *Canali* has been considered to be the inspirer of all objects of jewelry. Through his subor-dinates he directs and supervises all new fashions in jewelry, as for in-stance rings, bracelets, precious stones, in short any jewelry which is worn. Anyone who is engaged in the manufacture of jewelry is under his guardi-anship, such as gold miners, goldsmiths, gem cutters etc. In this regard the magician can learn quite a number of interesting things from *Canali*.

Fig. 231: *Aglasis* – (27° Libra) Everything that is linked to milk as it con-cerns mankind and animals is under the jurisdiction of this principal, who is deemed to be the patron of infants and mammals. In the course of time *Aglasis* taught human beings how to milk animals. Not only did he teach them to drink the milk, but also how to turn it into other products. That is how human beings learned to produce butter, cream cheese or cottage cheese, and cheese from milk, etc. The processing of milk has still a long way to go, for it has not even reached its peak, and the magician can learn many new and yet unknown things about milk from *Aglasis*.

Fig. 232: *Merki* – (28° Libra) Under the jurisdiction of this principal are all animals that live in the water, as well as their propagation. *Merki* is the patron of all fishermen on earth. He is the one who controls fortune and misfortune when fishing. *Merki* taught human beings how to preserve fish. Even this industry has not reached its peak. There are many new things in this field of endeavor yet to come for the enjoyment of mankind. The magician learns from this principal how the animals in the water can be controlled through the magic of the elements and through the Kabbalah, for example how they can be made to gather at particular locations etc. The magician can find out from *Merki* many other kinds of magical practices which concern the control of water animals.

Fig. 233: *Filakon* – (29° Libra) *Filakon* inspired humankind with a sense of order and cleanliness. During the course of human development, everything that has to do with the hygiene of healthy and ailing people came into being under this principal's rule. All those who are involved with hygiene in medicine and who occupy themselves with ethics are under this principal's protection. At the same time, *Filakon* is the originator of many ailments that are caused by infection, and he gives human beings ways and means to recognize these diseases and to employ precautionary measures. *Filakon* is the patron and initiator of all bacteriologists, toxicologists, and those who are involved in the research of bacteria, bacilli, viral diseases, and so on. This principal draws the magician's attention to those ailments which are presently considered to be a scourge or a plague to mankind, and which spread through infection. Not only does he disclose to the magician the true cause of the ailment, he also entrusts him with the manner by which they can be successfully controlled. At the magician's request this principal will disclose ailments which have remained unknown to this very day, and how they can be brought under control.

Fig. 234: *Megalogi* – (30° Libra) *Megalogi* is somewhat connected with the previous principal, for he protects all mineral springs i.e. healing springs on earth. He even urges animals to instinctively seek and enter particular waters when they are injured. With *Megalogi's* help, human beings have observed how animals help themselves when they are afflicted with certain ailments, and then they have learned how to apply this knowledge for their own benefit. The various kinds of hydrotherapies came into existence because of this knowledge, and wherever these healing springs were found, health resorts began to flourish in time. Not only does *Megalogi* show the magician healing springs which are yet undiscovered, he also initiates him completely into the entire subject of hydrotherapy and entrusts him with practices which still remain completely unknown to science.

The 30 Principals Of The Eighth Sign Of The Zodiac: Scorpio

All seals must be drawn in red.

Fig. 235: *Aluph* – (1° Scorpio) This principal is a guardian of fire on our earth. *Aluph* gives the magician precise information about all things connected with fire, including such magical matters as knowledge of the electric fluid, the beings of the Fire element, salamanders, and all the inventions and the practical uses of fire on the physical plane.

Fig. 236: *Schaluah* – (2° Scorpio) *Schaluah* is considered to be the arch-initiator of electricity. He has familiarized human beings with electricity and in the course of time he has urged suitable people to work on all kinds of inventions in this field and to make them public. Since there are many possibilities for the application of electricity in the future, there will be many more new inventions which will delight the world. A magician who contacts this principal will receive precise information about everything in this regard, especially the magical knowledge. For example, in the future the electric fluid will become a very important factor on all planes, because it will be employed in a great number of ways.

Fig. 237: *Hasperim* – (3° Scorpio) This principal has given human beings and animals the instinct for survival. He gave the animals in nature suitable means to protect themselves from any danger. *Hasperim* is the inspirer of the animal instinct. He urges human beings to care for their livelihood through diligence, perseverance and work. Therefore, every-thing that stimulates a human being's aspirations is under the jurisdiction of this principal. A magician who contacts *Hasperim* will be given enor-mous powers, either by this principal directly or through his subordinates, which can then also be transferred to others, and these powers will help to reach the desired goal at any time. *Hasperim* knows many secrets that concern the human spirit, and he is prepared to entrust them to the magi-cian, depending, of course, upon his maturity and development.

Fig. 238: *Adae* – (4° Scorpio) *Adae* is the guardian of children's love, motherly love, parental love and everything that keeps a family together. With the help of this principal a magician can resolve any quarrels, dis-putes, feuds and disagreements in a family. *Adae* is prepared to teach the magician how to solve any quarrels and disagreements by acquiring vari-ous practices.

Fig. 239: *Helmis* – (5° Scorpio) Everything on our earth that concerns milk, be it human or animal, is under the jurisdiction of this principal. He protects all wet nurses and mothers who breast-feed their babies. All mammals are likewise under the protection of this principal. His sphere of influence is extensive. He taught human beings over the course of time to use milk as part of their nourishment. Being inspired by this principal, humankind has learned that the milk from animals was not merely for drinking but could also be turned into various kinds of milk products. *Helmis* inspired human beings to employ a milk diet for certain ailments and also to prepare various healing remedies from milk. Many things that concern the utilization of milk will only become public domain in the distant future; however, a magician can find this out immediately from this principal.

Fig. 240: *Sarasi* – (6° Scorpio) *Sarasi* is an arch-initiator of all human ideals, without exception, whether they are ideals of the physical world, the astral world or the spiritual world. Through his subordinates, this principal controls the various ideals of every individual in accordance with his maturity and development. He creates situations and possibilities so that one or the other ideal will be realized in the mental, astral or physical world on a small or large scale. *Sarasi* gives human beings the necessary enthusiasm and perseverance to realize their desired ideals, again depending upon the maturity and destiny of the person. The magician can learn a great deal from this principal, for example how various ideals come into being on our world and also how they fall from grace again. Furthermore, *Sarasi* will show the magician ideals that are yet to come in the future.

Fig. 241: *Ugefor* – (7° Scorpio) This principal rules over the intellect of human beings and directs all intellectual attributes. In accordance with the maturity and development of a person, he allows certain knowledge to be available to him, depending upon the task that he has to fulfil on earth. *Ugefor* entrusts the magician with the knowledge whereby his intellect can be enlightened and he can attain an extraordinary memory. Any knowledge that can be rationally comprehended will be made accessible to the magician by this principal.

Fig. 242: *Armillee* – (8° Scorpio) *Armillee* protects human beings from all infectious diseases and urges them to care for themselves accordingly, so that they are always safe from such diseases. However, if it is a matter of karma or if it is imposed by destiny, then this principal allows an ailment to come into being through infection. Also, from the magical point of view the magician learns from *Armillee* about many protective remedies against the various infectious diseases. Since there are also mental and astral influences, the magician can be instructed by *Armillee* as to how to protect himself from negative astral influences and from the effects and influences of negative beings by acquiring particular magical practices.

Fig. 243: *Ranar* – (9° Scorpio) All human beings who occupy themselves with spiritual knowledge are protected by this principal from obsession and otherwise unfavorable psychic side effects, for example, oversensitivity, persecution complex, and paranoia. This principal has various methods at his disposal which make contact with the invisible in all spheres possible. In particular, *Ranar* acquaints the magician with the practices of mental and astral travel, and he teaches the magician specific methods on how to elevate his astral and mental body into the individual spheres. Consequently, the magician can consider this intelligence to be the inspirer of various magical practices on the path of perfection.

Fig. 244: *Caraschi* – (10° Scorpio) *Caraschi* protects and inspires all people who occupy themselves with healing magnetism. *Caraschi* teaches the magician the various methods of the magical healing arts, whether it is Od transference (i.e. vitalized life-magnetism) or prana treatments, so that they will pose no harm to the operator. It would fill many volumes to write about the sphere of influence of this principal. It is entirely at the magician's discretion if he wishes to be inspired by *Caraschi* and get his information on good authority.

Fig. 245: *Eralier* – (11° Scorpio) *Eralier* will convince the magician that the preparation of the Stone of the Sages is not an allegory or a symbolic esoteric notion. The magician learns from this principal how to prepare the Stone of the Sages in the most various degrees for the most various purposes. Furthermore, the magician will learn methods of transmuting metals, namely methods of how to prepare the Stone of the Sages through the dry process. (Those who are somewhat familiar with alchemy know what is meant by the dry process.) The preparation and realization of the Stone of the Sages is based on a variety of methods, with which *Eralier* acquaints the magician.

Fig. 246: *Sagara* – (12° Scorpio) *Sagara* is the initiator of all magicians. Every magician who comes in contact with *Sagara* receives valuable advice on how to influence human beings and animals magically and Kabbalistically, i.e. in a theurgic manner.

Fig. 247: *Trasorim* – (13° Scorpio) "Sun is Life!" Human beings have been inspired by this principal with the knowledge of this axiom. During the course of time, he has allowed human beings to come up with inventions which make use of the power of the sun. The magician learns from *Trasorim* how to make use of the sunrays with the help of colored filters for the various healing methods. This intelligence is therefore the initiator of color-light therapy. Healing remedies that are influenced by colored sunlight[25] analogous to the universal laws have a higher quality and capacity and exert a different dynamic effect than normally prepared remedies. This intelligence entrusts to the magician many magical methods on the basis of which the colored sunlight can be used for healing purposes, to dynamically charge healing remedies, and also for various magical operations.

Fig. 248: *Schulego* – (14° Scorpio) *Schulego* is a master of imitation in the physical world. For example, he taught human beings how to produce imitation gemstones. The invention of glass, porcelain, imitation leather, rubber and many other synthetic products can be attributed to this principal's inspiration. Through this intelligence, a magician can see the kinds of inventions in the art of imitation in the Akasha which are yet to come, and he will find that the supply of new inventions is inexhaustible. Under the seal of secrecy, *Schulego* also entrusts the magician with the manner in which they are manufactured.

Fig. 249: *Hipolopos* – (15° Scorpio) All the games which human beings of all races enjoy came into being through the inspiration of this principal. This also applies to all future games. *Hipolopos* will remain the initiator of all games for young and old, whether this be amusement, entertainment, betting, sporting events, etc. At the same time, this principal is also the creator of all children's toys. All card games and parlor games are also under his jurisdiction.

Fig. 250: *Natolisa* – (16° Scorpio) *Natolisa* is a guardian of the bees. He taught human beings how to culture bees and how to utilize the honey. In ancient times sugar was not known, and everything that required sweetening was sweetened with honey. It was through *Natolisa's* inspiration that humankind learned how to produce various sweets from honey. Only later, when the requirements for sweets could not be satisfied through bee

---

[25] For details read *The Healing Power of Sunlight* by Jakob Lorber (Merkur Publishing™ Inc.). – ED.

keeping, did *Natolisa* inspire human beings to extract sweeteners from other substances. In the Orient *Natolisa* had human beings discover the sugarcane, and in areas of the world which had a less favorable climate it was the sugar beet; these products contributed to the production of sugar. From this principal the magician can find out many interesting things about sugar and sugar-like products which up to this date are completely unknown to mankind. *Natolisa* will also most willingly give the magician information about the treatment of ailments which were either caused by too much sugar or a lack of sugar in the human organism.

Fig. 251: *Butharusch* – (17° Scorpio) Not only is the task of this principal to inspire people not to eat fruit in a raw state only, but to preserve and process it in sequence as it becomes available in nature. In the course of time *Butharusch* has taught human beings to prepare food with the help of the Fire element, i.e. roasting, baking and steaming. Furthermore how to bake bread, produce confectioneries, and invent meat dishes. He led mankind to its present state of achievement as far as the art of cooking is concerned. Therefore, *Butharusch* is considered to be the initiator of the art of baking and cooking.

Fig. 252: *Tagora* – (18° Scorpio) *Tagora* is a master of erotica. He is charged with the task of awakening and maintaining sympathy between a man and a woman. This principal will give the magician specific instructions as to how to enjoy great popularity and call forth sympathy, whether the person is a man or woman, and how to create peace in a marriage etc. *Tagora* knows about many magic love potions, which he will also entrust to the magician.

Fig. 253: *Panari* – (19° Scorpio) This principal has metallurgical chemistry under his jurisdiction. He taught human beings how to obtain various metals from ore and allowed them to recognize the elements of the metals and to produce metallic compounds or amalgamations from a diverse number of metals. *Panari* possesses various formulas and methods for producing metal alloys, metal compounds and metal processing. Furthermore, he possesses formulas and methods that dissolve various metals and

turn them into chemical products, synthetic products and healing remedies. This principal entrusts the magician in this respect with an abundance of secrets.

Fig. 254: *Nagar* – (20° Scorpio) This principal, just like *Panari*, will teach
the magician how to produce various healing remedies from various
metals and combinations thereof. *Nagar* is a great inspirer of all healing
remedies that are produced synthetically. A magician can expand his
medical knowledge by having *Nagar* instruct him as to how certain metals
can be utilized for medical purposes.

Fig. 255: *Kofan* – (21° Scorpio) Whosoever turns to this principal with a
sincere heart will have all his wishes fulfilled, provided they are within
Kofan's scope of possibility. His peculiarity is the ability to turn bad situations in life into good ones and to create a satisfactory existence for a
human being. *Kofan* shows the magician ways to improve his own situation in life and informs him as to how far his destiny is determined by
karma and how far Divine Providence will permit an intervention. However, since a magician is for the greater part master over his destiny, *Kofan's* help mostly affects the destiny of other people to whom the magician
can bring comfort and aid with the help of this principal.

Fig. 256: *Schaluach* – (22° Scorpio) This principal has almost the same
abilities and powers as the previous principal. Through intuition he gives
human beings advice and help, even in the most difficult situations of life
where, under normal circumstances, there is no escape. This intelligence
finds the right solution in every situation, and the magician comes into
the knowledge of this solution through *Schaluach's* inspiration.

Fig. 257: *Sipillipis* – (23° Scorpio) *Sipillipis* is considered to be a very
special principal of the zone girdling the earth, because he can teach the
magician the secrets of the power of belief and the powers of persuasion.
Through the acquisition of these two divine attributes the magician will
be able to achieve the greatest miracles in the mental, astral and physical

worlds. *Sipillipis* advises the magician how he can quickly and safely achieve the power of belief and powers of persuasion.

Fig. 258: *Tedea* – (24° Scorpio) *Tedea* is an outstanding diagnostician and an excellent analyst who will reveal to the magician all the causes of ailments in the physical, astral and mental bodies. At the same time *Tedea* will give the magician the remedies to dispose of the causes of the ailments or the disharmonies. A magician who has an interest in the healing arts will gain so much knowledge from *Tedea* that he will be able to develop into a master of those arts and of diagnosis.

Fig. 259: *Semechle* – (25° Scorpio) *Semechle* will also acquaint the magician with all the methods of naturopathy, whether that be healing with herbs (phytotherapy), hydrotherapy, physical culture, personal hygiene or other methods, which are presently employed and administered in naturopathy or whether they be methods which are still completely unknown.

Fig. 260: *Radina* – (26° Scorpio) *Radina* is an authority on the subject of Theurgy i.e. the Kabbalah. All theurgic healing methods on this planet are under his jurisdiction. He knows exactly how to cure even the most severe ailments through the Kabbalah. *Radina* entrusts the magician with many Kabbalistic formulas for curing the severest ailments. This may require that the magician record these Kabbalistic formulas in a book of formulas, and they might fill an entire book. Should the magician find it desirable, he will be instructed to such an extent by *Radina* that he will be able to achieve miraculous cures through the Kabbalah.

Fig. 261: *Hachamel* – (27° Scorpio) *Hachamel* is an outstanding authority on the subject of astronomy and orientation. He taught human beings to look up to the stars and to determine the individual course or direction of the constellations. In earlier times this knowledge was of great significance, especially for navigation. *Hachamel* is also the arch-initiator of the compass and the magnetic needle, without which navigation would be almost impossible. In time this principal will help humankind discover powers and produce inventions which will be important for orientation.

Under the jurisdiction of this principal are all instruments that measure ocean depths and water pressure, and in the future we will experience that all these instruments will be subject to tremendous improvement.

Fig. 262: *Anadi* – (28° Scorpio) *Anadi* is a specialist in hydrotherapy, just like the thirtieth principal of the zodiacal sign of Libra, *Megalogi*. *Anadi* has also all the methods of hydrotherapy under his jurisdiction. He teaches the magician how to make use of the electromagnetic fluid in connection with water for the treatment of a number of different ailments. Furthermore, he teaches the magician how to remove the causes of ailments through thermal stimulation and how to create the disposition for the harmony and health of the human body. Should the magician be interested in this field of endeavor, this principal will inform him on the many methods of hydrotherapy which are not known to this very day.

Fig. 263: *Horasul* – (29° Scorpio) *Horasul* oversees all man-made or artificial water regulations and controls on our earth. For example, he inspires human beings as to how they can utilize the powers of water such as an artificial irrigation system for the soil, or how to manage and control a water basin or water reservoir. *Horasul* is the inspirer for the most simple water mills, but also for the most modern hydroelectric power plants, manmade canals for navigation, and so forth. *Horasul* entrusts the magician with many new inventions regarding the regulation and utilization of water which are yet to be invented in the future.

Fig. 264: *Irmano* – (30° Scorpio) All things that live in the water are under the jurisdiction of this principal. Should fishery be of interest to the magician, *Irmano* will give him appropriate methods, and once the magician has become conversant with these methods he can have fish gather in one location where they can be caught very conveniently. The magician will furthermore learn methods with which fish become so docile that they can be controlled to such an extent that he can take them in his hands. In short, this also applies to any other animal that live in the water, whether sea snakes, crocodiles or sharks, because all animals in the water are under the jurisdiction of this principal.

The 30 Principals Of The Ninth Sign Of The Zodiac: Sagittarius

The seals of these principals have to be drawn in blue.

Fig. 265: *Neschamah* – (1° Sagittarius) Through intuition and inspiration, this intelligence gave human beings information by way of which they learned to process — i.e. to harden or temper — metals with the aid of fire and water, until they achieved our present-day modern steel-producing plants and metal hardening. In time, and also through the inspiration of this principal, human beings will invent other and even more complete procedures and methods to temper metals which must remain unknown for the time being.

Fig. 266: *Myrmo* – (2° Sagittarius) *Myrmo* drew the attention of mankind to steam and its many uses, whether it concerned the evaporation of liquids for multifarious purposes or whether for the purpose of building the most modern locomotives, all of which are under the jurisdiction of this principal. At the appropriate time *Myrmo* will inspire many inventors to improve, change and invent entirely new concepts in this field of endeavor, and they will pleasantly surprise the world then.

Fig. 267: *Kathim* – (3° Sagittarius) *Kathim* has all the fruit on earth under his jurisdiction. Without realizing it, human beings were inspired by this intelligence to enjoy fruit not only in its raw state, i.e. when the fruit is ripe, but also to have the benefit of fruit when nature is at rest and consequently fruit cannot be harvested at that time. And it happened that first of all some kinds of fruit were dried, and later on they were boiled down and preserved. Then humankind proceeded to make use of fruit by processing it accordingly, for example, they made jelly, fruit juices etc. However, *Kathim* has an unlimited supply of recipes and new ways of utilizing fruit and eventually everything will be made available to mankind.

Fig. 268: *Erimites* – (4° Sagittarius) Part of this intelligence's mission is to spread peace on earth among human beings. Ideals that truly represent the peace of humankind are directed and strengthened by *Erimites*. This principal gladly entrusts the magician with information as to how good influences can be called forth through the Akasha Principle to give rise to ideas of peace.

Fig. 269: *Asinel* – (5° Sagittarius) This intelligence of the zone girdling the earth was entrusted by Divine Providence with the pleasant task of bringing good fortune to every human being. A magician who is in contact with *Asinel* can be assured that he will be fortunate whenever he needs to be, whether it is in love, in gambling or in other matters. Not only can the magician secure this help for himself with the aid of this principal or his subordinates, but he can also help others who are not engaged in magic. *Asinel* also informs the magician in regards to employing his own powers as well as how far the principal himself can extend his powers.

Fig. 270: *Geriola* – (6° Sagittarius) *Geriola* is a particular authority on all moral virtues on our earth and he unveils to the magician the true secrets of magical equilibrium. He teaches the magician how to properly make use of introspection and draws his attention to the abilities and powers which can be obtained through introspection. If the magician carries out introspection in accordance with the information given by *Geriola*, this introspection which the magician employs on himself and on others will help him acquire great intuition and will also enable him to properly recognize the Akasha Principle. The magician can obtain much wisdom from this intelligence and he can also make it accessible to his intellect.

Fig. 271: *Asoreg* – (7° Sagittarius) From this principal humankind has learned the art of keeping pictures in multifarious ways through carving, engraving, embroidering, drawing or painting. Photographs, cinema, film and television are also under his jurisdiction. In the field of television, the future has prepared many magnificent inventions. *Asoreg* instructs the magician how pictures can be made visible over the greatest distances so that even an untrained eye can perceive them.

Fig. 272: *Ramage* – (8° Sagittarius) Besides other tasks, *Ramage* monitors the influence that the 28 Moon stations have upon our earth. *Ramage* can give the magician the best information in regards to rhythm and periodicity. He is always prepared to reveal to a magician all the secrets of the 28 Moon stations and the influences they have upon human life in a physical, astral and mental respect. At the same time he will also instruct the magician how to practically utilize all the knowledge he has gained.

Fig. 273: *Namalon* – (9° Sagittarius) *Namalon* protects the mentally ill. With the help of his subordinates, he protects all those who, according to their destiny, should not encounter evil. Somnambulists are also under his protection so that nothing happens to them while they are in their sleepwalking state. Furthermore, he protects all those human beings who suffer from Saint Vitus' Dance and those who suffer from epileptic seizures etc. The magician learns from this principal all the causes of these kinds of ailments and how to treat them.

Fig. 274: *Dimurga* – (10° Sagittarius) *Dimurga* is the guardian of travelers, especially those who travel by sea and undertake ocean voyages. *Dimurga* gladly gives the magician information about individual talismans which offer protection and help while traveling, and he teaches how to prepare them. When a magician is on an ocean voyage with *Dimurga's* protective talisman, the ship will survive the most severe hurricanes without ever being in danger of sinking.

Fig. 275: *Golog* – (11° Sagittarius) *Golog* is an outstanding initiator of evocative magic. This principal acquaints the magician with secret methods regarding the evocation of the various beings. *Golog* entrusts the magician with powerful magical words which force every being to absolute obedience, whether it is a positive or a negative being. The magician can find out from this intelligence a great amount of knowledge pertaining to the synthesis of evocative magic.

Fig. 276: *Ugali* – (12° Sagittarius) As the initiator of the highest level of magic which leads to the highest wisdom, this principal is very difficult to contact. In most cases, he is represented by his subordinates. Therefore, only a magician who has actually reached a high level of perfection will be successful in contacting *Ugali* directly. However, once contact has been established, the magician will find in *Ugali* the best initiator of the highest level of magic, especially of spherical magic. The magician will be initiated into the most secret teachings which reveal the highest wisdom.

Fig. 277: *Elason* – (13° Sagittarius) *Elason* is also very difficult to contact, just like *Ugali*. Should the magician succeed, despite these difficulties, in contacting *Elason,* then this high initiator will entrust the magician with secret methods pertaining to magical and Kabbalistic knowledge. By utilizing these methods, the magician will be able to realize all high ideals.

Fig. 278: *Giria* – (14° Sagittarius) The area of responsibility of this principal is trade, commerce and the monetary system, which also includes the minting of coins using various metals. He will also train human beings in this respect in accordance with their maturity and at the appropriate time. This principal can give the magician information about everything that concerns matters of trade, commerce, and the monetary system.

Fig. 279: *Hosun* – (15° Sagittarius) Every kind of educational method for young and old can be traced back to the inspiration of this principal. He is also the creator of all schools that exist to this very day, including the ancient schools of the prophets. The magician can find out from *Hosun* everything in regards to the education and upbringing of children. When the magician turns to this intelligence for help, he will pass all examinations. This intelligence or his subordinates will supervise all questions in the examination of the candidate.

Fig. 280: *Mesah* – (16° Sagittarius) *Mesah* is the creator of all traditions and customs of all the nations on earth, namely courting, love and marriage. This principal will show a magician all traditions and customs from the beginning of humankind to this very day, and also those which he will bring to humankind in the future.

Fig. 281: *Harkinon* – (17° Sagittarius) Under the special protection of this principal are orphans, those who have been abandoned, outcasts, and those who have been scorned and treated with contempt. This principal helps these people, in accordance with their karma, to bear their fate somewhat more easily, and he helps them wherever permitted by Divine Providence. The magician can obtain advice and help for all those who fall into this category.

Fig. 282: *Petuno* – (18° Sagittarius) *Petuno* is the patron of all huntsmen and all who are occupied with hunting wild animals. He is also the in-spirer of the appropriate weapons and all other tools and devices necessary to catch game or wild animals.

Fig. 283: *Caboneton* – (19° Sagittarius) To the sphere of influence of this principal belong astronomy, astrology and subjects related thereto. He instructs the magician thoroughly about the synthesis of astronomy and astrology. The magician learns from *Caboneton* about the visible universe, i.e. the stellar system, and he gains knowledge about the influence and the effects of the stars upon our earth, upon the destiny of individuals and entire nations.

Fig. 284: *Echagi* – (20° Sagittarius) *Echagi* gives advice and help in all cases of dangerous diseases, for example, epilepsy, cancer, spinal cord tuberculosis, Saint Vitus' Dance etc. Up to this date the cause for these diseases has not been found, and therefore they are still considered to be incurable. However, *Echagi* reveals to the magician the causes of these severe and mysterious diseases and at the same time entrusts him with methods and the preparation of appropriate remedies to heal all these difficult and dangerous diseases.

Fig. 285: *Batirunos* – (21° Sagittarius) The task of this principal is to bestow blissfulness, peace, pleasure and delight. Anything that contributes to the joy of human beings is created by this inspirer of blissfulness and his servants. Any questions that are raised by the magician in this respect will be answered by this principal to his complete satisfaction.

Fig. 286: *Hillaro* – (22° Sagittarius) *Hillaro* is a representative of right-eousness and justice. He provides everything that is required for the magician for true justice in matters that concern the court or in other issues. The magician will be supported by this intelligence in all legal matters.

Fig. 287: *Ergomion* – (23° Sagittarius) *Ergomion* is an inspirer in the science of colors,[26] and he instructs the magician thoroughly in the manufacture of colors and also color mixtures. Should the magician be interested in painting, this intelligence will supply him with mixtures of colors, inks, Indian ink, lithographic inks etc., which cannot be surpassed. Furthermore, the magician will also receive instructions on how to produce these mixtures of colors and how to use them practically. *Ergomion* is also an authority on synthetic inorganic chemistry and he can instruct the magician in this field of endeavor as well.

Fig. 288: *Ikon* – (24° Sagittarius) *Ikon* unveils to the magician the mysteries of magical equilibrium in the body, soul and spirit as they pertain to the Akasha Principle. *Ikon* makes the significance of true introspection perfectly clear to the magician and shows him how important it is to achieve magical equilibrium. *Ikon* also makes it perfectly clear that without introspection it is not possible to undergo physical, astral and spiritual schooling[27] and progress, nor is it possible to truly recognize the universal truths.

Fig. 289: *Alosom* – (25° Sagittarius) *Alosom* protects the most profound secrets of silence as well as the powers and abilities that are called forth through silence (negative state). Therefore, *Alosom* is the principal of the magic of silence.

Fig. 290: *Gezero* – (26° Sagittarius) *Gezero* guides the human conscience so that it always makes its presence known in a human being whenever the

---

[26] Colors include paints and dyes. – ED.
[27] The neophyte's entire progress depends upon his magical equilibrium, which is attained through proper introspection as described in *Initiation into Hermetics*. – ED.

occasion arises and in certain situations. Every magician knows that every expression of the conscience is an expression of the Akasha Principle, which makes itself known in a human being through the inner voice. *Gezero* and his subordinates make certain that even the most hardened criminal has pangs of conscience which will make him listen to reason.

Fig. 291: *Agasoly* – (27° Sagittarius) Under the jurisdiction of this principal is phenomena magic. He can give the magician hints, instructions and even help in this regard. With the help of *Agasoly* and his subordinates the magician can call forth the most incredible magical phenomena. *Agasoly* gave human beings the idea of imitating many occult phenomena by using technological inventions, because he is also the arch-initiator of all kinds of magical devices. Stage magicians and so-called amateur magicians make use of these magical devices. They delude the audience through dexterity, and by deceiving the senses they pretend to have the powers and abilities of a magician. The magician will get many ideas with *Agosoly's* help that lead to technological inventions with which other occult phenomena can be imitated.

Fig. 292: *Ekore* – (28° Sagittarius) *Ekore* guides the destiny of every person. A magician who evokes this principal will discover the exact difference between the influence of destiny and free will. *Ekore* has it within his power to change the destiny of a human being upon the magician's request. In any case, he will let the magician know how far he will be able to extend his free will when it comes to certain tasks.

Fig. 293: *Saris* – (29° Sagittarius) *Saris* teaches the magician how to load talismans and amulets through accumulated light projections and projections of accumulated elements. *Saris* also gives the magician exact instructions on how to banish the beings of the various spheres.

Fig. 294: *Elami* – (30° Sagittarius) *Elami* and his subordinates attend to all the waters which are under the surface of the earth. From this principal the magician can learn where to find healing springs and how large these springs are without using the common measuring devices. The magician will find drinking water even in the driest desert with the help of this intelligence and without using a divining rod, provided there is underground water in that particular area. All laborers who are employed in the discovery and utilization of subterranean water are under *Elami's* protection.

The 30 Principals Of The Tenth Sign Of The Zodiac: Capricorn

The seals of these principals must be drawn in black.

Fig. 295: *Milon* – (1° Capricorn) *Milon* will describe divine magic in more detail to the magician, particularly Akashic magic. He will teach him how to consciously create various causes in the Akasha in the magical manner in order to achieve particular effects in the mental, astral and physical worlds. Once the magician is in complete command of this practice, he can create causes in the Akasha Principle, which at times may take many years before they are realized. In this manner the magician becomes a consummate master in the control of destiny and thereby controls his karma as well as the karma of other people. However, always bear in mind that because of his ethical development the magician will never create any causes which could have an unfavorable and negative effect on any of the three planes. A magician who possesses these high ethical attributes will be entrusted by this principal with many magical secrets of which the magician has no idea at this point, because it is beyond the realm of his imagination.

Fig. 296: *Melamo* – (2° Capricorn) *Melamo* helps the magician to elevate his own personality, which places him at the top of his spiritual powers so that he can influence human beings and animals without any great effort. *Melamo* has magical practices at his disposal with which one can reach the highest level of powers. Should the magician wish to increase his powers, then *Melamo* and his servants will be only too pleased to help him in this endeavor.

Fig. 297: *Porphora* – (3° Capricorn) *Porphora* is an outstanding initiator of sympathetic or mummial magic, like many other principals of the zone girdling the earth which have already been mentioned. However, the difference lies in the fact that each principal uses different instructions and methods which he recommends to the magician, including how to practically apply them and carry out the magical operation. *Porphora* will inform the magician about many new practices that are completely unknown to him, for example how to use fluid condensers for sympathetic magic and also for many other magical operations.

Fig. 298: *Trapi* – (4° Capricorn) *Trapi* makes it easier for human beings to bear their disappointments and whatever destiny might have in store for them, especially in matters of friendship, love and marriage. Therefore, a magician who is in contact with this principal never has to fear these kinds of disappointments in his lifetime.

Fig. 299: *Jonion* – (5° Capricorn) *Jonion* is considered to be a mysterious principal of the zone girdling the earth. He is the custodian of those beings in the beyond who are preparing themselves for a new incarnation. In the invisible world, i.e. in the earth-girdling zone of departed human beings, he shows those beings that choose to incarnate on our earth again the most appropriate place and surroundings where they can develop. At the same time he instructs them how to establish a bond of sympathy between themselves and the maturing fruit in the mother's womb.

Fig. 300: *Afolono* – (6° Capricorn) *Afolono* is the master of Mercurial Kabbalah. This principal teaches the magician how he can Kabbalistically transfer the influences of the Mercurian sphere to the zone girdling the earth and from there to our physical world as well as to the mental, astral and also the physical bodies. The magician can find out from *Afolono* how to attain a particularly receptive intellect with which he can attain enlightenment in every field of science on our earth.

Fig. 301: *Paruchu* – (7° Capricorn) All human beings whose field of endeavor is writing or acting, whether drama, tragedy, comedy etc. will find in this principal an outstanding inspirer. Should the magician be a writer or an actor, then *Paruchu* can offer him many opportunities which will contribute to the magician's fame as an actor or writer.

Fig. 302: *Pormatho* – (8° Capricorn) *Pormatho* has the task of monitoring all earth rays[28] on our planet. From this principal the magician can find out which earth rays he can use for himself and for the benefit of others and which are harmful to one's health. At the same time the magician will learn from this principal how he can protect himself from the harmful earth rays. All instruments which our technology presently has in its possession to measure earth rays exist on account of the inspiration of this principal.

Fig. 303: *Ampholion* – (9° Capricorn) *Ampholion* initiates the magician into the entire anatomy of the astral body of humans and animals. At the same time the magician receives from this principal the knowledge of occult anatomy and how to employ this knowledge practically in the magical sciences. Therefore, you can consider *Ampholion* to be the teacher of occult anatomy, and the magician can learn a great deal in this respect.

Fig. 304: *Kogid* – (10° Capricorn) *Kogid* is one of the best initiators on the path of cognition. He guides the cognizance of every human being in accordance with his maturity, and he gives the necessary enlightenment to one who is on the path of cognition. This principal entrusts the magician with methods with which to attain enlightenment and omniscience. *Kogid* is the patron of all students of spiritual knowledge, namely those whose field of endeavor is Jnana Yoga, i.e. the yoga of cognizance.

Fig. 305: *Cermiel* – (11° Capricorn) *Cermiel* is appointed by Divine Providence to monitor the incarnation of every human being, just like *Jonion,* the fifth principal of this sign of the zodiac. *Cermiel* knows how long every person must stay in the invisible world so that he becomes mature enough to see the light of day on our earth again and to continue

---

[28] Ground radiation. – ED.

with the school of life. Should a magician request it, this principal will give him the exact time he will depart from this earth as well as the departure of any individual. In addition, he will give the magician the location and point in time of the next incarnation.

Fig. 306: *Erimihala* – (12° Capricorn) *Erimihala* is in control of higher astral magic. He unveils many secrets of the invisible world to the mature magician. For example, he informs the magician about the influences of the elements in the astral plane, the manner in which an abandoned astral body gradually decomposes through the astral elements while the spirit has already incarnated again on our earth. The magician can increase his knowledge with the help of this principal and expand his horizons in regards to working and being effective with the elements in the astral world.

Fig. 307: *Trisacha* – (13° Capricorn) *Trisacha* has many methods at his disposal which will lead to the swift development of television technology. He teaches the magician how time and space can be spanned in a very simple manner. *Trisacha* is the initiator of all optical instruments, and he allowed me to view new inventions in the Akasha that were far in the future. For example, in the future it will be possible with the aid of a small device to transmit and receive at the same time. All one has to do is aim this device at any spot on earth and it will be possible to see everything that takes place there immediately. The particular people one wishes to observe need not have a transmitter or receiver. But what is even more surprising is that the people who are observed will have no idea that this is occurring. Today's state of development of television technology is just in the beginning stages. Before this principal permits the aforementioned invention and similar others to be disclosed, humankind must first develop spiritually and astrally to a higher level. At their present level, human beings would only misuse these types of inventions. Presently, only a magician with his developed clairvoyant eyes is able to see over time and space; however, the possibility exists that in the future this type of viewing will be achieved with a form of television through appropriate inventions in the physical sense. The future will confirm my prognosis.

Fig. 308: *Afimo* – (14° Capricorn) *Afimo* is the arch-inspirer of all those who are in the field of physics and chemistry, particularly those who are engaged in the invention and production of all kinds of gases, all of whom are under the particular protection of this principal. *Afimo* initiates the magician into the secrets of evaporation in nature, the absorption of liquids and returning them as water in the form of rain or snow. All physical procedures on our earth which are in any way connected with evaporation are under the direction of this principal. Furthermore, the magician will learn from this principal how to produce rain and fog in nature or to prevent this from happening. The magician will also be shown how to transform liquids and solid matter into gases. *Afimo* gives the magician the opportunity to view inventions which can only become a reality in the distant future.

Fig. 309: *Garses* – (15° Capricorn) Similar to *Pormatho* — the eighth representative of the zodiacal sign of Capricorn who monitors the earth rays and their measuring devices — *Garses* also has the same abilities and can teach the magician the magical practices necessary to detect earth rays. In particular, he teaches how earth rays can be detected in a magical manner with the help of a divining rod, sidereal pendulum and some other aids, without having to revert to complicated physical measuring devices. The magician will receive precise information from this intelligence about many new and completely unknown methods of detection.

Fig. 310: *Masadu* – (16° Capricorn) *Masadu* is the principal who encourages human beings to be thrifty and teaches them to provide for leaner times, i.e. to stock up supplies for the winter etc. This principal shows the magician under which circumstances a meager harvest can be expected, the kind of fruits that will be in short supply, and through his subordinates he offers the magician protection so that he never has to suffer famine.

Fig. 311: *Arabim* – (17° Capricorn) *Arabim* has the qualifications to instruct the magician on occult botany and anything related thereto. This principal teaches the magician about botany from the Hermetic point of view and how to utilize it practically in magic and in the healing arts.

Fig. 312: *Amia* – (18° Capricorn) *Amia* monitors all crystallization on and under the surface of the earth. All the kings of the gnomes and their subordinates are subject to this principal of the zone girdling the earth. *Amia* permits the magician to penetrate more deeply into the secrets of crystallization, and he shows him the location of crystals, rock crystals, and various kinds of salts, as well as precious and semi-precious gemstones. Should the magician have reached a certain level of maturity and magical development, he will also learn how to transmute crystalline compounds into semi-precious or precious gemstones through an alchemical process.

Fig. 313: *Kamual* – (19° Capricorn) *Kamual* monitors all ores and coal mines on earth. He is the initiator of all human beings who are employed in the mining of ore and coal. All miners and mining engineers are under his particular protection. Should this subject be of interest to the magician, this principal can give him many valuable instructions.

Fig. 314: *Parachmo* – (20° Capricorn) *Parachmo* acquaints individuals with all the various species of healing herbs that grow on earth, and he also protects all those who gather these herbs. This principal teaches the magician to prepare healing herbs in an alchemical-spagyric manner and turn them into healing remedies for various ailments. At times he can even cure ailments which are deemed incurable. *Parachmo* will even disclose to the magician alchemical-spagyric essences and quintessences, the preparation of which is to this day known only to very few initiates. The magician can learn much more from *Parachmo* than what he believes or assumes he could.

Fig. 315: *Cochaly* – (21° Capricorn) Under the protection of this intelligence are all athletes, especially hunters and mountain climbers. Any magician who has an interest in sports will find it very beneficial to contact this principal. For example, the magician can find out from *Cochaly* how to get his body in extraordinary condition in order to achieve outstanding performances in sports.

Fig. 316: *Ybario* – (22° Capricorn) *Ybario* is considered to be a very special guardian of divine justice. He monitors the activities of the negative forces in the entire zone girdling the earth, as well as on our planet, namely in all three planes, i.e. the mental, astral and physical worlds. *Ybario* makes certain that the negative forces never gain control, thereby creating chaos in these spheres, which would then have to be brought back into equilibrium by the positive forces. *Ybario's* fundamental attributes are harmony and justice.

Fig. 317: *Lotifar* – (23° Capricorn) In the zone girdling the earth, this principal has a very difficult task to fulfil. It is *Lotifar's* task to warn desperate people, through the inner voice, not to commit suicide and if possible to prevent them from doing so. Those who are in great difficulties or who have suffered great disappointments and despair are inspired through *Lotifar's* subordinates to realize that life is holy and cannot be replaced by anything. Through this intuition *Lotifar* has saved the lives of millions of human beings from such an ill-considered step. He did this by creating for such wretches a good situation at the very last moment or by giving them à positive inspiration to chase away any thoughts of suicide. Human beings who could not be dissuaded in this manner and who committed suicide in spite of it are watched over by *Lotifar* and his servants so that they do not gain full consciousness in the astral world until their normal lifespan on earth has come to an end. When a suicide victim awakens from this semi-conscious state to full consciousness, another principal, which guides and watches over the incarnation of human beings, takes over. This principal cares for this person when he reincarnates, in that he will be placed in a situation where he will be able to catch up on what he missed, i.e. what he should have learned through his destiny during his last incarnation. Anyone who entertains thoughts of suicide should realize that in reality it is the greatest nonsense and blunder he could commit to end his life prematurely and by force. Because in reality this violent act does not change anything as far as his destiny is concerned; on the contrary, he unnecessarily prolongs the time of schooling and the development of his spirit whilst increasing his suffering.

Fig. 318: *Kama* – (24° Capricorn) *Kama* is a ruler of the physical atmosphere of our earth. He directs the air, warm and cold currents, and he determines the conditions for the vegetation. Cold and warmth, heat, drought, storms and frost are under this principal's sphere of influence. Even the atmosphere has its secrets, and there is no one who has the ability to form a clear picture of this; however, *Kama* is only too willing to unveil all the secrets of the atmosphere to a true magician.

Fig. 319: *Segosel* – (25° Capricorn) *Segosel* reveals to the magician the secret of matter, i.e. the matter of our physical world in so far as it concerns chemical and physical effects. This principal can enlighten the magician about everything that concerns our physical world.

Fig. 320: *Sarsiee* – (26° Capricorn) As a mysterious principal of the zone girdling the earth, *Sarsiee* enjoys the very special interest of every magician. He is the custodian of all magical keys; therefore he takes great care of these magical keys and ensures that the immature never have access to them because enormous powers can be set into motion with them. *Sarsiee* himself makes certain that the true mysteries remain hidden from the profane and the vulgar, even if they are published in hundreds of books. Therefore, this principal can rightfully be considered the principal who keeps the magical keys secret.

Fig. 321: *Kiliosa* – (27° Capricorn) *Kiliosa* renders magical help when a magician is in great danger. This principal will come to the aid of every magician who has ever been in contact with him and he will momentarily save the magician from any predicament and danger that might threaten his life. *Kiliosa* will also entrust Kabbalistic formulas to the magician, provided he is mature enough, which can only be used in times of grave danger and which contain the power to save the magician immediately. For example, as soon as a particular Kabbalistic formula or word is spoken, a murderer would die instantly or it would permit a magician to become invisible, or he could escape in another fortunate manner; many other difficult situations could be changed through such Kabbalistic words. The effects of these Kabbalistic words or formulas sometimes occur in just a tenth of a second after they have been uttered. Therefore, any magician who practices evocation will not neglect contacting this principal of the zone girdling the earth, in order to be entrusted by him with some of these Kabbalistic formulas which could save him.

Fig. 322: *Rosora* – (28° Capricorn) In our physical world this principal is a master of acoustics. Humankind owes *Rosora* its progress in acoustical communication over vast distances, beginning with primitive communication such as drums etc., to the present-day modern telephone, radio, and all the other inventions that belong to this field of endeavor. From the magical viewpoint, the magician will learn from this intelligence the manner by which he can direct his attention in order to hear anything he wishes, even over vast distances, i.e. clairaudience. Furthermore *Rosora* can teach the magician how to materialize acoustical vibrations over great distances, i.e. how spoken words and sentences can be condensed acoustically over great distances and how they can be heard. Should the magician attain a certain level of mastery in this respect, he will be able to materialize this phenomenon to such a degree that even people who are not magically trained will be able to hear what is said with their physical ears at a far distance. The magician will also receive from *Rosora* precise information about other phenomena in regards to acoustical transmission over any distance.

Fig. 323: *Ekorim* – (29° Capricorn) Since time immemorial this principal has taught humankind how to sculpt the most multifarious forms out of earth in the form of clay and gypsum. *Ekorim* has inspired humankind in accordance with its maturity to produce pots, vessels, statues etc. out of clay. Later this principal inspired human beings to make bricks from clay, which to this day represent an important part of the building trade. Not only can the magician learn all about the things clay can be turned into, but this principal can also instruct him in the healing powers of clay in naturopathy, and other kinds of natural remedies which can be added to the clay so that certain healing effects are achieved. *Ekorim* can also inform the magician about entirely new yet unknown healing therapies which are yet to be discovered by humankind in the future.

Fig. 324: *Ramgisa* – (30° Capricorn) This principal mainly guides and watches over the fishing trade. It was *Ramgisa* who taught humankind how to preserve fish in many different ways. The magician can gain great insight into this matter through this principal.

The 30 Principals Of The Eleventh Sign Of The Sign Of The Zodiac: Aquarius

The seals of these principals have to be drawn in violet.

Fig. 325: *Frasis* – (1° Aquarius) This principal gave human beings the inspiration to sharpen their tools. In the beginning, human beings were inspired by this principal to sharpen their knives, axes, swords and all other weaponry, and later they began to cut and polish gemstones for jewelry. Also all the tools, for example the grindstone, which are required to sharpen tools and to cut and polish gems reached today's perfection through the inspiration of this principal. *Frasis* is the guardian of all who are in this field.

Fig. 326: *Pother* – (2° Aquarius) *Pother* is a lord and master of warfare. This does not actually mean that he incites humankind to make war; on the contrary, this principal secures the peace and, through inspiration, he teaches those who are attacked by an enemy how to take control of the war successfully. *Pother* is also the initiator of all protective measures that can be employed against an enemy. He can be considered the strategist in warfare.

Fig. 327: *Badet* – (3° Aquarius) The assignment of this principal of the zone girdling the earth is to inspire human beings with creative imagination. Should the magician have little fantasy, all he has to do is contact this intelligence and he will assist the magician in this respect. The magician will attain fabulous powers of the imagination with the help of particular methods which will be entrusted to him by *Badet*. In addition, the magician will learn how to properly think creatively and how to transfer certain trains of thought into the Akasha in such a way that the desired result can actually be achieved.

Fig. 328: *Naga* – (4° Aquarius) As the inspirer of poetry, this principal will help the magician attain a good ability to judge, and to have an all-around talent. However, *Naga* prefers spiritual and astral motives when it comes to poetry; therefore, through the methods recommended by *Naga,* the magician can attain the ability to easily express all spiritual subjects and problems in the form of poetry.

Fig. 329: *Asturel* – (5° Aquarius) *Asturel* represents divine mercy and, through his pleasant vibrations, he helps every person to bear his cross more easily. He helps wherever it is possible and as long as the lawfulness is not violated. The magician can also turn to this principal to help other people. *Asturel* gives the magician the opportunity to recognize the limits of justice and mercy from the universal point of view.

Fig. 330: *Liriell* – (6° Aquarius) *Liriell* is an arch-initiator of cosmic philosophy and he teaches the magician the various philosophies, from the very beginning of humankind to the present. *Liriell* will allow the magician access to the distant future, through which he will gain knowledge over all philosophical directions which are yet to come. The magician will also attain rational knowledge of unimaginable profundity through this intelligence of the zone girdling the earth.

Fig. 331: *Siges* – (7° Aquarius) This principal teaches the magician the various mummification procedures that stop the decomposing influence on the astral and physical bodies. If the magician makes use of this procedure he ceases to age, and he withdraws to such a degree from the influence of destiny that he is in a position to extend his life as long as he pleases. A magician who has astrally and physically mummified himself is no longer subject to any ailments. If the magician follows the instructions of this principal he will be able to produce many other experiments through magic. For example, if he so wishes he will be invulnerable to fire, water, and poison; he will not need to eat or drink for years and he will remain young, fresh and resilient as long as he wishes. In this case Divine Providence alone decides the magician's life and death.

Fig. 332: *Metosee* – (8° Aquarius) To this principal's sphere of influence belong manual skills. He bestows these skills in the professions as well as in the arts. *Metosee* influences all needlework done by women such as embroidery, crocheting, sewing, spinning and all the other work that requires certain manual skills. *Metosee* entrusts the magician with methods to raise to another level those talents that require very precise manual skills.

Fig. 333: *Abusis* – (9° Aquarius) *Abusis* assists everyone who seeks the truth. All those who seriously strive for truth, knowledge and cognizance will be helped by *Abusis* himself or by his subordinates. In accordance with the seeker's development, *Abusis* will arrange that they come into the vicinity of those who are initiated in spiritual knowledge. He even arranges an opportunity to come into contact with a true guru, i.e. a teacher, who then initiates the seeker into the truth for which he has yearned.

Fig. 334: *Panfodra* – (10° Aquarius) *Panfodra* can reveal to the magician the most secret methods that reveal the spiritual development of a person. This principal also determines the secret method of spiritual development that is to be released to the individual seeker of truth. *Panfodra* like many other principals is an outstanding initiator of true magic and guardian of the keys to the magical-Kabbalistic secrets.

Fig. 335: *Hagus* – (11° Aquarius) Besides the many methods that concern magical knowledge, the magician will also receive detailed instructions from this principal about the mental, astral and physical emanations. *Hagus* teaches the magician in which manner he can determine the degree of maturity of every human being through the emanations of the mental and astral bodies. This principal of the zone girdling the earth has special methods for the multifarious practical utilization of these emanations that he gladly entrusts to a true magician.

Fig. 336: *Hatuny* – (12° Aquarius) On his travels in the zone girdling the earth, a magician will certainly not neglect contacting this particular principal. *Hatuny* is an excellent initiator of Kabbalistic magic, because he teaches the magician how to employ Kabbalistic magic in the mental, astral and physical planes. *Hatuny* is in possession of secret practices of Kabbalistic magic which up to now he has entrusted only to a few initiates.

Fig. 337: *Gagolchon* – (13° Aquarius) *Gagolchon* is an inspirer of all naturalists on our earth. In accordance with humankind's maturity and development, the secrets of Nature are released successively. A magician who is engaged in the natural sciences will strive to contact this principal, because with the appropriate means he will awaken an extraordinary genius in the magician in this respect.

Fig. 338: *Bafa* – (14° Aquarius) This principal inspires authors of mysticism, occultism and spiritual knowledge by giving them wonderful ideas so that they commit to paper the mysteries in the form of very selective poetry or rare and wonderful verse. This also applies to playwrights whose plays contain mysticism, as they are inspired by this intelligence. A magician who is an author receives many useful suggestions for his work from this principal.

Fig. 339: *Ugirpon* – (15° Aquarius) This principal can teach the magician about astronomy and its influence on the mental, astral and physical planes. He is also an excellent initiator on the entire subject of astrophysics. *Ugirpon* gladly gives a mature magician information about the inhabitants of other planets and constellations, about their spiritual maturity and development, and about their technological achievements, in short everything that the magician deems worthwhile knowing in this respect.

Fig. 340: *Capipa* – (16° Aquarius) *Capipa* is considered to be the guardian of affluence, wealth and reputation. *Capipa* and his servants are the custodians of all treasures which are located under the surface of the earth, whether these be precious stones or other treasures that were buried by human hands. Should the magician decide to become rich quickly in this manner, without this wealth becoming a hindrance to his spiritual development, this then assures the magician that *Capipa* will help him to obtain the desired wealth. Of course this principal would inform the magician if this wealth would be detrimental to his spiritual development.

Fig. 341: *Koreh* – (17° Aquarius) *Koreh* is an excellent initiator in Kabbalistic mysticism, as are many other principals. This principal acquaints the magician with very special methods regarding the spiritualization of divine virtues in the mental, astral and physical worlds. If the magician acquires all these magical-Kabbalistic abilities by following the methods he received from *Koreh*, then he may use these abilities to help others.

Fig. 342: *Somi* – (18° Aquarius) The magician can be initiated by this principal into many alchemical secrets, especially the preparation of fluid condensers for various magical practices. Should *Somi* consider the magician mature enough, he will also teach him the knowledge of the most secret sexual magic, i.e. love magic, and how to load these fluid condensers effectively. In this respect, the magician can be initiated by *Somi* into high mysteries which are without a doubt completely unknown to him.

Fig. 343: *Erytar* – (19° Aquarius) *Erytar* is an outstanding authority and initiator of alchemy and electrophysics and he can acquaint the magician with special procedures — for example, how the oscillations of the electrons of metals can be changed at the magician's discretion through the electromagnetic fluid in order to bring about the transmutation of the metal's primary matter. *Erytar* teaches the magician how to make use of electrophysics in magic, so that various effects can be brought about, not only in the physical plane but also in the astral and mental planes.

Fig. 344: *Kosirma* – (20° Aquarius) *Kosirma* acquaints the magician with special healing methods for ailments that are presently considered incurable. This principal entrusts the magician with many recipes and methods to prepare alchemical and spagyric healing remedies for all kinds of severe ailments. He also teaches him how to favorably influence these healing remedies through the electromagnetic fluid and how to load these remedies through various methods. In addition, the magician will receive precise information from this principal about all secret alchemical healing methods.

Fig. 345: *Jenuri* – (21° Aquarius) The magician receives information from this principal about all kinds of protective measures that can be employed against all negative influences, whether they are negative elementals, negative elementaries, negative beings of the elements of the zone girdling the earth, or negative beings from the other spheres. This principal can give the magician protective measures for all the various practices, evocations etc., where the possibility of negative influence exists. The magician will also receive instructions from this intelligence on how to prepare protective amulets, talismans and so-called magical lightning rods etc.

Fig. 346: *Altono* – (22° Aquarius) Similar to *Asturel*, the fifth principal of this sign of the zodiac, *Altono* makes decisions regarding justice and injustice. He will always make certain that a magician is dealt with in a just manner, whether in a court of law or when dealing with his fellow man. *Altono* is also the comforter of all people who are without rights, all victims of persecution, all innocent prisoners etc. Through his vibrations *Altono* bestows on all these human beings the blessing of mercy, through which they find their inner peace. At the same time, this intelligence provides great assistance in the most difficult situations in life.

Fig. 347: *Chimirgu* – (23° Aquarius) *Chimirgu* initiates a magician who is in contact with him into the mysteries of creation on all planes and spheres. The magician learns through this intelligence all about the Akasha Principle, i.e. the causal principle, and through this the mysteries of wisdom are revealed to the magician.

Fig. 348: *Arisaka* – (24° Aquarius) *Arisaka* is a consummate master of magical incarnation. This principal awakens in the magician the understanding of the music of the spheres, and he teaches him how to express every idea, every train of thought, through music or song. The magician will attain an excellent musical sense of hearing, or, as it is commonly known, "an ear for music" through the methods entrusted to him by *Arisaka*.

Fig. 349: *Boreb* – (25° Aquarius) *Boreb* is considered to be the judge for the entire zone girdling the earth. It is his duty to strictly monitor through his subordinates all oaths that human beings take on earth, whether they are oaths taken in a court of law, oaths of faithfulness, love etc. The magician learns from this principal to fully understand what it means to take an oath, especially as it pertains to a magical oath and what can be achieved when complying with a magical oath. *Boreb* also instructs the magician under which circumstances an oath can be broken without having any karmic consequences for the magician. The magician will also learn many other things concerning this subject matter from this intelligence.

Fig. 350: *Soesma* – (26° Aquarius) As an authority on universal ritualistic magic, *Soesma* is only too willing to reveal to a magician the secrets of all magical-Kabbalistic rituals. Through this principal of the zone girdling the earth, the magician acquires the very best information about individual rituals or rituals of an entire society such as a lodge, as well as rituals that are bound to a demiurge (i.e. a personified divinity) or to particular religious systems, and rituals that express the cosmic analogy (i.e. rituals that are of universal origin). Whenever the magician requires a suitable ritual for a very particular purpose, all he has to do is ask this intelligence.

Fig. 351: *Ebaron* – (27° Aquarius) *Ebaron* entrusts the magician with special methods that not only make it considerably easier to travel mentally and astrally in the three planes of the mental, astral and physical worlds, but to rise to the other spheres as well. If the magician so wishes, this principal or his subordinates will accompany him on his mental and astral travels to the zone girdling the earth and also to the other individual spheres, where the magician will become acquainted with the laws and the mysteries that prevail there. This principal will also instruct the magician how to deal with these laws.

Fig. 352: *Negani* – (28° Aquarius) *Negani*, like the previous principal *Ebaron*, can also familiarize the magician with the secrets of magical spheric Kabbalah, and he can give the magician suitable methods of spheric magic for practical use in all three planes. Any magician who succeeds in contacting this intelligence will have access to incredible possibilities.

Fig. 353: *Nelion* – (29° Aquarius) This principal has abilities that are on the same level as the two previous principals. *Nelion* is well-versed in analogy, i.e. the lawfulness of synthetic alchemy, magic and Kabbalah, so that the magician can place himself confidently under the guidance of this intelligence. *Nelion* will enrich the knowledge of the magician with many unknown methods.

Fig. 354: *Sirigilis* – (30° Aquarius) *Sirigilis* is a very special initiator and at the same time the guardian of the high mysteries that are concerned with alchemical magic. The magician learns from this principal how to magically impregnate the semen and blood of a human being in many various ways for very particular purposes. If a magician strives to contact this principal and is successful in this endeavor, he will be richly rewarded from a magical point of view.

The 30 Principals Of The Twelfth Sign Of The Zodiac: Pisces

The seals of these principals have to be drawn in blue.

Fig. 355: *Haja* – (1° Pisces) This principal will gladly entrust special secret methods to the magician that elevate the creative powers. These special methods will enable the magician to summon the dynamics (energies) necessary for Kabbalistic magic and to endure this state without any danger to himself, provided that he carefully observes the instructions of this intelligence. The magician gains in *Haja* an outstanding teacher for the magic of powers, and in addition he will also learn how to condense the various fluids to such an extent that phenomenal effects can be achieved.

Fig. 356: *Schad* – (2° Pisces) *Schad* constantly makes every effort, if possible, to ease the workload of every person, i.e. the work which one has to accomplish while here on earth. For example, this principal inspires people who have the abilities with technological inventions of all kinds, so that manual work can be replaced as much as possible by machines.

Fig. 357: *Kohen* – (3° Pisces) *Kohen* also inspires human beings with new technological inventions, and he pays special attention to inventions in agriculture. Provided that it is the interest of the magician, this principal can show him technological achievements in the Akasha Principle in the field of agriculture which will contribute to save humankind a considerable amount of manual labor in the distant future.

Fig. 358: *Echami* – (4° Pisces) *Echami* monitors the activities of people on our earth and therefore he can enlighten the magician about the secrets of Karma Yoga. To properly pursue Karma Yoga means to do good deeds strictly for the sake of doing a good deed, but under no circumstances to reap rewards of any kind. However, on account of *Echami's* teachings the magician will be cognizant of the fact that unselfish deeds are evaluated in the Akasha Principle and are rewarded with various magical abilities and various releases from karma. On the basis of this knowledge the magician will certainly long for situations that allow him to unselfishly perform as many good deeds as possible. *Echami* and his subordinates can assist the magician to attain these kinds of situations.

Fig. 359: *Flabison* – (5° Pisces) Under *Flabison's* jurisdiction are all kinds of arts, entertainment, amusements of all kinds, good fortune and the comforts of life. This principal can help the magician in that he can create situations for him which are desirable for amusement. Should the magician himself seek some kind of change and diversion in order to relax from his magical studies, all of which are certainly of a serious nature, all he has to do is turn to *Flabison* and he will find that this principal will pave the path for him.

Fig. 360: *Alagill* – (6° Pisces) With the help of this principal, the magician will experience sweeping success in his profession. *Alagill* has a great fondness for the arts and crafts and therefore he likes to help in this field of endeavor. However, since mere success in one's profession is not enough, this intelligence also ensures financial success. That is why the magician should see in this principal a helper in all material matters who will never refuse him help; on the contrary, he will draw the magician's attention to everything, so that his successes will never be unfavorably influenced.

Fig. 361: *Atherom* – (7° Pisces) *Atherom* makes a person fortunate in all fields of knowledge and successful in learning or any kind of intellectual work. He helps every person when it comes to the acquisition of study material, whether through his direct influence or through that of his subordinates. This intelligence will make a magician omniscient in every field of knowledge upon request, so that nothing remains hidden or unexplained to him in an intellectual respect.

Fig. 362: *Porascho* – (8° Pisces) *Porascho* has a similar sphere of activity as the previous principal. The only difference is that *Porascho* supports knowledge that is dispensed in the school system, whereas *Atherom* takes care of the erudition of human beings in their private lives. Therefore, *Porascho* supports those who are subject to school examinations and courses, should the magician require the services of this principal for someone who is not on the path of magic.

Fig. 363: *Egention* – (9° Pisces) All things that concern travel and are connected with travel fall under the jurisdiction of this principal. Any magician who turns to this intelligence will always be fortunate when he travels, and all his projects, undertakings and plans will be successful. He will be safe from all accidents, whether traveling on land, water or in the air. A magician who carries this principal's seal on his person will never have a traffic accident.

Fig. 364: *Siria* – (10° Pisces) Very special occult methods that are entrusted by *Siria* to the magician help him in accordance with his maturity to be fortunate, affluent, honored, wealthy and held in high esteem without burdening his karma and suffering negative consequences. *Siria* can fulfil all the magician's requests in this respect.

Fig. 365: *Vollman* – (11° Pisces) This principal initiates the magician into the most exalted mysteries of light. If the magician works in accordance with the instructions which he receives from this principal, he will attain a level of maturity that will enable him to employ the mysteries of light in regards to magic, Kabbalah and alchemy so that he will be able to achieve all things in all the mental, astral and physical spheres. Besides that, his entire being will be filled with bliss that is beyond description.

Fig. 366: *Hagomi* – (12° Pisces) *Hagomi* entrusts the magician with Kabbalistic methods that empower him to mentally travel and rise into other spheres outside our planetary system. In these spheres the magician will gather knowledge which a person who is not magically trained will not comprehend at all. The magician learns from *Hagomi* how to influence the zone girdling our earth mentally, astrally and physically from the other spheres to which he travels with his mental body.

Fig. 367: *Klorecha* – (13° Pisces) This principal helps those who seriously strive and long for the truth to attain true occult knowledge by making it possible for them to be taught directly by a true initiate, or at least to receive the appropriate books for their studies. *Klorecha* is a great friend of occult philosophy.

Fig. 368: *Baroa* – (14° Pisces) *Baroa,* like many other principals of the zone girdling the earth, is a friend and patron of the arts. He promotes all ideals and everything that is beautiful. He inspires authors, journalists, editors, poets and other artists at their work and helps them to achieve an all-around success. Should the magician turn to this principal, he can count on his support.

Fig. 369: *Gomognu* – (15° Pisces) *Gomognu* is an arch-initiator of languages that are expressed through gestures, movement of hands etc. The blind owe their alphabet,[29] a system of raised dots, to the inspiration of this principal. In the course of time the blind and the deaf and dumb, with this principal's help and with the progress of technology, will have considerably better means of communication at their disposal. However, a magician can now take a look into the future to see all new inventions.

Fig. 370: *Fermetu* – (16° Pisces) This principal can be considered the great peacemaker, because all matters of peace are under his jurisdiction, whether it concerns the peace of entire nations, peace in the family, or peace in a marriage etc. *Fermetu* makes it possible for a magician to find blissful love; he helps the magician find friendships and he makes it possible that all sympathies are permanent, i.e. between a man and woman.

Fig. 371: *Forsteton* – (17° Pisces) This principal will give advice to female magicians who are infertile. If they follow his advice they will become fertile and be able to conceive. He will also provide methods of determining the sex of the child in advance. *Forsteton* will remove emotional frigidity, whether in a woman or a man, and enormously increase the sexual drive. The methods of this principal make it possible for the magician to retain his mental alertness and vigor and the sexual powers of a young man until a ripe old age. When the magician's sexual powers are waning, and for some reason the magician wishes to raise them to the proper level again, he will find in *Forsteton* an excellent advisor and a willing friend in need.

---

[29] The Braille system. – ED.

Fig. 372: *Lotogi* – (18° Pisces) *Lotogi* has in his possession secret methods to manufacture extremely effective amulets and talismans for love, marriage and friendship. *Lotogi* is quite willing to reveal his secrets to a magician, and he is even prepared to load the amulets and talismans for him. The jurisdiction of this principal is quite extensive, therefore establishing contact with him offers the magician many other advantages. For example, the magician can learn from *Lotogi* how to easily contact the beings of the Venusian sphere. Not only does he give the magician the methods by which to achieve this, but also to contact the human beings that live there. As a matter of interest, *Lotogi* accompanied me in my mental body to Venus, where I observed their way of life and their activities. The color of the skin of the inhabitants of Venus is light silver. They are considerably more advanced in their spiritual development than the humans on earth, and consequently so is their technology. On account of their technological achievements, they can leave their planet without any effort, and visiting other planets presents no obstacle to them, in contrast to human beings on earth who at this point have no means to travel past the stratosphere.[30] The inhabitants of Venus are somewhat smaller in stature than the human beings on earth. Whenever a magician wishes to contact human beings on other planets, he must change his mental body so that it has the same size as those that live on that planet. The method of how to transform the mental body is described in my first work, *Initiation into Hermetics*.

Fig. 373: *Nearah* – (19° Pisces) *Nearah* is a very good inspirer when it comes to inventions in the chemical field, especially new pharmaceutical inventions. *Nearah* has a great penchant for dentistry and, under the seal of secrecy, he allows the magician to look into his sphere of activity in the Akasha Principle, to see how far pharmaceuticals and dentistry will progress in the future. For example, *Nearah* allowed me to look into the future in regards to chemistry and dentistry, and not only did he show me that artificial teeth were made from very resistant materials, but he also showed me new magnificent inventions whereby adults will grow

---

[30] This book was first published in 1956. – ED.

completely new natural teeth. As soon as humankind has reached that particular degree of maturity, then *Nearah* will inspire the appropriate people with this secret. By using the proper chemical-pharmaceutical preparations, the decayed teeth will fall out by themselves without being pulled by an instrument, whereupon in a surprisingly short time new and healthy teeth will grow. In this manner, people will become masters over growing new teeth. This also applies to the growth of new hair. Losing one's hair and becoming gray will then be a matter of the past. Every person can also determine the color of his or her hair without the use of any kind of hair dye. These statements appear to be utopian, and it might evoke a sneering grin from the skeptical reader. However, these statements are not utopian; they are the truth and the future will confirm it. A magician who can span time and space will prefer to keep his silence to prevent from becoming the target of ridicule by the immature.

Fig. 374: *Dagio* – (20° Pisces) It is the task of this intelligence to take care of the development of the human spirit in an intellectual respect. If the magician observes the secret methods which *Dagio* gladly entrusts to him, he will attain an excellent memory, his intelligence will increase rapidly, he will emerge as the victor in any battle of words, and he will be surprisingly good at repartee in every situation of life.

Fig. 375: *Nephasser* – (21° Pisces) As a bearer of good fortune, this principal helps the magician, like many other intelligences of the zone girdling the earth, with good luck, happiness, wealth, success and contentment in the material sense. *Nephasser* also possesses a tremendous treasury of spiritual knowledge, and should the magician request anything in this respect, *Nephasser* will certainly be quite generous.

Fig. 376: *Armefia* – (22° Pisces) A magician would rarely require the help and support of this principal for himself. However, should he wish to help immature, magically untrained individuals, then this principal will certainly not refuse to help him. *Armefia* provides protection for important people. He makes certain that proper justice will be administered in court trials where the defendants are innocent, and that those that are guilty will be given the greatest possible leniency. He also protects all those who are exposed to great danger.

Fig. 377: *Kaerlesa* – (23° Pisces) *Kaerlesa* is the master of the natural sciences. He bestows upon the magician a profound understanding of the lawfulness of nature, particularly of the higher laws in all three kingdoms, mineral, vegetable and animal. He allows the magician to penetrate deeply into the lawfulness of nature and teaches him how he can magically make use of this knowledge. This principal can be of great benefit to any magician who is a nature lover or a naturalist.

Fig. 378: *Bileka* – (24° Pisces) *Bileka* initiates the magician into the various kinds of meditation and teaches him how to make proper use of them for magical-Kabbalistic purposes. On the basis of the instructions he receives from *Bileka,* the magician can develop abilities within himself that border on the incomprehensible and appear to be unbelievable to any other person — provided that he follows these instructions. A fundamental condition to establish contact with this principal would be that the magician possess a certain magical maturity. When the magician summons this principal for the very first time he is usually represented by his subordinates, who give the magician instructions on how he should prepare himself in order to establish a direct and good contact with *Bileka.* Even though I know exactly the method of how to approach this principal, I cannot disclose it. Also, any other magician who has been in contact with *Bileka* cannot reveal this method, because there are mysteries that can never be made public.

Fig. 379: *Ugolog* – (25° Pisces) There are only a few initiates on our earth who are acquainted with the methods that this intelligence of the zone girdling the earth has at his disposal. These methods offer the magician who is entrusted with them the ability to plainly read the karma of every human being in the mental, astral and physical world directly from the Akasha Principle. A magician who works in accordance with the methods of this principal will learn how to read all the thoughts of any human being, whether they belong to the past, present or future. The magician can also see any human being's astral development from the very beginning to his consummate maturity and the physical destiny of past and future incarnations. The magician can become a famous prophet through *Ugolog's* methods, the kind of prophet encountered but seldom in the history of humankind. In antiquity these methods were entrusted by the high priests only to very mature neophytes of magic.

Fig. 380: *Tmiti* – (26° Pisces) This principal is the guardian of secret methods which he will entrust only to a mature magician. These methods allow the magician to draw planetary powers from the planets and spheres in a magical-Kabbalistic manner and use them for particular magical operations in the zone girdling the earth and also on our physical world in all three planes, the mental, astral and physical. The effects that are released by using these powers are of such enormous range that they would appear as absolutely unbelievable to the uninitiated.

Fig. 381: *Zalones* – (27° Pisces) The magician will learn from this principal of the zone girdling the earth about all the mysteries of the microcosm and macrocosm. Besides that, he will be taught in which manner he can attain consummate divine cognizance without having to enter upon the path of saintliness and without losing his magical individuality. A magician who works in accordance with the instructions of this intelligence will be entrusted by Divine Providence with particular tasks and missions in the zone girdling the earth. Under certain circumstances the magician may also be assigned a task on our earth to support and help humankind as a teacher and an assistant by employing magic and the Kabbalah without anyone being aware of it.

Fig. 382: *Cigila* – (28° Pisces) As a very special initiator and teacher of magical-Kabbalistic mysticism, this principal can familiarize the magician with secret methods which, with the help of magic and the Kabbalah, will enable him to unfold within himself the divine virtues to the fullest extent, mentally, astrally and physically. The divine virtues that the magician will develop will help him attain all the abilities that belong to these virtues. At the same time the magician matures on account of following these secret methods to the level that he can fulfil particular tasks precisely in accordance with Divine Providence's will. However, *Cigila* entrusts these secret methods, which are under his guardianship, exclusively to those magicians who in previous incarnations reached a particular level of maturity in magic and in the Kabbalah. A magician who developed in accordance with these methods is godlike; he is a personified Divinity, endowed with all the virtues, powers and abilities that can be compared with those of Divine Providence.

Fig. 383: *Ylemis* – (29° Pisces) *Ylemis* reveals to the mature magician the most secret mysteries of divine love and he allows the magician to become cognizant of Her (divine love) sphere of activity in the mental, astral and physical plane from a magical-Kabbalistic point of view. Understandably so, the realization of this divine virtue calls forth a feeling of blissfulness in the magician that will lead him to the highest level of ecstasy.

Fig. 384: *Boria* – (30° Pisces) The magician will be thoroughly instructed by the last principal of the zone girdling the earth about the reciprocal effects of the elements and fluids in the entire microcosm and macrocosm, i.e. on all spheres and planets of the zone girdling the earth, in all three planes, the mental, astral and physical. He will also receive precise information about the magical use of these effects. Should the magician make the request, then this principal will also reveal to him the chemical compounds and primary substances that exist on other planets, as well as their effects and influences, which are completely unknown on our earth. Furthermore, *Boria* instructs the magician on how to utilize these compounds and primary substances, not only in magic and Kabbalah, but also in technology and chemistry. Through *Boria's* guidance the magician becomes omniscient and omnipotent as far as the microcosm and macrocosm are concerned and no one except the One and Only Unpersonified Divine Providence can be his master and command him.

This concludes the description of the 360 principals of the zone girdling the earth. Every magician must admit that it is unquestionable that the actual existence of these principals is known only to a few high initiates on earth. The scope of this book does not allow that I commit to paper all the details about every principal. Therefore, I shall publish in a very few words only what pertains to the overall Hermetic knowledge. If I endeavored to give a detailed description of the appearance of each principal I have summoned personally, and give an account of everything under his jurisdiction, his sphere of activity, his work and his tasks in the zone girdling the earth in regards to the Akasha Principle, in regards to the elements, in regards to the cause and effect of the lawfulness, in regards to the laws of analogy, polarity, the electromagnetic fluid etc., I would have to write a book containing hundreds of pages for every principal. In the case of some of the principals whose sphere of activity is rather extensive, the description would take not only one book but would require several volumes.

These short descriptions about the intelligences should suffice for a mature magician, and they should give him ample points of reference, which is actually the purpose of these descriptions. Should the magician wish to establish contact with a particular intelligence, he has many possibilities by which to do so.

It will definitely not escape a magician that many principals have similar and even common spheres of activities or jurisdictions. This idea became more prominent when I described the various tasks of the principals, especially when I described these tasks from the Hermetic point of view. The magician will certainly welcome this circumstance, because it gives him a much greater choice. Later, the magician will realize that although there exists a similarity in their spheres of activities, the methods, directions and practices are fundamentally different. Therefore, should the magician entertain certain wishes, he can realize them through different sources and means and he is not dependent upon one single method or upon the instruction of one single principal. That is also why it is impossible to describe all the various instructions of the principals that could be given to the magician to fulfil his wishes, besides the fact that many principals demand that their methods remain secret.

Therefore, the zone girdling the earth is something entirely new for the magician, something completely unknown, but of great importance. Thus far there has been no author of astrology or the Kabbalah who has known of the existence of the zone girdling the earth. An astrologer who has been trained in magic will be able to increase his knowledge by studying the information in this book regarding the existence of the zone girdling the earth. When a magically trained astrologer now ascertains particular influences, besides the signs of the zodiac and the planets which are the common property of all astrologers and the basis of determining and calculating these influences, he now can also include the knowledge that the influence of the zone girdling the earth has upon the destiny of human beings. From an astrological point of view, the zone girdling the earth can be considered as the 360 degrees of the ecliptic of our earth. From sunrise to sunrise, according to our calculations, the duration of influence of every principal of the zone girdling the earth lasts exactly four minutes. When the astrologer knows the time of birth of a person exactly, then it is easy to calculate which principal made his influence known at the moment of birth. As a result of that, this principal is well disposed towards that person. Even the inclinations and talents of a person can be established when the zone girdling the earth is included in these calculations. When the astrologer casts a horoscope and considers the influences of the other constellations, he will obtain surprising results. If the astrologer considers the mantic or prophetic aspect of a horoscope, and he also considers all the favorable planetary aspects or positions which can be calculated to a specific degree of the ecliptic, he will be able to gain profound insight into synthetic astrology. And with this knowledge he will achieve what would be impossible to achieve on the basis of conventional astrology.

For example, if the astrologer now calculates the kind of influence the cosmic elements of the spheres beyond have on our physical world, he will calculate it in a different manner, and he will look at it from an entirely different point of view than he did in the past. This will give him the opportunity to get closer to the truth than he has up to now. An entire voluminous book could be written about synthetic astrology pertaining to the entire Hermetic knowledge in consideration of the zone girdling the earth. Perhaps later I shall publish such a book, provided however that the impulse to do so is given to me by Divine Providence. An astrologically trained magician can therefore calculate, beginning from sunrise, the exact time when an intelligence exerts an influence on our earth. He can make use of this knowledge when evoking an intelligence from the zone girdling the earth for the first time. This will to some extent make his work easier. Of course, a magician who is well trained does not have to calculate the exact time when it is astrologically most favorable to evoke an intelligence.

Parallel to the positive principals of the zone girdling the earth are also the opposite intelligences at work, who represent the negative principle in their spheres of influence. I purposely did not describe these negative principals and I refrained from mentioning their names and seals, so that a magician is not tempted to evoke them and thereby suffer unnecessary consequences.

A magician should always strive to contact those principals that appeal to his ideals. Because if a magician should want to get acquainted with the entire zone girdling the earth, with all principals and all the beings, one incarnation would not suffice, even if he lived for one hundred years. Even if a magician looks at this from a theoretical point of view, he will conclude that the principals can reveal the highest level of wisdom and allow him to acquire the greatest knowledge and understanding. He will also realize that they can supply him with the highest powers that open up and pave the way to the greatest magical abilities. There is nothing on this earth that a magician is not capable of achieving, since he can call all the keys of wisdom, authority and power his own. It is within his powers to fulfil all wishes.

Chapter 4
The Intelligences Of
The Lunar Sphere

Once the magician has become familiar with the zone girdling the earth to the extent that he is at least in contact with some of the principals, especially the masters of magic, only then should he proceed to contact the intelligences of the sphere of the Moon. This is achieved by mental travel or through a carefully prepared evocation, either on our physical world or in the zone girdling the earth; or he may even strive to contact the intelligences of the Moon sphere directly. At this point the magician should take instructions from one of the many principals of the zone girdling the earth in regards to the Moon sphere, i.e. in order to control the Moon sphere he must undergo a certain amount of training.

When the magician undertakes his first journey to the Moon sphere, it is best if he is accompanied by a principal of the zone girdling the earth, provided that he is well-versed in rising to other spheres. A personal guide, a guru, can also introduce the magician to the Moon sphere by following the magician in thought during his mental travels or during evocative practice into the Moon sphere. A well-trained magician who has strictly followed the instructions in *Initiation into Hermetics* can proceed to the Moon sphere without an escort and without help, and he does not have to worry about encountering any dangers. In due time the magician becomes accustomed to the vibrations of the Moon sphere, which differ somewhat from the vibrations of the zone girdling the earth, the vibration of the physical world and the vibrations of the kingdom of the elements. As soon as the magician has overcome these initial difficulties he will be at home in the Moon sphere, just as in all the other spheres.

The Moon is the closest to our earth and, as a satellite, the Moon is completely dependent upon earth. Through mental travel, the magician will discover there are no living beings and no vegetation and therefore no human beings on the side of the Moon facing the earth. The Moon is surrounded by the Moon zone, which is called the Moon sphere by initiates, as the earth is surrounded by the zone girdling the earth. The Moon sphere, like the zone girdling the earth, is inhabited by countless beings of various ranks. It is not possible to list and describe all the beings of this sphere, because it would surpass the scope of this book. The initiates of the Moon sphere, like the initiates of the zone girdling the earth, have to fulfil various tasks for Divine Providence, and they are endowed with special authorities and powers. They also have the ability to release particular causes and effects directly in the Moon sphere and on our earth. Some intelligences of the Moon sphere have particular tasks to fulfil on other planets and in their respective spheres.

Some principals of the zone girdling the earth can already enlighten the magician about Moon magic. It does not have to be emphasized that the Moon, in its orbit around our earth, quickly passes through the various electromagnetic force fields and vibrations of its aura and the aura of our earth; yes, one could say that the Moon traverses directly through it and influences the existence and the destiny of planet earth.

A spheric magician can calculate the influence of the Moon in the four degrees of the ecliptic, i.e. the zone girdling the earth. Due to his knowledge of the laws of analogy, the spheric magician can likewise calculate the Moon's influence upon the zone girdling the earth and on our world. It is entirely at the discretion of the magician as to how he makes use of these influences. Spheric magic is not at all pure fantasy; instead, it is a very secretive knowledge and only the Kabbalah can be put on the same level.

Now I shall describe the 28 principals of the Moon sphere who exert the greatest influence upon the zone girdling the earth and on our physical world in all three planes of human existence. In many instances these intelligences are considered to be the rulers of the 28 Moon stations and they are well known to the Kabbalistic astrologer in a positive and a negative sense. There are 28 positive principals and 28 negative principals of the Moon sphere. The positive principals have the task of creating good causes and effects, whereas the negative principals do exactly the opposite. In order to prevent any misuse, I shall only describe the positive principals of the Moon sphere. If it seems to be desirable for the magician, he can then contact the negative principals on a temporary basis without having to risk his life or soul. Only very few initiates know the names and seals of the principals of the Moon sphere. All my statements are based on numerous personal contacts with all the beings and principals of all the spheres, which includes the beings and principals of the Moon sphere.

The 28 Principals Of
The Lunar Sphere

Fig. 1: *Ebvap* – is the name of the first principal of the Moon sphere. One of his duties is to monitor the regularity of ebb and tide. *Ebvap* is an excellent initiator into the electric and magnetic fluids and how they can be utilized in Moon magic. If the magician attentively follows the explanations of this principal and follows his instructions exactly, he will be able to accomplish almost miraculous things in the zone girdling the earth and on our physical world, i.e. in all three planes, the mental, astral and physical. This is accomplished with the help of the magnetic influences of the Moon in connection with the electric fluid of the earth. Besides that, *Ebvap* protects the magician with his subordinates from all unfavorable influences which could occur when he is working with the lunar influences. The first principal of the Moon sphere can give the magician information about many mysteries which to this very day are still unknown.

Fig. 2: *Emtircheyud* – is the second principal of the Moon sphere. He monitors the rhythm of our physical world. This principal has this rhythm produced in the causal world through the appropriate intelligences of the zone girdling the earth. The magician learns from this principal the laws of biorhythm and periodicity on our earth and also their utilization for mantic and magical purposes. The magician will also learn about the relationship of the nine-month pregnancy period to the Kabbalistic number nine, which is the number of the Moon and to which it has a special significance. The magician will also receive precise information in regards to the analogies of a woman's menstrual cycle in respect to the Moon, about periodicity, polarity and many other pertinent facts in this regard.

Fig. 3: *Ezhesekis* – is the third principal of the Moon sphere. The magician will learn from this principal how to secure good fortunes for himself and everything that is good in the Akasha Principle through the reciprocal influences of the Moon sphere. Since the influence of this principal is predominantly extended to the physical world, with his servants he helps the magician attain good fortunes and success in all his earthly undertakings.

Fig. 4: *Emvatibe* – is the fourth principal of the Moon sphere. He protects the magician from all acts of maliciousness and vengeance of those who are hostile. *Emvatibe* or his subordinates, which he gladly places at the disposal of the magician as *spiritus familiaris*, will disclose to the magician all secret plans of his enemies in advance, and all acts of vengeance and maliciousness. He also gives the magician advice on how he can protect himself from deceitful human beings. *Emvatibe's* spirit-servants possess the ability to stop all acts of vengeance at the onset. *Emvatibe* entrusts the mature magician with magical formulas, i.e. magical words, with which he can instantly paralyze any person, and if necessary entire groups of people. Indeed, these magical formulas will give the magician the power to kill. This does not require the presence of the magician; he can accomplish this even over great distances. The person for whom this is intended will die instantaneously of a heart attack. It should also be understood that these kinds of magical formulas can also cause temporary or lifelong paralysis. It should also be obvious that these formulas can only be entrusted to a magician who would *never* misuse them.

Fig. 5: *Amzhere* – is the fifth principal of the Moon sphere. This principal can secure for the magician the good graces and protection of high public figures, besides many other things. *Amzhere* will entrust the magician with simple Kabbalistic methods with which he will be able to melt even a heart made of stone, and turn an enemy promptly into a friend. He allows love and sympathy to emerge in anyone who is of interest to the magician. The magician can also make any person he wishes compliant.

Fig. 6: *Enchede* – is the sixth principal of the Moon sphere. *Enchede* gives rise to love in people who are not magically schooled, i.e. a man to a woman and vice versa. However, when it comes to a magically schooled magician he teaches him the mysteries of sexual magic as it applies to Moon magic. Besides that, *Enchede* instructs the magician how to load all kinds of talismans and amulets, which are prepared with a fluid con-denser, in a magical manner through sexual magic with the influences of the Moon for various purposes, especially for the purpose of attaining love, sympathy, having strong attractive powers, popularity etc.

Fig. 7: *Emrudue* – is the seventh principal of the Moon sphere. Should a magically untrained person constantly wear the seal of this principal on his person, it will bring him good fortune and success and it will especially fulfil his earthly wishes. The seal must be made and engraved on a silver plate during the astrological time period of the seventh Moon station. When a magically schooled magician contacts this principal, *Emrudue* will disclose how he can realize all his wishes with the help of Moon magic, whether these wishes concern the mental, astral or physical worlds. *Emrudue* will help the magician attain good fortune and success and he will gladly place his subordinates as *spiritus familiaris* at the magician's disposal.

Fig. 8: *Eneye* – is the eighth principal of the Moon sphere. He is an outstanding authority of all diplomatic and political events. He can help a magician in this respect by assisting him in embarking on a political career and becoming successful in all diplomatic matters. Above all, this principal loves peace; that is why in times of war he stands beside anyone who pursues the highest ideals of peace, truth and justice. Any magician who pursues and is active in this respect can win any dispute, any war, with the help of this principal. It does not really matter in which manner these disputes or wars were conducted.

Fig. 9: *Emzhebyp* – is the ninth principal of the Moon sphere. He is a very special friend and protector of the ailing whose ailments were caused by the unfavorable influences of the Moon or the negative beings of the Moon sphere. These ailments are usually epileptic seizures, menstrual problems, obsession, possession, insanity, hysteria, Saint Vitus' Dance, somnambulism, and the like. This principal will instruct a magician how to cure these diseases with the help of Moon magic.

Fig. 10: *Emnymar* – is the tenth principal of the Moon sphere. It is the responsibility of this principal to monitor the entire duration of pregnancy and the birth of humans. Together with the appropriate principal of the zone girdling the earth, *Emnymar* sees to it that human beings will see the light of day i.e. will be born. That is why all gynecologists and

282

obstetricians, midwives and their assistants are under his influence. He also reveals to the magician how he can induce a painless delivery in a magical manner whenever the magician deems it necessary. He will also reveal, while the child is still in the mother's womb, whether the child is a boy or a girl. The magician can also find out from this principal the precise point in time for copulation during which a boy or girl can be procreated consciously. *Emnymar* is also the patron of all magnetopaths and those who are in engaged in healing magnetism. He familiarizes the magician with various methods that concern the treatment of ailments with the help of the magnetic fluid. *Emnymar* also has very reliable healing remedies for venereal diseases. If the magician has a good relationship with this principal of the Moon sphere, he can learn a great deal from him.

Fig. 11: *Ebvep* – is the eleventh principal of the Moon sphere. With his methods, *Ebvep* gives the magician the opportunity of magically establishing respect and esteem for himself among individuals, regardless of their position. Furthermore, he teaches the magician to call forth phenomena that would cause horror and fear in any uninitiated person. Although it is not easy to contact this principal directly, a magically well developed magician should succeed. There is also another possibility: he can contact this principal under the guidance of a principal of the zone girdling the earth or his personal guru. Then the magician can discover for himself that this principal is an excellent initiator who can initiate him in phenomenal Moon magic.

Fig. 12: *Emkebpe* – is the twelfth principal of the Moon sphere. He is a great admirer of marital bliss and marital peace. Whatever concerns matters of good fortune, love and sympathy, this principal is somehow involved. He teaches the magician to fully enjoy the high ideals of love and to pass them on to people who are not trained in magic. The magician learns from this principal of the Moon sphere what a magical transmutation of love really is. *Emkebpe* entrusts the magician with the process of producing love amulets, which are loaded with the aid of Moon magic.

Fig. 13: *Emcheba* – is the thirteenth principal of the Moon sphere. He is an outstanding initiator of mummial magic, in as far as it is connected with the influence of the Moon. Therefore, the magician learns from this principal how to connect mummial magic with Moon magic, to work successfully with them and at the same time utilize the magnetic influence of the Moon. This principal instructs the magician in many magical practices, for example, a harmless manner in which astro-magical pacts can be established through mummial magic without the magician having to sell his body and soul. These kinds of astro-magical pacts are carried out with a mummy, where the magician with the help of a fluid condenser calls forth a great variety of effects without affecting himself personally in any way. In this case the magician does not leave any trace in the causal world or in the Akasha that could be detrimental to him personally. This principal has in his possession many other secrets in this respect, and any magician who is interested in and occupies himself with Moon magic would fare well to contact him.

Fig. 14: *Ezhobar* – is the fourteenth principal of the Moon sphere. This principal can be of benefit to the magician in that he can reveal the secret of how to easily develop within himself various occult and magical abilities with the aid of Moon magic, which he can also make use of in other spheres. At the same time the magician learns how to polarize powers and how to levitate himself, other human beings and objects in a very particular manner through Kabbalistic Moon magic by changing the polarity of gravitation. The magician will further learn how to properly interpret symbols that can be seen clairvoyantly in Moon magic. *Ezhobar* teaches the magician to understand and practically master, from a magical-Kabbalistic point of view, all the laws pertaining to the Moon sphere. *Ezhobar* is considered to be a fabulous initiator of Kabbalistic Moon magic.

Fig. 15: *Emnepe* – is the fifteenth principal of the Moon sphere. Any magician who contacts the intelligences of the Moon sphere should not neglect to contact this principal, because he can be initiated into many things which to this point are completely unknown to him. For example, the magician will receive information regarding the kind of influence that the divine virtues have upon the beings of the Moon sphere as well as how the Akasha Principle has an effect in the Moon sphere directly and from there upon the zone girdling the earth. *Emnepe* gladly entrusts the magician with special methods. If the magician follows these methods, he will acquire the ability to read in the Akasha Principle with his mental body while in the Moon sphere and also work there magically. It is not possible to list all the advantages and details that are offered to the magician through an association with this principal. Therefore, it is at the discretion of the magician to contact him.

Fig. 16: *Echotasa* – is the sixteenth principal of the Moon sphere. The magician learns from this principal how to control and force the negative beings of the Moon sphere to absolute obedience, either through evocation or mental travel. *Echotasa* familiarizes the magician with various magical protective measures which not only protect him from any unfavorable influences but also help the magician to become a magical authority and to be respected by positive and negative beings alike. This principal is, in accordance with his character, a very good-natured intelligence who will be quite helpful in every respect to the mature magician, and will therefore reveal the secrets of Moon magic to him.

Fig. 17: *Emzhom* – is the seventeenth principal of the Moon sphere. Magical banishment is one of the peculiarities of Moon magic. Under the seal of secrecy, this principal can give a mature magician precise information on this subject by entrusting him with various Kabbalistic and magical formulas, i.e. banishment formulas. These formulas can be used for a wide variety of purposes. For example, *Emzhom* has in his possession banishment formulas that render any enemy instantly harmless and which prevent thieves from escaping so that they cannot take another step with their stolen goods. There also exist banishment formulas that immediately paralyze any attacker and make him completely lifeless, or banishment formulas that immediately eliminate any negative influence. The magician can also learn banishment formulas that render even the most rapacious wild animal immediately harmless, whether it be an animal of the air, land or water. Besides these, *Emzhom* has an entire selection of banishment formulas which he can reveal to the magician. However, a magician will never make use of these formulas unless he is in grave danger. *Emzhom* is held in high esteem in the Moon sphere and all the beings of the Moon are in great awe of him.

Fig. 18: *Emzhit* – is the eighteenth principal of the Moon sphere. *Emzhit* familiarizes the magician with secret methods that allow him to become invisible with the help of Moon magic, Moon Kabbalah, the beings of the Moon and the Akasha Principle. Besides that, *Emzhit* instructs the magician about the laws of dematerialization and materialization, not only as far as the astral body is concerned, but also physical matter. This principal is considered to be the initiator of magical transmutation.

Fig. 19: *Ezheme* – is the nineteenth principle of the Moon sphere. He is the arch-initiator who thoroughly instructs the magician on all the influences of the lawfulness and analogy of the Moon and the Moon sphere so far as it concerns the zone girdling the earth and our physical world in all three planes, mental, astral and physical. He also teaches the magician how to practically utilize the knowledge that he has acquired through magic and the Kabbalah. The magician can gain much more knowledge and wisdom from this principal than he could ever imagine.

Fig. 20: *Etsacheye* – is the twentieth principle of the Moon sphere. He is an outstanding master of initiation, especially on the subject of ecstasy, ecstasy that is triggered through magic dances and appropriate rituals in connection with Moon magic and Moon Kabbalah. It is known to only a very few initiates that special powers and abilities can be developed through ecstatic dances and rituals, and this principal will point this out to the magician. The magician will learn how to control all the influences of the Moon sphere and how to get the positive and negative beings of the Moon under his control. It is a foregone conclusion that through this, the magician becomes an authority in the Moon sphere.

Fig. 21: *Etamrezh* – is the twenty-first principal of the Moon sphere. From this principal the magician will learn how to make himself firm and resistant with magical and Kabbalistic methods against all visible and invisible enemies, against all influences of the elements etc. The magician acquires what is known as magical untouchability. There is not one person on earth who would be able to attack and cause a magician harm when he works and is under the protection and guidance of this principal. Such a magician is safe from all persecution and all magical attacks. He is in a position to resist the greatest heat — he can walk through an immense fire without a single hair on his head being singed. The magician's body will become as hard as a diamond by following the appropriate methods that are entrusted to him by this principal. From a magical point of view, he has become invulnerable and is the consummate master over his life and death.

Fig. 22: *Rivatim* – is the twenty-second principal of the Moon sphere. He teaches the magician to fully and consciously understand the concept of time and space in the Moon sphere. This enables the magician to immediately transport not only his mental body but also his astral and even his physical body over great distances. A magician who entrusts himself to the guidance of this principal of the Moon sphere can safely walk on the surface of the oceans without sinking, and he can rise into the air and travel to wherever he wishes. In short, he can span any distance with his spirit, soul and physical body. Under these conditions, the concept of time and space begins to fade away for the magician, not only in the spirit but also in the astral and physical bodies, and matter in any respect is no longer an obstacle to him.

Fig. 23: *Liteviche* – is the twenty-third principal of the Moon sphere. A magician who gains the trust of this principal will be initiated into the greatest secrets of magic and the Kabbalah. As a result of this, he will have magical formulas at his disposal with which he can immediately calm the greatest ocean storms and hurricanes, annihilate entire armies, win wars etc. A highly ethical magician will certainly not dare to misuse these magical formulas which have been entrusted to him, for he would only oppose the lawfulness and harm himself. Under the guidance of this principal the magician will attain such powers, not only in the Moon sphere, but also in the zone girdling the earth and on our physical world, which would be incomprehensible to a non-initiated person.

Fig. 24: *Zhevekiyev* – is the twenty-fourth principal of the Moon sphere. He is considered to be the alchemist of this sphere. The magician is initiated by this principal into the effectiveness of the elements on the Moon. Through the ability to control the electromagnetic fluid, the magician is taught the appropriate methods for alchemical transmutation of metals. Furthermore, *Zhevekiyev* will reveal to the magician the secret of true magical rejuvenation of the physical and astral bodies. And he will also explain the laws of life and the laws of death in the Moon sphere, while also taking into consideration the zone girdling the earth and our physical world. Every magician will welcome establishing contact with this principal, because it will offer him many advantages.

Fig. 25: *Lavemezhu* – is the twenty-fifth principal of the Moon sphere. It is the task of this principal to influence and control the world of plants. He reveals to the magician all the mysteries of life, germination and growth, and he teaches him how to control the plant kingdom through Moon magic. This will give the magician the ability to promote, accelerate or stop growth. With the help of Moon magic and certain Kabbalistic formulas, a magician who follows the instructions of this principal will be able to make an entire field, regardless of size, so fruitful that it by far exceeds any expectations, or he can also do the opposite and transform it into a desert.

Fig. 26: *Empebyn* – is the twenty-sixth principal of the Moon sphere. When a magician contacts this principal, he reserves the right to explain the causes and effects of the Sun and its light in a mental, astral and physical respect upon the Moon itself, the Moon sphere, as well as the effects of these influences upon the zone girdling the earth and also on our physical world, its mineral, plant and animal kingdoms. *Empebyn* will give the magician information about the influences of sunlight upon the

Moon and reflecting from there to our human body, in a mental, astral and physical respect, and *Empebyn* also teaches the magician how to use all this knowledge magically.

Fig. 27: *Emzhabe* – is the twenty-seventh principal of the Moon sphere. He teaches the magician about all those minerals on our earth that are analogously connected with the Moon itself and the Moon sphere. An association with *Emzhabe* can have great advantages for the magician, because he is a fabulous initiator when it comes to the mastery of Moon magic.

Fig. 28: *Emzher* – is the twenty-eighth and last principal of the Moon sphere. The magician learns from this principal how to completely control the Water element in the Moon sphere and on our physical world through Moon magic and the Kabbalah. Not only will the magician reach the level where he attains power over all living animals in the water, he will also become master over the temperature. A magician who works with this principal can be doused with boiling water without suffering any burns. Under *Emzher's* tutelage the magician will also be able to change boiling hot water into ice in the greatest summer heat.

This concludes the description of the 28 principals of the Moon sphere. The first time these principals are evoked, their seals must be drawn in white or in a silvery color. A magician who has already become master of the zone girdling the earth should not neglect to contact at least a few principals of the Moon sphere, because it will not be to his detriment; instead, it will offer him great advantages.

Chapter 5
The 72 Genii Of
The Mercurian Zone

The Mercurian sphere is the next sphere that awaits the magician. The magician must pass through this sphere and learn to control it. In order to withstand the influences and the vibrations of the Mercurian sphere, the magician must be able to completely control the influences and vibrations of the previous sphere, the Moon sphere. Besides the description of the individual genii of this zone, there are also some references made which will be of interest to the magician.

One of the greatest initiates before Christ was without a doubt the Egyptian high priest, Hermes Trismegistos. He left with his book of wisdom, which is known as Thoth, the highest knowledge known to mankind. It is also the most exalted knowledge that will ever be understood by humans on this planet. His *Tabula Smaragdina*, i.e. the Hermes Tablet, serves as proof of the macrocosmic and microcosmic laws of analogy. This knowledge, which is known as "Hermetic knowledge," was named after Hermes Trismegistos, although it has always been available only to those who have reached the level of maturity that is necessary for initiation. The book of wisdom, which was authored by this high initiate, originally consisted of 78 tablets, which later became commonly known as the 78 Tarot cards. In spite of the fact that in time these Tarot cards were degraded to mere gaming cards, the secret meaning of the Tarot is known to this very day to a chosen few.

A magician who meditates will discover that there is a certain connection between the 78 Tarot cards and the 72 genii of the Mercurian zone, whereas the 6 remaining cards are to be attributed as follows: 4 cards to the elements and 2 cards to polarity.

The first Tarot card is symbolic of the spiritual development of a human being. My first work, *Initiation into Hermetics,* contains a system that has been devised in a very precise manner, especially for this kind of development.

The second Tarot card refers to contact with the spiritual beings of all spheres. The practice of the procedure of how to contact these be-ings is explained and described in this book.

The third Tarot card refers to the cosmic language, which is the Kabbalah, about which I give a detailed account in my third work *The Key to the True Kabbalah.*

In accordance with the written records that are still available, Hermes Trismegistos was a representative of the highest knowledge. He was a shining example of human intelligence with an enlightened intellect corresponding to the Mercurian sphere, because this sphere is ascribed to the immortal spirit and therefore it is also analogous to the immortal spirit.

Although the 72 genii of the Mercurian sphere are numerically in accord with the original Tarot cards, they are not represented, one after the other, by various Tarot cards. Instead, all 72 genii together form only a portion of the second Tarot card. It has already been mentioned that the entirety of spherical magic is represented by the second Tarot card. However, there is a very secret Kabbalistic key to the Mercurian sphere concealed in the numerical connection of the 72 genii with the 78 Tarot cards.

Many Kabbalists mistakenly consider the 72 genii of the Mercurian sphere as the *Shemhamphorasch*, which is the unspeakable name of God, composed of 72 letters. Rather, the *Shemhamphorasch* is the unspeakable name of God, as expressed through the four syllable-letters, YOD-HEH-VAU-HEH, the well known Tetragrammaton or Adonai.

True initiates and Kabbalists are well aware of the fact that nomenclatures which also have numbers affixed to them are numerical keys which refer to the proper use of the methods and directions given. The magician will find the details in *The Key to the True Kabbalah,* which deals with Kabbalistic mysticism and formula magic, i.e. the practice of Theurgy.

The Cosmic Order
Of Precedence

The following represents a small overall view of the cosmic hierarchical order, which will also refer to the zone of Mercury and its sphere. It will familiarize the magician with the structure of our universe from a magical-Kabbalistic point of view, i.e. the Hermetic point of view.

Earth: Our physical world, with its three kingdoms, mineral, plant and animal, is the lowest of the spheres. The physical body of a human being has an analogous connection with these three kingdoms.

Moon: As a planet, the Moon influences all the liquids on our earth. However, the Moon sphere is also analogous to the astral body and the astral matrix of a human being. On the other hand, the zone girdling the earth also has an effect upon the vital energy of a human being.

Mercury: Mercury influences the gaseous state of our earth. The mental body of an individual is subject to the Mercurian sphere.

Venus: As a planet, Venus influences the fruitfulness of our earth in the plant and animal kingdoms. On the other hand, the Venusian sphere is responsible for the sympathy, love and reproduction of mankind.

Sun: As a planet, the Sun influences the physical life on our planet in all three kingdoms, whereas the sphere of the Sun maintains the life of the mental, astral and physical bodies through the individual matrices.

Mars: The influencing of all powers, forces or energies in all three kingdoms is subject to Mars. As a planet, Mars has the greatest effect in the animal kingdom and on human beings in the form of self-preservation, i.e. survival instinct, whereas the Martian sphere awakens the impulse and propensity for life within a human being. The Martian sphere affects one's character, attributes, and all energies, powers and abilities.

Jupiter: As a planet, Jupiter has an effect on harmony and lawfulness, whereas the sphere of Jupiter controls the karmic evolution and righteousness or fairness in a person, guides him on his path to perfection and in his endeavor to strive for the highest in accordance with his maturity.

Saturn: On our earth, Saturn, as a planet, has an effect upon the destiny of all three kingdoms, mineral, plant and animal. In its most subtle form here on earth, Saturn is known as ether. On the other hand, the Saturnian sphere controls the destiny of human beings, also known as karma. Humans are indebted to this sphere for its greatest influence, which is the gift of intuition by which Divine Providence reveals Herself in accordance with the individual's maturity. Divine Providence also expresses Herself in the conscience of those who are not magically schooled.

Uranus: The planet Uranus is responsible for magical development on our earth, whereas the Uranian sphere allows human beings to recognize all the phenomena of magic.

Neptune: Neptune keeps the cosmic order of precedence of planet earth in equilibrium. Human beings are indebted to the influence of the Neptune sphere, which gives mankind the knowledge of the path of perfection, but also the knowledge of the cosmic language, i.e. the Kabbalah.

Only the Divine Light, the incomprehensible and the indescribable, is beyond these spheres, and that is what we call Divine Providence. In our cosmic order of precedence there is nothing higher.

In the Kabbalah the cosmic order of precedence with all its influences is known as the Kabbalistic Tree of Life. My third work, *The Key to the True Kabbalah,* contains more details and also describes the practice of the Kabbalah.

Going back for a moment to the Mercurian zone, let me reiterate that the Mercurian sphere is analogous to the mental sphere of human beings. That is why the genii of the Mercurian sphere exert the greatest influence upon the spirit, i.e. the mental body, of a human being. If, for example, a genius of the Mercurian zone wanted to have an effect upon the astral sphere of a human being, he would have to make the effort and assert his influence in accordance with the laws of analogy by way of the Moon sphere and then the zone girdling the earth. Even a magician would have to follow the same laws of analogy. The 72 genii of the Mercurian zone are the subject matter in many Kabbalistic works; however, they are depicted as independent genii without any affiliation to a particular sphere. The true significance of the 72 genii of the Mercurian zone was not known to any of the many authors of these writings, nor were any of them in touch personally with the genii. Although the names of the genii are correct, there are great differences in the drawings of the seals which

so that it is doubtful whether they were ever passed on in
_ ial form.

In order that we do not have to be satisfied merely with assumptions, and to save time for any additional explorations, I have personally contacted all 72 genii of the Mercurian zone. As a result of that, I can now provide the magician with their true seals and a short description of their spheres of influence. You will notice that the seals of the genii also have some letters; these letters contain secret keys and these keys will be explained to the magician by the particular genius when he contacts him. At the first evocation, the seals of these genii are generally drawn in yellow. However, in talismanology it is important that the seals be reproduced in the colors as depicted in this book. Sometimes it occurs that individual genii request that their seals be drawn in another color, which the magician must honor under all circumstances.

The 72 Genii Of
The Mercurian Zone

Fig. 1: *Vehuiah* – is the name of the first genius of the Mercurian sphere. From this genius the magician will learn how to attain an iron will and make his belief as solid as a rock, in order to increase his powers of conviction to such a degree that he can perform absolute miracles. The magician can also find out from this genius in which manner he can easily and quickly attain magical abilities of a special kind.

Fig. 2: *Jeliel* – is the name of the second genius of the Mercurian sphere. He initiates the magician into the mysteries of sympathy and love. Since he has all the secret mysteries of sexual magic under his control, he is prepared to reveal them at any time to a mature magician. Through contact with this genius the magician learns how to change animosity into friendship, awaken and increase love in a magical manner in a man and in a woman and, should it prove necessary, have love subside again, and how to become a consummate master of love. The magician will also be able to prompt thieves to return stolen goods, banish murderers and criminals in various ways, cause and stop earthquakes, understand, master and speak every language in the world through special methods, attain esteem and respect, power and wealth, and also have unworthy people lose their reputations and wealth. Contact with this genius assures the magician of many advantages.

Fig. 3: *Sitael* – is the name of the third genius of the Mercurian sphere. He is an authority on the subject of hypnosis, suggestion and spiritual telepathy. Through this genius a magician can attain the ability to become absolute master over man and animal, namely through deception, illusion etc. In addition, the magician will learn the art of easily reading the past, present and future in the Akasha Principle.

Fig. 4: *Elemiah* – is the name of the fourth genius of the Mercurian sphere. This genius teaches the magician how to become master over his own destiny and also how to be in control of the destiny of any person or animal. Furthermore, the magician learns to load magical words through Kabbalistic methods and to transfer them into the Akasha Principle, in order to attain the desired influence in the mental, astral and physical worlds, and to contact the departed through various methods of passive communication.

Fig. 5: *Mahasiah* – is the name of the fifth genius of the Mercurian sphere. With special Kabbalistic methods he teaches the magician how to completely control the elements and to produce all kinds of phenomena with very little effort, to successfully treat incurable diseases with magic and Kabbalah, to understand the laws of analogy of the macrocosm and microcosm and derive profound wisdom therefrom.

Fig. 6: *Lelahel* – is the name of the sixth genius of the Mercurian sphere. As the initiator of the sexual mysteries, he teaches the magician to load things magically with the aid of sexual magic. This genius is especially fond of talismans and amulets, which are loaded through love magic. He directs the magician's attention to all aids that can be used for this purpose. He gives the magician detailed information about all fields of knowledge on our earth. He teaches the magician how to produce talismans for good luck and protection in a very particular way. This genius is well disposed towards all artists, and should the magician be an artist, then he will be especially inspired by this genius.

Fig. 7: *Achaiah* – is the name of the seventh genius of the Mercurian sphere. He teaches the magician to effortlessly remove any obstacles, how to quickly advance in magic, to change enemies into friends, how to make friends, to call forth love and how to read the destiny of individuals and of entire nations in the Akasha Principle.

Fig. 8: *Kahetel* – is the name of the eighth genius of the Mercurian sphere. He teaches the magician how to control the electromagnetic fluid through the magic of the elements, so that the magician can call forth various kinds of phenomena in nature. The magician also learns from this genius how to influence the growth of plants through the electromagnetic fluid in a positive and negative manner. This genius entrusts the magician with certain magical words, i.e. magical formulas, which he can utter in order to cause and stop rain, snow, thunderstorms, hail etc.

Fig. 9: *Aziel* – is the name of the ninth genius of the Mercurian sphere. He teaches the magician about divine justice and divine mercy, and he also shows the magician the extent of effectiveness of these two divine virtues on all planes and spheres. Under the guidance of this genius the magician learns to reconcile enemies, to call forth love and make peace. The magician may also learn how to protect himself in a magical manner from his greatest enemy and his attacks, and how to acquire honor, wealth and fame. The magician receives from *Aziel* information about everything that is under the surface of the earth, whether hidden treasure, metals or subterranean waters.

Fig. 10: *Aladiah* – is the name of the tenth genius of the Mercurian sphere. He teaches the magician about the occult anatomy of a human being, about harmony and disharmony, and he teaches him how to protect himself Kabbalistically from disharmonious influences. Furthermore, he teaches the magician how to determine the causes of ailments and successfully treat any kind of ailment. *Aladiah* is a very good initiator of chemistry and alchemy and of magic and Kabbalah. He instructs the magician how to use powers and plants for various kinds of magical practices.

Fig. 11: *Lauviah* – is the name of the eleventh genius of the Mercurian sphere. He entrusts the magician with banishment formulas which allow the magician to control severe storms, and to control and banish enemies. As an initiator, *Lauviah* instructs the magician in warfare. He also instructs the magician in which manner he can become an authority in magic and how he can acquire honor and fame. This genius helps the magician solve the most difficult problems with amazing ease.

Fig. 12: *Hahaiah* – is the name of the twelfth genius of the Mercurian sphere. As the initiator of the laws of analogy, he teaches the magician the language of all symbols, even to completely comprehend and therefore correctly explain the most complicated symbols and also how to properly express any idea in the form of symbols. He shows the magician how to solve the most difficult problems in the Hermetic sciences and he reveals profound truths and secret mysteries which to this day are only understood by very few magicians. This genius is also an excellent initiator in magic and Kabbalah. On account of his powers he can turn the greatest foe into a friend and strengthen the bond of love between friends, etc.

Fig. 13: *Jezalel* – is the name of the thirteenth genius of the Mercurian sphere. He helps all authors and artists by inspiring them in their artistic endeavors, and he also helps them to achieve sweeping successes. He shows the magician ways that allow him to develop a talent for eloquent speech. After having awakened and developed the talent to articulate, he helps politicians to climb the ladder of political success and reach the top. This genius has at his disposal particular methods that lead to a clear intellect and a good memory and which allow the magician to acquire an excellent perceptiveness and a talent for repartee in every respect. Through *Jezalel* the magician has the possibility to obtain the good graces of personalities in high positions and to be successful in love affairs, to discover the secret plans of his enemies, and so on.

Fig. 14: *Mebahel* – is the name of the fourteenth genius of the Mercurian sphere. This genius allows wars to be won and realizes plans for peace. He inspires politicians and allows them to realize their plans. As a special friend of justice, this genius is a protector of injustice and in legal matters or matters of the courts he helps to achieve justice. He helps prisoners who are innocent get out of jail. The magician learns from this genius the art of mind reading. Furthermore, the magician will learn to detect and control his pursuers and enemies.

Fig. 15: *Hariel* – is the name of the fifteenth genius of the Mercurian sphere. *Hariel* is an outstanding initiator of occult philosophy, of magic and the Kabbalah. In the Mercurian sphere he is an initiator of evocation. He gives the magician the means to protect himself against the negative beings of the Mercurian sphere. *Hariel* teaches the magician to make use of the influence of the Mercurian zone inductively and deductively in all three planes of our existence. As a great friend of peace, this genius gives rise to circumstances that bring about peace, as it becomes necessary. Should the magician require the protection of personalities in high positions, this genius will be able to secure this for him.

Fig. 16: *Hakamiah* – is the name of the sixteenth genius of the Mercurian sphere. He helps the magician through occult means to acquire honor, fame, high esteem and wealth. Should the magician request it, *Hakamiah* will secure him the love of women and entrust him with methods on how he can successfully treat women who suffer from infertility, and he will also give the magician the appropriate amulets for this purpose.

Fig. 17: *Lanoiah* – is the name of the seventeenth genius of the Mercurian sphere. The magician learns from this genius how to view the past, present and future in the Akasha Principle, in particular all technological inventions. Various new inventions in technology, chemistry and electricity have been made on account of the inspiration of this genius. He helps musicians and composers through intuition to achieve great successes in their art as well as with the audiences. *Lanoiah* is considered to be an excellent initiator of sound magic. The magician will find in *Lanoiah* a teacher of cosmic metaphysics.

Fig. 18: *Kaliel* – is the name of the eighteenth genius of the Mercurian sphere. This genius is an outstanding initiator of high magic and Kabbalah. A magician who contacts this genius will achieve great things through him. For example, he will receive magical formulas which the magician has only to utter should the situation demand it, whereupon a Mercurian being will momentarily come to his aid. In magic these formulas are known as the "magical-Kabbalistic distress call." However, a magician will only make use of these magical formulas in cases of great danger, because he can completely annihilate his enemies in an instant with such a distress call. *Kaliel* instructs the magician about the various kinds of formula magic, for example, how mental, astral and physical invisibility can be achieved through the appropriate magical formulas. Furthermore, the magician will learn how to dematerialize himself mentally, astrally and physically and become visible again at a distant location. *Kaliel* teaches the magician to span time and space and become the consummate master in the Akasha. Should the magician request it, *Kaliel* will point out all the herbs and precious gems and stones that are necessary for magical knowledge. He will also instruct the magician how to use these herbs and precious stones as fluid condensers in alchemy, and how to load the stones magically. The magician will also find in this genius a friend, a helper and an advisor in every respect.

Fig. 19: *Leuviah* – is the name of the nineteenth genius of the Mercurian sphere. The magician learns from this genius how to attain a high level of intelligence, an excellent memory and fabulous powers of judgement. Should a magician make a mistake in his dealings or actions, this genius will help him to correct his mistake. Furthermore, the magician will learn how to awaken and reinforce love in men and women, friend and foe through magical-Kabbalistic methods.

Fig. 20: *Pahaliah* – is the name of the twentieth genius of the Mercurian sphere. This genius instructs the magician about the lawfulness of the macrocosm and microcosm, initiates him into the evolution of human beings, and explains the actual value of asceticism and magical equilibrium. Furthermore, he explains to the magician the synthesis of all religious systems that exist on our earth from the Hermetic point of view, so that the magician is able to distinguish the chaff from the wheat. Furthermore, *Pahaliah* gives the magician the opportunity to be cognizant of the various effects which the divine virtues have in all three planes.

Fig. 21: *Nelekael* – is the name of the twenty-first genius of the Mercurian sphere. *Nelekael* is an outstanding initiator of the entire Hermetic sciences. He helps occult authors in that he gives them plenty of inspiration and he also bestows upon them a good imagination. He provides the sincere seeker of truth with the appropriate study material and he creates the opportunity for such a person to come into contact with a real teacher of magic, i.e. a guru. *Nelekael's* methods, instructions and formulas provide protection from negative influences of any sphere. This genius gives precise information about the magical powers of herbs and precious stones which are of particular importance for magic, Kabbalah and alchemy, and he also gives precise information about the effectiveness of the Akasha Principle and provides the method of how to read in the Akasha Principle.

Fig. 22: *Jeiaiel* – is the name of the twenty-second genius of the Mercurian sphere. He helps the magician attain wealth and high esteem through magic and Kabbalah, and he allows the magician to become famous, provided that he harbors such a wish. At work and while traveling, he ensures success and entrusts the magician with protective means which safeguard him from accidents. A talisman that is made and worn in accordance with the instructions given by this genius will protect anyone from injustice and accidents. Should the magician be an inventor, he will find in this genius a fabulous initiator, besides which he will show the magician anything in the past, present and future, should it be of interest to him.

Fig. 23: *Melahel* – is the name of the twenty-third genius of the Mercurian sphere. *Melahel* entrusts the magician with Kabbalistic formulas that protect him from any weapon. Amulets that are made in accordance with the instructions of this genius protect the wearer from ambush, muggings and assaults while traveling. Furthermore, this genius has Kabbalistic formulas at his disposal which momentarily extinguish any large blaze, and whoever is in possession of these Kabbalistic formulas will be able to endure the greatest heat or fire without singeing one single hair. This genius is also well-versed in phytotherapy, i.e. healing with herbs; hence, he can give the magician excellent herbal remedies, for example, a blend of herbs and the proper dosages for treating diseases.

Fig. 24: *Hahuiah* – is the name of the twenty-fourth genius of the Mercurian sphere. The magician receives from this genius banishment formulas to control even the most dangerous animals, to influence thieves to return stolen goods, to have murderers confess their shameful deeds, etc. A single magic word will instantaneously place a murderer into a state of complete paralysis. This genius is an excellent initiator in magic and Kabbalah, and he familiarizes the magician with the various magical arts and entrusts him with methods that allow him to awaken and unfold the talent of eloquent speech in other persons. This genius also helps to win back honors and dignities that were lost. Since this genius is well-versed in formula magic, he has at his disposal the most multifarious formulas, i.e. protective formulas. Some formulas regarding Kabbalistic mysticism I shall disclose to the reader in *The Key to the True Kabbalah*.

Fig. 25: *Nith-Haiah* – is the name of the twenty-fifth genius of the Mercurian sphere. *Nith-Haiah* is the greatest arch-initiator of the Mercurian sphere as far as magic and the Kabbalah are concerned, and he also strictly protects all the secret mysteries. He makes certain that not one single immature person is given the *abhisheka,* i.e. the knowledge or cognizance of magic and the Kabbalah. However, he initiates a mature magician into the most profound mysteries of these subjects. He also makes it possible for the magician to recognize the most profound secrets of the cosmic order of the worlds, and the magician will learn how to make practical use of these laws. The magician will find in this genius an arch-initiator of all knowledge, as well as the greatest wisdom that can be made available to a human being. *Nith-Haiah* is the guardian of all magicians on our earth.

Fig. 26: *Haaiah* – is the name of the twenty-sixth genius of the Mercurian sphere. As the guardian of justice, he will allow a magician who is in contact with him to win any court case as long as the magician is within his rights. *Haaiah* is a friend of high diplomacy and he will help a magician attain a high position in this field, provided that the magician belongs to the diplomatic profession. The magician will also find out from this genius the manner in which he can attain the good graces of personalities in high positions, how he can attain knowledge and wealth, and how to respond to his opponents in order to reveal all treason, all secret talks, plans and undertakings.

Fig. 27: *Jerathel* – is the name of the twenty-seventh genius of the Mercurian sphere. This genius can bestow upon the magician an excellent talent for languages and can also secure for him the favor of friend and foe. He allows the magician to view, in the Akasha Principle, what his opponents have in mind and how he can protect himself from them. For this purpose he entrusts the magician with various kinds of banishment formulas. Should the magician be engaged as an author, he can help him become famous by bestowing upon him an excellent perceptiveness; or he can show him how this can easily be attained.

Fig. 28: *Seeiah* – is the name of the twenty-eighth genius of the Mercurian sphere. *Seeiah* can entrust the magician with power formulas which, when employed, will cause thunder and lightning, cause and stop severe thunderstorms, and cause or extinguish severe fires, even at the greatest distance. The magician may even choose the location. He can destroy entire cities, or he can protect cities and houses that they remain untouched, for instance, in times of war. No one ever need worry about any misuse of these formulas, because never will the mysteries be released to an immature person. A magician who is in contact with this genius does not have to worry about anything because he is under special protection.

Fig. 29: *Reiiel* – is the name of the twenty-ninth genius of the Mercurian sphere. He is the genius who makes the greatest truths accessible and understandable to the magician. Furthermore, *Reiiel* makes the magician aware of the plans of his enemies, whether they be visible or invisible, and he gives him advice as to how he can protect himself from them and how he can change their minds and make friends out of them. This genius is prepared to reveal many secrets to the magician which have remained undisclosed to this very day. The magician can also receive from this genius information about the cosmic hierarchy and the reciprocal effect of its powers.

Fig. 30: *Omael* – is the name of the thirtieth genius of the Mercurian sphere. He is a great friend of the animal kingdom. Consequently, he can give the magician many remedies with which he can successfully treat sick animals. This genius is also well disposed toward physicians, in particular gynecologists and surgeons, and should this be a magician's profession he will bestow upon him excellent skills and will also initiate him into occult anatomy and medicine. *Omael* is also well-versed in chemistry and alchemy, and the magician can profit greatly from this genius in this field of endeavor. *Omael* gives the magician detailed information about prenatal education. A magician who is in contact with this genius will never suffer from any plight or grief, and he will always feel the favorable influence of his guardian.

Fig. 31: *Lekabel* – is the name of the thirty-first genius of the Mercurian sphere. He is an initiator and therefore he initiates the magician into love magic and all sexual mysteries. Besides that, *Lekabel* can teach the magician Kabbalah and talismanology, and how to acquire various magical abilities through the Akasha Principle or by utilizing light, for example, clairvoyance, invisibility etc. The magician will also find in *Lekabel* an excellent teacher of alchemy. Should the magician follow the instructions of this genius, he will be able to prolong his life at his discretion. There are many more advantages which present themselves to the magician by being in contact with this genius of the Mercury sphere; for example, the magician can become wealthy after this genius allows him to discover valuable treasures under the earth. The magician will learn in a magical manner how to coerce thieves to return stolen goods or else give themselves away. The magician will also be entrusted by this genius with methods whereby he can develop the talent to become a fabulous orator etc.

Fig. 32: *Vasariah* – is the name of the thirty-second genius of the Mercurian sphere. The magician finds in him a multifarious initiator and guardian whom he can summon at any time. He helps the magician to attain his rights; *Vasariah* will urge thieves, robbers and liars to tell the truth. *Vasariah* has the ability to bestow upon the magician the talent to become an eloquent speaker and can also teach him the Kabbalistic manner in which these talents can be obtained. In instances of severe danger, *Vasariah* can provide the magician with power formulas or power words, i.e. magical-Kabbalistic formulas, which will render even the greatest assailant harmless. This genius can also instruct the magician in astrophysics, space magic and the Kabbalah as well as in all magical arts. He can also instruct artists in their given fields. He will entrust to the mature magician magical power formulas that will make him invisible and invulnerable to any type of weapon.

Fig. 33: *Jehuiah* – is the name of the thirty-third genius of the Mercurian sphere. This genius can instruct the magician on all earthly sciences. Should the magician have to undergo any examinations, this genius will help him to pass them successfully. He will also show the magician all the occurrences of the past, present and future, and make it possible for him to recognize his enemies. *Jehuiah* teaches him how to turn animosity into friendship, awakens love in men and women, and reinforces love between friends. Furthermore, *Jehuiah* teaches the magician the art of levitation, i.e. how to make practical use of levitation from the magical point of view. He teaches the magician how to dematerialize and materialize bodies and objects, and he also instructs him how to master space magic. *Jehuiah* makes the most profound truths accessible to the magician and, when it comes to a very difficult magical problem, *Jehuiah* will provide the magician with the solution through inspiration.

Fig. 34: *Lehahiah* – is the name of the thirty-fourth genius of the Mercurian sphere. The magician will receive power formulas from this genius that allow him to calm storm spirits, whereby he gets these spirits under his control. He will also become the master over lightning, thunder, and storms on land and water. Should the magician undertake a voyage while under the protection of this genius, the ship will pass through the greatest storms and arrive safely in the harbor. The magician will achieve great deeds while under the guidance of this genius. Upon the magician's special request, *Lehahiah* will initiate him into the most profound divine mysteries and will also entrust the magician with many secrets in magic and Kabbalah, so that tremendous possibilities will unfold for him.

Fig. 35: *Kevakiah* – is the name of the thirty-fifth genius of the Mercurian sphere. This genius will show the magician ways to completely gain control over the most dangerous influences of negative beings. He turns the magician's fiercest enemy into a friend, and wherever there is a yearning for peace, he makes peace — and that applies to individuals as well as nations. Should the magician request it, *Kevakiah* will help him attain honor and wealth.

Fig. 36: *Menadel* – is the name of the thirty-sixth genius of the Mercurian sphere. He is an excellent initiator of synthetic astrology. He will teach a magician how to practically utilize astrological knowledge in spagyric healing and alchemy. He will teach him at which time and for what purpose to make and to load talismans. He will also teach the magician in which manner the desired powers can be banished into precious gemstones through magic and the Kabbalah. In addition, he will give the magician instructions as to the exact time to gather herbs, how to prepare them for healing purposes and magical practices. This genius also has the ability to set prisoners free. It does not matter how the prisoner is incarcerated or where the prison is located. The prison release takes place in a magical manner either by influencing the guards to leave the prison doors open or else by having the prisoner set free through a legal procedure of pardon. *Menadel* provides the magician with good fortune in his chosen profession, with the good graces of personalities in high positions, and a whole array of other things.

Fig. 37: *Aniel* – is the name of the thirty-seventh genius of the Mercurian sphere. He is a friend of poets, dramatists, composers and everything that is connected with the arts. A magician who has an inclination towards the arts can count on this genius' support. The magician can become acquainted with all the sciences on earth, and he can also be initiated into many magical arts. *Aniel* will reveal to the magician the most profound secrets in nature, the entire occult philosophy and the most secretive initiation mysteries in magic and the Kabbalah. *Aniel* awakens in the magician the talent to translate these high mysteries into an intellectual language.

Fig. 38: *Haamiah* – is the name of the thirty-eighth genius of the Mercurian sphere, and is very well liked in that sphere. He willingly opens to a mature magician all spherical treasuries, i.e. he reveals the most profound wisdom through which he leads the magician to the greatest and highest bliss. He helps the magician to make his earthly existence bearable by strengthening his health and providing him with contentment, good fortune and a good reputation. This genius can fulfil any wish the magician might have.

Fig. 39: *Rehael* – is the name of the thirty-ninth genius of the Mercurian sphere. He is a very special initiator of alchemy and occult anatomy. The magician can learn how to prepare the Stone of the Sages through the wet process and the dry process for the purpose of impregnating and rejuvenating the astral and physical bodies. Through this, the magician is given the possibility of prolonging his life as long as he wishes. *Rehael* is a great friend of children and he sees to it that people or parents who love children have a large family. When their children have ailments, he gives the parents or others precise information and he willingly provides them with all the help they require. Whenever the magician requests it, this genius will kindle love and loyalty in those people whom he selects.

Fig. 40: *Ieiazel* – is the name of the fortieth genius of the Mercurian sphere. Should the magician request the release of someone from prison or the rescue of someone from an enemy, he should turn to this genius. *Ieiazel* will support the magician either through direct intervention or by having his subordinates influence those people who have it within their powers to release or liberate those who are imprisoned. The magician will learn many things from *Ieiazel:* for example, how to dematerialize objects at great distances and materialize them again, and how to influence humans, animals and matter itself through element magic. In addition, he will learn how to determine the past, present and future of any thing or any person, how to turn enemies into friends, how to cause and stop thunderstorms with power formulas with which he is entrusted, and how to eliminate any emotional (psychic) disharmony or melancholy with magical formulas etc. This genius is well disposed towards all artists, and he helps them through inspiration to achieve success and makes them well liked by their audiences. The same applies to people who are occupied with publishing books and written works.

Fig. 41: *Hahahel* – is the name of the forty-first genius of the Mercurian sphere. This genius confers success in warfare and allows mankind to come up with new inventions in this field of endeavor, and he helps to discover the plans and projects of one's enemies. Whenever it is necessary, this genius will place the appropriate power formulas at the disposal of the magician to annihilate armies, or to cause and stop thunderstorms. In addition, the magician will learn from *Hahahel* how to raise his energy to an amazing level, how to become invulnerable, and how to recognize the effectiveness of the Akasha Principle in the mental, astral and physical worlds. The magician will be able to increase his magical powers to the highest level by using the methods he receives from this genius, as well as learning how to increase his belief and persuasiveness to such an extent that he will be able to perform miracles.

Fig. 42: *Mikael* – is the name of the forty-second genius of the Mercurian sphere. In order to get his enemies under his control, the magician can receive from this genius magical-Kabbalistic formulas with which he will be able to discover and thwart his enemies' plans. The magician will also learn how to bedazzle his enemies through magic and, through subterfuge, have his enemies do as he wishes. This genius helps politicians and diplomats to embark on a successful career, and in addition he bestows upon them the gift of intuition and premonition.

Fig. 43: *Veubiah* – is the name of the forty-third genius of the Mercurian sphere. The magician learns from this genius how to see through his enemies' schemes and how to thwart all their plans which are directed toward him. On the basis of special magical methods which the magician will receive from this genius, he will learn how to become a complete master over his enemies. Furthermore, he will learn how to make talismans which will protect a soldier from annihilation during an offensive attack in a state of war, and he will also learn through magic and Kabbalah how to heal the worst wounds in a matter of a few moments, and many other things.

Fig. 44: *Ielahiah* – is the name of the forty-fourth genius of the Mercurian sphere. This genius entrusts a magician who is in contact with him with special Kabbalistic formulas with which he can make the blind see, the deaf hear and liberate the insane from their unfortunate state. *Ielahiah* also gives the magician the appropriate instructions to transfer objects over the greatest distances, either by spiritual beings or through dematerialization and materialization. He also teaches the magician how to read correctly in the Akasha Principle, and furthermore to be successful in every respect and realize all wishes for himself and other people.

Fig. 45: *Sealiah* – is the name of the forty-fifth genius of the Mercurian sphere. This genius teaches the magician how to recognize all those who are engaged in sorcery and witchcraft and who evoke negative spiritual beings. *Sealiah* gives the magician methods that enable him to render any attacker or aggressor harmless. The magician can either prevent any hostile plans against himself or he can cover his enemies with a so-called magic cap, which does not permit any magical experiments against him to succeed. *Sealiah* will disclose to the magician the magical method of how a magic cap is made, one which no black magician can penetrate. As with other genii from this sphere, the magician can find out power formulas from *Sealiah* that, when uttered, will cause severe earthquakes which can completely destroy entire cities. However, these kinds of power formulas will never be entrusted to a magician who is ethically undeveloped; therefore there is no danger that these formulas will ever be misused. It is obvious that the magician is master over land and water. He can force thieves to return stolen goods, he can humble the arrogant and prideful, he can help human beings that have been wronged to attain their rights. All these things are feasible for a magician with the help of this genius. *Sealiah* will also allow the magician to become master over this earth.

Fig. 46: *Ariel* – is the name of the forty-sixth genius of the Mercurian sphere. This genius can bestow the gift of prophecy upon the magician. He can guide the magician so that he will completely control the Akasha Principle in regards to viewing the past, present and future, and he will also teach the magician how to load volts, and many other things. Should it be the magician's wish to become wealthy, provided he has a good reason, then this genius will assist him in finding all the treasures on our earth. Not only will *Ariel* do that for the magician, he will also familiarize him with the greatest secrets of nature and the greatest mysteries of life, for example in which manner dreams can arbitrarily be called forth over the greatest distances, how precious stones can be loaded with particular powers, and how any kind of elementary can be created with magical-Kabbalistic methods. *Ariel* can also make it possible for the magician to contact positive beings of other spheres and he can also instruct him in talismanology and other magical arts, which at this point are unknown to the magician.

Fig. 47: *Asaliah* – is the name of the forty-seventh genius of the Mercurian sphere. This genius instructs the magician in the laws of justice and lawfulness and how to recognize them and also to understand them, i.e. he teaches the magician the art of staying constantly in equilibrium in respect to the worldly and the spiritual laws. Besides that, he can teach the magician how to understand the most profound truths. He can show the magician the past lives, the present life and future of any human being in the Akasha. *Asaliah* will gladly familiarize the magician with special methods with which this ability can be developed in a human being. There is no doubt that this genius will help the magician to attain his rights. He can also give rise to love among human beings, strengthen love between friends, change animosity into friendship etc. *Asaliah* can help the magician attain the good graces of personalities in high positions.

Fig. 48: *Mihael* – is the name of the forty-eighth genius of the Mercurian sphere. This genius is considered to be the teacher of alchemy. His particular field of endeavor is transmutation, i.e. the transmutation of metals, and he can instruct the magician on this subject in detail. *Mihael* will disclose methods to the magician with which he can change the oscillations of the electrons of any metal and change even the most inferior metal into gold. One will also learn to work in the exact opposite mode, for example to change the gold and silver of a greedy person into lead or iron through magic and Kabbalah. With this method the magician can also change common stones into precious stones. From this same genius, the magician can learn how to increase and decrease love and passions in men, how to create an atmosphere where human beings have to do whatever the magician wishes them to do, how to eliminate infertility in women, how to make peace, and how to create unity and faithfulness between husband and wife so that no power on earth can separate them except death.

Fig. 49: *Vehuel* – is the name of the forty-ninth genius of the Mercurian sphere. The magician learns from this genius every kind of prophecy from the most simple to the most consummate, namely reading in the Akasha. Not only will the magician become acquainted with these methods, he will also learn how to master them himself. Furthermore, the magician will learn how to increase his consciousness so that he will be able to transfer it anywhere he wishes. He will learn how to immediately read any person's mind, and find out from that person's aura anything he wishes to know about his character in the wink of an eye, regardless whether that person is friend or foe. This genius can teach the magician every method regarding influence. Contact with this genius offers the magician the opportunity to enjoy his life without worries and in peace.

Fig. 50: *Daniel* – is the name of the fiftieth genius of the Mercurian sphere. This genius enables the magician to look into Divine's Providence's workshop and understand the lawfulness and activities and effects of the Akasha Principle. *Daniel* also gives the magician the opportunity to comprehend the effectiveness of the divine virtues, which knowledge enables him to influence the vibrations of love and compassion within himself. Consequently, this will place the magician into a state of bliss, and only one who has been under the guidance of this genius will experience this state. There are also other advantages that arise from having contact with this genius, for example, the magician learns how to distinguish right from wrong or justice from injustice, how to develop good judgement, and how to act prudently in all matters. He will learn to be successful as an author, attain the excellent talent of eloquent speech, attain the talent for repartee, attain the most profound intuition, and recognize the true philosophy in every religious system. This genius will always give the magician the appropriate intuition in critical situations.

Fig. 51: *Hahasiah* – is the name of the fifty-first genius of the Mercurian sphere. He is an arch-initiator of Hermetic knowledge. This genius will give the magician correct information about magic and the Kabbalah, and he will also teach him astrophysics, astro-chemistry and alchemy. In addition he will teach the magician to elevate his spirit to the various planes and spheres and to act consciously in those spheres. On the basis of special methods that the magician receives from this genius, he will be able to make his mental, astral and physical bodies invisible.

Furthermore, the magician will be able to change particular causes in the Akasha Principle in order to avert the consequences. There are also additional advantages that the magician will derive from contact with this genius. He will learn how to prepare various healing remedies, be they spagyric or alchemical herbal mixtures or medicinal-pharmaceutical preparations. Should the magician's field be the art of healing, he can develop into an excellent physician under the guidance of this genius, and he will have success in healing his fellow man, and he will enjoy a great popularity among his patients.

Fig. 52: *Imamiah* – is the name of the fifty-second genius of the Mercurian sphere. This genius gives the magician the opportunity to become master over his fellow man, in particular over his adversaries. He shows the magician ways to control them. With the help of *Imamiah*, prisoners can regain their freedom, either through direct magical intervention or through influencing the particular authority who decides the release or pardon of prisoners. *Imamiah* is a special initiator of astrology in regards to magic and Kabbalah, so that the magician will gather valuable advice from the instructions given by this genius. The magician can also receive information about every science on earth. *Imamiah* is also very fond of cheerfulness, entertainment and amusement, and he will bring about situations so that the magician will receive his share in this respect and not be disappointed.

Fig. 53: *Nanael* – is the name of the fifty-third genius of the Mercurian sphere. It must certainly be the wish of every advanced magician to have the ability to understand and control every species of animal. *Nanael* can initiate the magician into this art, so that he will be able to understand the language of all animals. The magician will be able to magically transform his mental and astral bodies to such a degree that any animal will be aware of him. The magician will also welcome the opportunity for *Nanael* to familiarize him with all the laws of magic and the Kabbalah. Eventually the magician will penetrate into the profoundest problems through appropriate meditation and attain many magical abilities. The magician can receive from this genius many magical methods which will enable him to control animals and the elements as well as the astral body of people and animals.

Fig. 54: *Nithael* – is the name of the fifty-fourth genius of the Mercurian sphere. As a great friend of all artists, authors and speakers who pursue high ideals, *Nithael* will help them to become very famous. He makes a magician very popular among personalities in high positions in the earthly sense, but he also makes the magician popular with higher spiritual beings. He gives the magician the opportunity to walk on the path of good fortune and success and leads him to blissfulness. *Nithael* can give the magician information on every subject on this earth and he is always ready to assist the magician.

Fig. 55: *Mebaiah* – is the name of the fifty-fifth genius of the Mercurian sphere. *Mebaiah* helps infertile women by giving the magician instructions on how to eliminate the causes of infertility. Wherever it is welcome, he calls forth love and helps the magician attain success, honor, esteem, fame, dignity and authority. He is an arch-initiator of true cosmic religion and a faithful helper on the path of perfection.

Fig. 56: *Poiel* – is the name of the fifty-sixth genius of the Mercurian sphere. Everything that the magician requires for his livelihood, his studies, his profession and for his earthly life in general can be attained with the help of this genius. The magician can always depend on *Poiel's* support. The magician can always find out from this genius everything from the past, present and future, and *Poiel* will call forth love and sympathy wherever it is desirable. The magician will be given information that is unknown to him about occult philosophy, magic and Kabbalah, and he will be given extensive support by this genius during his studies.

Fig. 57: *Nemamiah* – is the name of the fifty-seventh genius of the Mercurian sphere. This genius can reveal to the magician the secret of magical transformation, i.e. the magician will attain the ability to transform his own mental and astral bodies into any kind of form or figure. He will also be able to transform the mental and astral bodies of any other person into any kind of form. It should be obvious that this ability is of great significance, because it offers the magician valuable possibilities in regards to magical knowledge. Another ability which the magician attains under the guidance of this genius is the ability to magically mummify the elements in order to be protected against any influence of the elements. *Nemamiah* entrusts the magician with magical practices which enable him to make the blind see, to become clairvoyant, to make his body resistant and thus able to effortlessly endure all the trials and tribulations of life, to be successful in every respect, to eliminate any passion, to call forth love and to increase and decrease love, to release prisoners and much, much more. This genius is especially fond of inspiring technical engineers and helping them develop new inventions, especially in the steel industry.

Fig. 58: *Jeialel* – is the name of the fifty-eighth genius of the Mercurian sphere. This genius is an initiator. He initiates the magician into spheric magic and the astrology of the spheres. The magician can learn great wisdom from the instructions of this genius. He will learn about the various powers and effects of the individual spheres and their common influence upon the zone girdling the earth and upon our physical world. He will also learn how to calculate these influences for mantic purposes and then practically apply this knowledge for magic and the Kabbalah. In addition, the magician will learn how to become an absolute master over all the beings of the elements and the spheres and he will learn how to increase his magical powers and authority.

Fig. 59: *Harahel* – is the name of the fifty-ninth genius of the Mercurian sphere. This genius is also an authority on astro-magic. He teaches the magician how to transfer magical powers into precious stones. A magician who is in contact with this genius will be entrusted with special methods for the prenatal education of children. Furthermore, he will be taught methods which will eliminate infertility in women. *Harahel* is a friend of all gynecologists, obstetricians, midwives, etc. This genius is well-versed in all the sciences that exist on earth. Therefore, he can give the magician precise information about everything. Should the magician be a businessman and should his interests include stock market transactions, then *Harahel* will give the magician good tips by pointing out the stocks that will increase in value as well as those which will lose their value.

Fig. 60: *Mizrael* – is the name of the sixtieth genius of the Mercurian sphere. Should the magician require dexterity and skillfulness in his chosen profession, he should turn to this genius, because he will help him in this respect. If religious philosophy and other sciences are of interest to the magician, he can be initiated by *Mizrael* into all fields of knowledge and he can achieve greatness as a self-taught scholar. This genius is also well-versed in alchemy, and a magician can learn how to prolong his life through alchemical-spagyric remedies and how he can mummify his body, and furthermore how mental illnesses can be successfully healed. This genius is willing to give the magician information about the divine virtues and their influence and also about the most multifarious magical abilities. He will teach the magician to liberate those human beings who are persecuted by their enemies and how to render such enemies harmless.

Fig. 61: *Umabel* – is the name of the sixty-first genius of the Mercurian sphere. No magician will neglect to contact this genius, because he will achieve considerably more through this contact than he imagines. For example, he will achieve in his earthly life good fortune and contentment, friendship and love, recreational and rejuvenating excursions with the necessary financial means, instructions in alchemy, specifically about the utilization of the elements for various alchemical purposes, such as turning water into wine and vice versa. He will receive instructions about the transmutation of metals, and instruction in magic and Kabbalah. *Umabel* possesses such tremendous powers that he can, without exaggeration, turn total fools into wise men.

Fig. 62: *Jah-Hel* – is the name of the sixty-second genius of the Mercurian sphere. He teaches the magician the following: to realize the divine virtues within himself; the art of meditation and concentration; to recognize the activities and effects of the Akasha Principle; to gather profound wisdom from magic and the Kabbalah; to comprehend the essence of all philosophies. *Jah-Hel* initiates the magician into the various arts, for example how to change a staff or cane into a snake and vice versa, similar to what Moses did before the Pharaoh. He teaches the magician how to have all snakes gather in one location and how to make himself immune to snake poison so that even the most poisonous snake cannot harm him. Should the magician request it, this genius will have him discover hidden treasures.

Fig. 63: *Anianuel* – is the name of the sixty-third genius of the Mercurian sphere. The magician will be initiated by this genius in all the different kinds of treatments for ailments, whether it be with the help of remedies or through magic and the Kabbalah. The magician learns how to prepare special protective amulets against various kinds of ailments and negative influences, and how to load them accordingly. Furthermore, the magician will receive power formulas, i.e. magic words, with which he will be able to control any negative being of the Mercurian sphere and protect himself from any undesirable influences. This genius helps all those human beings that are engaged in trade and money transactions and he helps them to make money. He helps them to make inventions of any kind a reality; he shows them ways and means to hone their intellect and to attain an excellent intuition, and he will gladly give the magician information at any time about any field of knowledge on earth.

Fig. 64: *Mehiel* – is the name of the sixty-fourth genius of the Mercurian sphere. This genius entrusts the magician with power formulas, i.e. magical formulas, which will change any enemy into a pile of ashes should the life of the magician be in danger, because these powers momentarily develop an incredible amount of heat. Other power formulas will tame the most rapacious animal, or immediately calm a hostile and out-of-control mob. The magician who is in contact with this genius will be initiated into many mysteries which to this day are still completely unknown, and he will also be initiated into all the sciences which are of interest to him. Any magician who is under *Mehiel's* guidance will achieve a high level of erudition. Furthermore, the magician can also become a famous literary figure, be able to develop within himself a great oratory talent, learn how to become immune to decomposition through the elements, and consequently prolong his life as long as he wishes.

Fig. 65: *Damabiah* – is the name of the sixty-fifth genius of the Mercurian sphere. The magician can be initiated by this genius into symbolism and talismanology, i.e. how to magically produce talismans and amulets. Furthermore, under the guidance of this genius the magician can reach the source of the highest wisdom which exists on our planet. He will teach the magician the laws of the microcosm and macrocosm and how to make use of these laws in magic and the Kabbalah. And he will learn how to make the element of Water subject to his will in order to have any water animal under his control. This genius willingly discloses all the treasures that are hidden under the surface of the water, and he allows new mineral springs, i.e. healing springs, to be discovered. *Damabiah* is an initiator in hydrotherapy; therefore not only does he teach the magician how to load the Water element magically and Kabbalistically with particular powers, he also teaches the magician how to employ the Water element for healing purposes. This genius helps the magician in all his undertaking in word and deed.

Fig. 66: *Manakel* – is the name of the sixty-sixth genius of the Mercurian sphere. If the magician is trying to recover lost goods, he should turn to this genius for help, for he will help him discover all things and treasures that are hidden. Besides that, he entrusts the magician with methods whereby he will attain an enlightened intellect. He also teaches him how to express any idea Kabbalistically and numerically. Furthermore, this genius will teach the magician how to equilibrate disharmonies, in particular those caused by the influence of the Moon. Through this the magician is given the opportunity to cure any kind of epilepsy, Saint Vitus' Dance, somnambulism, etc. in a magical-Kabbalistic manner or through talismanology. Furthermore, the magician learns how to get vegetation under his control and to influence it at his discretion, for example how to promote and stop the growth of plants. In addition, he learns how to influence water animals, to gather fish in one location, even the largest and most dangerous, and he learns how to tame crocodiles. Furthermore, he learns how to influence the character of any person and change it at his discretion. He will learn how to correctly interpret dreams that depict the truth. The magician is offered many other magical possibilities in regards to our physical world through contact with this genius.

Fig. 67: *Eiaiel* – is the name of the sixty-seventh genius of the Mercurian sphere. *Eiaiel* is a fabulous initiator of occult knowledge, in particular magic and Kabbalah. He teaches the magician to attain the highest enlightenment through this knowledge, to attain absolute perfection, and to overcome all influences and obstacles on the path of perfection. Under the guidance of this genius the magician will be able to control nature, above all the world of plants, and he will be able to perform miracles through nature magic which are known to only a very few magicians. This genius will gladly assist any magician who endeavors to contact him in attaining success, honor, fame and esteem, provided this is the magician's request.

Fig. 68: *Habuiah* – is the name of the sixty-eighth genius of the Mercurian sphere. This genius teaches the magician all the various treatments for ailing humankind, even if it concerns the most difficult cases. At the same time he initiates the magician into occult anatomy and Hermetic medicine. The magician learns the preparation of alchemical remedies for various ailments. He also learns how to achieve great things in nature magic, for example, how to increase the fruitfulness of the soil in a magical-Kabbalistic manner. Of course he will also learn the opposite, i.e. how to make entire tracts of land barren. With the help of *Habuiah,* the magician will turn enemies into friends, and he will also be able to awaken love among people, whether male or female, and he will also be able to raise their level of love for each other.

Fig. 69: *Rochel* – is the name of the sixty-ninth genius of the Mercurian sphere. He teaches the magician how to locate a thief, even the most ingenious one, regardless of where he might hide. This is accomplished either through the Akasha Principle or with the help of spiritual beings. The magician also learns, through special methods, how to influence thieves to such an extent that they betray themselves or return the stolen goods. He will also learn how to stop thieves who endeavor to escape and, through Kabbalistic methods, he will be able to paralyze them as long as he deems it necessary. *Rochel* is a patron of justice and he helps the magician at any time to attain his rights and to win his court case. This genius can be called upon in any kind of predicament.

Fig. 70: *Jabamiah* – is the name of the seventieth genius of the Mercurian sphere. *Jabamiah* is an excellent initiator of ceremonial magic. He teaches the magician how to call forth the greatest magical phenomena with magical-Kabbalistic methods. The magician learns how to read in and be effective through the Akasha Principle, and he learns how to use the light magically in all three planes. Furthermore, the magician will become acquainted with special methods that concern the ability of astral and mental travel. In addition, the magician will learn how to dematerialize and materialize his own person as well as other people and objects, and he will also learn how to acquire the ability to transfer objects over vast distances. *Jabamiah* leads the magician to the path of enlightenment and the highest bliss. He can also initiate the magician into all sexual mysteries, whether concerning the procreation of a child or a magic volt. The advantages that this genius can offer a magician cannot be expressed in mere words.

Fig. 71: *Haiel* – is the name of the seventy-first genius of the Mercurian sphere. Under the guidance of this genius the magician learns to be the absolute master over every situation. He also learns how to get out of even the most oppressive situations, and how to make his enemies subservient and help all those who are persecuted by their enemies and by destiny. *Haiel* has methods at his disposal with which the magician can increase his magical powers to such an extreme as to eventually achieve miracles. This genius is in every respect an excellent teacher and aide to the magician.

Fig. 72: *Mumiah* – is the name of the seventy-second and last genius of the Mercurian sphere. He is an outstanding initiator of magic and the Kabbalah. Under his guidance the magician will be able to succeed in any sphere with every magical operation. This genius helps the magician become aware of any obstacle in his path and he tells him how these obstacles can be removed. At the same time *Mumiah* is also an arch-initiator in alchemy, metaphysics, astro-physics and particularly in occult medicine. Therefore, he has the ability to instruct the magician how any ailment can be successfully treated and how total health and a long life can be attained with magical-Kabbalistic or alchemical methods. This genius can give the magician information about the preparation of the Stone of the Sages, about alchemical quintessences and about many other things in this respect. He is considered to be the patron of all physicians who occupy themselves with magic, Kabbalah and alchemy.

*

This concludes the informative description of the seventy-two genii of the Mercurian sphere. Should the magician completely control this sphere as well, then he has become an excellent spheric magician. I place great importance on the control of the intelligences of the zone girdling the earth, the Moon sphere and the Mercurian sphere, since these three spheres are closest to the magician and correspond to the physical, astral and mental worlds. Therefore, I urge the spheric magician to become absolute master of these three spheres and their intelligences. During his magical and evocative operations, the magician will discover on his own that through contact with these three spheres and their intelligences, genii and subordinate beings, he can attain anything he wishes to an extent of which a magically untrained person has not the slightest idea. This book offers the magician such a great choice of intelligences to fulfil his wishes that he does not require a second book for this purpose.

I should also like to bring to the attention of the magician the fact that each intelligence described in this work, regardless to which zone or sphere it belongs, can bestow knowledge and wisdom upon the magician in accordance with his maturity and development to such an extent that an entire book could be dedicated to each intelligence, the content of which would be riveting and extremely fascinating. My brief descriptions are merely points of reference for the magician and they are to serve him in his future practical work. How many different kinds of methods and practices, how much knowledge and wisdom he gains is his own affair. However, one thing is certain: on account of his contact with the intelligences and having the intelligences of the cosmic hierarchy under his control, the spheric magician is walking on the path of perfection. Therefore, the possibility exists that he can become a true adept.

Chapter 6
The Intelligences Of
The Venusian Sphere

The next task for the spheric magician is to contact the intelligences of the Venusian sphere, in order to get them gradually under his complete control. The magician accomplishes this task either through evocation or mental travel. Having completed the previous three spheres, which are extremely important for his magical development because they have given him the opportunity to train and properly prepare his magical abilities, he has broadened his abilities and thus exalted his spirit over everything. The magician is therefore well prepared to safely contact the intelligences of the Venusian sphere.

It has to be mentioned at the outset that all intelligences of the Venusian sphere are ravishing beauties and extremely attractive. Unfortunately, these alluring attributes have become the downfall for many spheric magicians. And even if this is not the case, it is still true that in many instances the magician's further development has been brought to a standstill. Should the magician allow himself to become intoxicated by the Venusian intelligences' extraordinarily breathtaking beauty, then he is as good as lost for any further magical advancement, for he will be drawn back to the Venusian sphere again and again, so that any further contact with that sphere can only be compared to a pact. Not only the positive, but also the negative intelligences of the Venusian sphere are devilish beauties and they all have a very seductive character; therefore the magician must possess a considerable amount of steadfastness in order to resist their lures.

The vibrations of the Venusian sphere are intoxicated with love, which places every spheric magician into a blissful state that can be compared to love ecstasy. Through this the magician is quite often overcome by the temptation to remain with his mental body in the Venusian sphere (which would undoubtedly cause his physical death) or by the constant urge to visit this sphere. If a magician gives in to these temptations he will gradually become completely spellbound by this sphere and it will be extremely difficult to free himself from there. When this occurs, the magician is irretrievably lost for a long time, if not for his entire life, for any further development on the path of perfection. However, a magician who has worked systematically on his development and who has diligently completed every sphere properly in the sequence described, who possesses strength of character, has achieved complete magical equilibrium, is the master over his abilities and attributes, and possesses a spirit that is exalted above everything — such a magician can proceed without reservation to visit the higher spheres, and therefore he can also visit the Venusian sphere without hesitation.

Therefore, every magician must examine himself quite thoroughly as to whether he possesses the necessary maturity, power and steadfastness before he takes this step.

Now follows the description of the ninety intelligences of the Venusian sphere. In the past I have been in contact with these intelligences; their names and seals are known only to very few spheric magicians and initiates. Besides these intelligences, there are a few more in the Venusian sphere that can be found in books written by other authors. For example, one of those intelligences is *Hagiel*. Since the names and seals of these intelligences are generally known and are accessible to every magician, I have not included them in my book. I shall describe the positive intelligences of the Venusian sphere in only a few words, in order that this work does not become too voluminous. The possibility exists for the spheric magician to contact each intelligence personally, and he can extend his knowledge and enrich his understanding through his practical work.

The Ninety
Venusian Intelligences

In general, for the first evocation, the seals of the Venusian intelligences are to be drawn in the color green. In talismanology, attention has to be paid to the fact that the seals must be reproduced in the colors requested by the intelligence during the first evocation. The graduation, i.e. the division into degrees in the analogy of the zodiac, which is noted under each seal in the appendix, denotes the particular influence of each intelligence upon the zone girdling the earth and from this zone upon humans in all three planes, the mental, astral and physical bodies. Being cognizant of this is of the utmost significance for attaining astro-Kabbalistic knowledge.

1. *Omah*	2. *Odujo*
3. *Obideh*	4. *Onami*
5. *Osphe*	6. *Orif*
7. *Obaneh*	8. *Odumi*

The eight intelligences of the Venusian sphere mentioned above have the same sphere of influence. They can be regarded as outstanding initiators of all erotic and sexual mysteries. These intelligences are also in complete control of the electric and magnetic fluids, particularly as these fluids pertain to the magic of love. The magician can learn from these intelligences how to work sexually-magically with the help of these fluids, how volts and talismans are loaded, how to make love amulets, and in which manner the vibrations of the Venusian sphere can be produced. These intelligences will gladly give the magician more information about many other magical practices.

9. *Orula*	10. *Osoa*
11. *Owina*	12. *Obata*
13. *Ogieh*	14. *Obche*
15. *Otra*	

The intelligences of the Venusian sphere from No. 9 to No. 15 are initiators of fertility for men and women and are the representatives of peace and wedded bliss. With the help of these intelligences the magician gives rise to love between a man and a woman, secures the good graces of women and men, and achieves everything in connection with love and propagation.

16. *Alam*	17. *Agum*
18. *Albadi*	19. *Aogum*
20. *Acolom*	21. *Achadiel*
22. *Adimil*	23. *Aser*

This group of eight Venusian intelligences is charged with the task of monitoring, supporting and helping to realize the divine ideas of philosophy, of inspiration, of the arts, of beauty, of music, as well as all the talents in accordance with the instructions given by Divine Providence.

24. *Aahum*	25. *Acho*
26. *Arohim*	27. *Ardho*
28. *Asam*	29. *Astoph*
30. *Aosid*	

To the sphere of influence of these seven intelligences of the Venusian sphere belong the acquisition of magical abilities, the achievement of personal beauty, the achievement of personal appeal or the power of attracting someone, knowledge in mummial magic pertaining to love, and so on. These intelligences gladly give a magician information as to how to acquire various magical abilities through love-magic. The aforementioned intelligences inspire love and bring about its realization. Not only does this apply to the beings of the zone girdling the earth, but also to the beings of the other spheres.

31. *Iseh*	32. *Isodeh*
33. *Idmuh*	34. *Irumiah*
35. *Idea*	36. *Idovi*
37. *Isill*	38. *Ismee*

From this group of eight intelligences the magician can learn how to acquire friendship, love and sympathy in spheres and planes through magic and the Kabbalah with the help of the appropriate rituals, ceremonies and gestures.

39. *Inea*	40. *Ihom*
41. *Iomi*	42. *Ibladi*
43. *Idioh*	44. *Ischoa*
45. *Igea*	

This group of seven intelligences of the Venusian sphere has the task of awakening intellectual abilities and bringing them to a higher level. Furthermore, they make beauty, love and harmony comprehensible and make these concepts understandable in order that they can be expressed in all intellectual languages. The monitoring, inspiration and realization of the arts and also all the various kinds of inventions are under the jurisdiction of these intelligences.

46. *Orro*	47. *Oposah*
48. *Odlo*	49. *Olo*
50. *Odedo*	51. *Omo*
52. *Osaso*	

These seven intelligences control the laws of harmony in the plant and animal kingdoms. They explain to the magician the effects the influences of the Venusian sphere have upon these two kingdoms on our earth and on all the planets in our universe. Under the jurisdiction of these intelligences and in their field of knowledge are the monitoring and regulation of fertility and growth on all planets.

53. *Ogego*	54. *Okaf*
55. *Ofmir*	56. *Otuo*
57. *Ohoah*	58. *Ocher*
59. *Otlur*	60. *Ogileh*

The aforementioned eight intelligences familiarize the magician with the technical inventions on Venus and on the other planets. Furthermore, they inform the magician in more detail about all the laws that are in effect on Venus.

61. *Gega*	62. *Gema*
63. *Gegega*	64. *Garieh*
65. *Gesa*	66. *Geswi*
67. *Godeah*	68. *Guru*

These eight intelligences initiate the magician into the laws of the plus and minus principle. Furthermore, they instruct him on the effectiveness of divine virtues on the planet and in the sphere of Venus. Besides that, they entrust the magician with special methods with which the good graces of the spiritual beings of the Venusian and the other spheres can be attained through mummification of the vibrations of the Venusian sphere in a magical-Kabbalistic manner. These intelligences inform the magician about many other theories and practices in magic and the Kabbalah.

69. *Gomah*	70. *Goldro*
71. *Gesdri*	72. *Gesoah*
73. *Gescheh*	74. *Gehela*
75. *Gercha*	

These seven intelligences permit the magician to look into Divine Providence's workshop, through which the magician will become cognizant of the effectiveness of Divine Providence or the Akasha Principle on Venus and in its sphere. With the help of these intelligences the magician will be able to view in the Akasha Principle the entire history of the evolution of Venus and its sphere. The magician will also be instructed in the Kabbalah by these intelligences.

76. *Purl*	77. *Podme*
78. *Podumar*	79. *Pirr*
80. *Puer*	81. *Pliseh*
82. *Padcheh*	83. *Pehel*

This group of eight intelligences teaches the cosmic language and its use in the Venusian sphere. The magician will also learn about the reciprocal influences of the individual spheres on Venus and in its sphere. Besides that, the magician will be instructed as to how he can practically apply his knowledge in magic and the Kabbalah.

84. *Pomanp*   85. *Pitofil*
86. *Pirmen*   87. *Piomal*
88. *Piseph*   89. *Pidioeh*
90. *Pimel*

The magician will be instructed by these intelligences about the divine worldly order in the universe, especially as far as this order pertains to the Venusian sphere, about its lawfulness, the manner in which it is symbolically expressed, etc. These Venusian intelligences can also initiate the magician in spherical Kabbalistic magic as it pertains to love. By practicing the Kabbalah and magic that is in force in the Venusian sphere, the magician will learn to call forth the state of blissfulness and ecstasy of love. These intelligences can instruct a magician who is in contact with them on many other things as well.

*

For the experienced spheric magician these brief descriptions and pointers will certainly suffice. I could describe each individual intelligence in more detail, but for technical reasons, I have refrained from that endeavor. A precise description of the entire sphere of influence of each intelligence of the Venusian sphere in regards to the individual planets and their spheres, in regards to human beings, in regards to the powers of the causal world, their working methods etc., would fill the pages of an entire book. Therefore, I leave it up to the individual magician to gather his own practical experiences through personal contact with these intelligences. However, I must warn the magician again not to remain constantly in contact with an intelligence, even if she is a ravishing beauty and is endowed with a great amount of wisdom. In time it would turn out to be a great disadvantage for the magician and eventually it would lead to a standstill on his path to perfection.

Should the magician set foot on Venus, he will find that this planet is inhabited by very beautiful human beings. Besides that, he will find that in knowledge and wisdom the inhabitants of Venus are considerably further advanced on the evolutionary scale in terms of magic, the arts, literature, technology etc., than are the inhabitants of our earth. The magician will gain a considerable amount of knowledge and, under the seal of secrecy, he will be entrusted with many valuable teachings, advice and methods. A well-trained magician who can cross planets and spheres with his mental body will find human beings on Venus who are initiated in magic and the Kabbalah, and, if he wishes, he may contact them. In this case he does not even have to assume the form of a Venusian, because the initiates on Venus will see him; of course the other inhabitants on the planet will not. These initiates will inform the magician about any topic that is of interest to him. For good reason, the magician will not disclose any information to anyone about his experiences or the knowledge he has gained, because in the eyes of the uninitiated his account of his experiences would be considered nothing more than fairytales and delusions, and in the end he would only be subject to ridicule.

Chapter 7
The Genii Of The Solar Sphere

On the assumption that the magician has also become the master over the Venusian sphere — namely that after contacting at least a few of the intelligences, he has not fallen victim to their lures and is in control of the vibrations of the Venusian sphere and the previous spheres — he is now ready to proceed to the sphere of the Sun and learn all about it and control it.

The sphere of the Sun has an entirely different vibration than the Venusian sphere. Not every spheric magician is in a position to remain in this sphere for longer periods, especially if he visits the sphere of the Sun with his mental body through mental travel. It would take too much time to give a more detailed description of the vibrations of this sphere.

However, after the magician has made numerous visits there, he gradually becomes accustomed to it and becomes more and more the master of the situation, which enables him to stay longer and eventually establish contact with the genii there. The initiates consider the sphere of the

Sun to be the so-called light-sphere. In our cosmos the sphere of the Sun is the most difficult to control. When the spheric magician gets to the point that he knows and controls the sphere of the Sun well, then the other spheres are no longer a difficult task for him and he will control them with great ease.

A brief description of the individual genii of the sphere of the Sun should give the magician additional points of reference for his practical operations. The first time the magician evokes these genii the seals must be drawn in a golden-yellow color. The graduation, i.e. the division into degrees under each seal at the back of the book, have the very same significance as those of the Venusian sphere. It is very important from the Kabbalistic point of view to know exactly the kind of influence every genius exerts on the zone girdling the earth and from there on our planet. Furthermore, in the Kabbalah of the spheres it is also of the greatest importance to know the demarcation of the influences or of a vibration.

The Sun sphere influences all life on all planets and spheres. In the case of human beings, this influence, as I previously mentioned in the description of the cosmic hierarchy of the Mercurian sphere, expresses itself in vital energy which holds together the mental, astral and physical matrices.

The Forty-Five Genii Of The Solar Sphere

The sphere of the Sun is ruled by forty-five genii altogether. Their ruler, expressed in Hermetic terms, is the "Lord of the Sun Sphere." In the Kabbalah he is called *Metatron*. In the original Kabbalistic writings *Metatron* is referred to as the mediator between God and human beings.

Fig. 1: *Emnasut* – is the first genius of the sphere of the Sun. He monitors and rules over the primary element of fire in the entire cosmic hierarchy on all planets and spheres.

Fig. 2: *Lubech* – is the second genius of the sphere of the Sun. In his sphere of influence this genius has the electric fluid on all planets and spheres in our universe under his control, which comes into being from the fire principle. This applies also to the mental, astral and physical planes.

Fig. 3: *Teras* – is the third genius of the sphere of the Sun. This genius is responsible for the plus (positive) and minus (negative) effects of the fire element and the electric fluid in the entire cosmic hierarchy on all planets and spheres.

Fig. 4: *Dubezh* – is the fourth genius of the sphere of the Sun. The power of the active principle in human beings as well as in the mineral, plant and animal kingdoms is under his jurisdiction.

Fig. 5: *Amser* – is the fifth genius of the sphere of the Sun. This genius takes care of enlivening matter in our physical world through the plus and minus principle, i.e. through electricity and magnetism, and through the electric and magnetic fluids on all planets and in all spheres of our cosmic hierarchy.

Fig. 6: *Emedetz* – is the sixth genius of the sphere of the Sun. This genius monitors and cultivates the germinative power of human beings, animals and plants.

Fig. 7: *Kesbetz* – is the seventh genius of the sphere of the Sun. He takes care of the growth of human beings, as well as of the mineral, plant and animal kingdoms.

Fig. 8: *Emayisa* – is the eighth genius of the sphere of the Sun. It is the task of this genius to maintain and nourish the instinct of self-preservation in everything that is created.

Fig. 9: *Emvetas* – is the ninth genius of the sphere of the Sun. All beings in the entire cosmic hierarchy who possess an intellect and hence full consciousness, regardless of rank, are under his influence.

Fig. 10: *Bunam* – is the tenth genius of the sphere of the Sun. This genius is responsible for all intellectual abilities in human beings and beings on all planets and spheres.

Fig. 11: *Serytz* – is the eleventh genius of the sphere of the Sun. This genius is a high arch-genius of this sphere. Under his jurisdiction is the air principle as the mediator between the active and passive, and as such the equilibrating principle in all phases, in all beings, in all things that are created in our cosmic hierarchy, and furthermore the cosmic equilibrium between the plus and minus powers.

Fig. 12: *Wybiol* – is the twelfth arch-genius of the sphere of the Sun. It is the task of this genius to monitor and guide the wisdom and knowledge of human beings and beings on all planets and spheres.

Fig. 13: *Lubuyil* – is the thirteenth arch-genius of the sphere of the Sun. Under the jurisdiction of this arch-genius are the tasks of guiding and directing the principle and the element of water in all phases of cause and effect in all regions, all planets and spheres of the cosmic hierarchy.

Fig. 14: *Geler* – is the fourteenth arch-genius of the sphere of the Sun. As such he has the task of monitoring the magnetic fluid in its purest and subtlest form of effectiveness in all phases of development on all planets and spheres, including all three planes, namely the mental, astral and physical.

Fig. 15: *Wybitzis* – is the fifteenth arch-genius of the sphere of the Sun. He controls the principle of feelings in all beings and humans on all planets and spheres of our cosmic hierarchy.

Fig. 16: *Wybalap* – is the sixteenth genius of the sphere of the Sun. Under the jurisdiction of this genius is the effectiveness of the light principle on all levels of existence in everything that is created, on all planets and spheres of the entire cosmic hierarchy.

Fig. 17: *Tzizhet* – is the seventeenth arch-genius of the sphere of the Sun. It is the task of this arch-genius to make the lowest to the highest form of divine enlightenment accessible to all human beings and beings on all the planets and spheres of the cosmic hierarchy, whether through intuition, inspiration or other abilities.

Fig. 18: *Dabetz* – is the eighteenth arch-genius of the sphere of the Sun. It is the task of this arch-genius to transfer the cognizance of divine virtues upon the human beings and beings of all the planets and spheres, and to acquaint them with the influence of these virtues and help them to realize these virtues.

Fig. 19: *Banamol* – is the nineteenth arch-genius of the sphere of the Sun. Under his jurisdiction is the materialization of the divine primary light in the ambit of creation on all planes and spheres of our cosmic hierarchy to the lowest level, wherever vital energy is expressed.

Fig. 20: *Emuyir* – is the twentieth arch-genius of the sphere of the Sun. This arch-genius controls the primary principle of health, i.e. the consummate harmony regarding the laws of analogy and magical equilibrium of human beings and the beings of all planes and spheres.

Fig. 21: *Dukeb* – is the twenty-first arch-genius of the sphere of the Sun. Under the jurisdiction of this arch-genius are the laws of meeting[31] through the plus and minus principle in the created universe, i.e. in the entire cosmic hierarchy, as well as monitoring the lawfulness.

---

[31]Meeting by attracting each other in the broadest sense of everything that exists in the universe, triggered by the plus and minus principle. – ED.

Fig. 22: *Emtzel* – is the twenty-second arch-genius of the sphere of the Sun. Under his jurisdiction is the law of dynamics or expansion on all planes of existence, i.e. on all planets and spheres of our cosmic hierarchy.

Fig. 23: *Tasar* – is the twenty-third arch-genius of the sphere of the Sun. Under the control of this arch-genius is the reproductive drive of everything that is created on all planets and spheres of our universe.

Fig. 24: *Fusradu* – is the twenty-fourth arch-genius of the sphere of the Sun. The laws of attraction and repulsion, i.e. the laws of sympathy and antipathy on all planets and in all spheres of our cosmic hierarchy are under the control of this arch-genius.

Fig. 25: *Firul* – is the twenty-fifth arch-genius of the sphere of the Sun. The law of solidity, of cohesion on all planets and in all spheres is monitored and controlled by this arch-genius.

Fig. 26: *Ebytzyril* – is the twenty-sixth arch-genius of the sphere of the Sun. The law of gravity or attraction, i.e. the law of weight and the force of gravity on all planets and in all spheres is under the control of this arch-genius.

Fig. 27: *Lhomtab* – is the twenty-seventh arch-genius of the sphere of the Sun. The control of all laws of transmutation on all planets, in all spheres and also in all regions is under the jurisdiction of this arch-genius.

Fig. 28: *Tzybayol* – is the twenty-eighth arch-genius of the sphere of the Sun. Under the jurisdiction of this arch-genius is the protection of all laws of vibration and oscillation on all planets and in all spheres of our cosmic hierarchy.

Fig. 29: *Gena* – is the twenty-ninth arch-genius of the sphere of the Sun. Any kind of radiation or emanation on all planets and spheres is in accordance with the lawfulness that is controlled by this arch-genius.

Fig. 30: *Kasreyobu* – is the thirtieth arch-genius of the sphere of the Sun. The quality of anything that exists in creation is under the control of this arch-genius.

Fig. 31: *Etzybet* – is the thirty-first arch-genius of the sphere of the Sun. Besides other things, the proper compliance with the universal laws in all spheres and planes is under the jurisdiction of this arch-genius.

Fig. 32: *Balem* – is the thirty-second arch-genius of the sphere of the Sun. This arch-genius is in charge of all the laws of analogy on all planets, and in all spheres and planes of our cosmic hierarchy.

Fig. 33: *Belemche* – is the thirty-third arch-genius of the sphere of the Sun. This arch-genius has been given the task of monitoring the lawfulness of appearances in our universe so that they are truly in harmony with the universal laws.

Fig. 34: *Aresut* – is the thirty-fourth arch-genius of the sphere of the Sun. This arch-genius has the equilibrium on all planets and in all spheres of our cosmic hierarchy under his control.

Fig. 35: *Tinas* – is the thirty-fifth arch-genius of the sphere of the Sun. He guards solidification, crystallization, fixation etc.

Fig. 36: *Gane* – is the thirty-sixth arch-genius of the sphere of the Sun. This arch-genius has control of the evolution of human beings and animals on all planets, and in all spheres and planes under his jurisdiction.

Fig. 37: *Emtub* – is the thirty-seventh arch-genius of the sphere of the Sun. The karma and destiny of anything that is alive and has been created, from the smallest to the largest, is under the control of this arch-genius.

Fig. 38: *Erab* – is the thirty-eighth arch-genius of the sphere of the Sun. This arch-genius is the arch-initiator and also monitors time and space on all planets in our universe.

Nota Bene: The spheric magician knows that time and space only exist where there are forms and created things, whether they are so-called dead or living creatures. Whereas all spheres, beginning with the zone girdling the earth to the highest sphere of our cosmic hierarchy, in contrast to their planets, are timeless and spaceless.

Fig. 39: *Tybolyr* – is the thirty-ninth arch-genius of the sphere of the Sun. He is the ruler over all the ideals of human beings and beings on all planets and in all spheres.

Fig. 40: *Chibys* – is the name of fortieth genius of the sphere of the Sun. This genius has under his jurisdiction the control of the spiritual development of human beings and beings on all planets and in all spheres in respect to evolution, lawfulness and karma.

Fig. 41: *Selhube* – is the forty-first arch-genius of the sphere of the Sun. He is the arch-creator of all arch-symbols in their primary language, the cosmic language, and he is also the helmsman of all original ideas that have become reality.

Fig. 42: *Levum* – is the forty-second genius of the sphere of the Sun. He is the original creator of all magical knowledge and the Kabbalah.

Fig. 43: *Vasat* – is the forty-third genius of the sphere of the Sun. He is an arch-initiator of the principle of water and its magnetic fluid in all levels of density and effects on human beings and beings on all planets and in the spheres of our universe. All things that are created in which the principle of water is active are monitored by *Vasat*.

Fig. 44: *Ezhabsab* – is the forty-fourth genius of the sphere of the Sun. Under his control are all beings that live in the water on our earth as well as those that live in the water on all the other planets.

Fig. 45: *Debytzet* – is the forty-fifth genius of the sphere of the Sun. Under his protection are all the different kinds of evocative methods, furthermore all burning and combustion processes and also fermentation.

In accordance with their jurisdictions or spheres of influence in the cosmic hierarchy, the arch-genii of the sphere of the Sun are to be considered as mediators of the Primary Creator of the planetary system. For reasons of information and for the purpose of obtaining a better overall view, the descriptions which I have attached to each genius of the sphere of the Sun have been expressed as abstract ideas. However, there are, in regards to the effects of these abstract ideas, many parallels which the magician can arrange by himself intuitively or regarding which he will receive the appropriate explanations from the genii of the Sun when he establishes contact with them. In any case, the magician will gain so much knowledge that words cannot suffice to explain it.

As soon as the magician has become master over the sphere of the Sun, there are no longer any problems that he cannot solve. Furthermore, there are no longer any gaps in his knowledge. He can achieve consummate adepthood through the sphere of the Sun. A magician who is somewhat conversant with the Kabbalah now fully realizes why, in most Kabbalistic initiations, the statement that a connection with the Divinity occurs in *Tiphareth* is made. According to the Kabbalistic Tree of Life, *Tiphareth* is the sphere of the Sun. Therefore, the sphere of the Sun is the sphere in which the magician can achieve divine unification. In the Kabbalistic Tree of Life it literally states that the magician must have traveled halfway back to God, i.e. he must have traveled through the aforementioned spheres inclusive of the sphere of the Sun and he must have them under his control. Then, on the second half of the way, God will meet him, so that it comes to a divine unification. This does not mean that it comes to unification with a personified God, rather knowledge and wisdom, might and power are united into one.

Chapter 8
The Intelligences Of
The Martian Sphere

The magician who has fought his way honestly through the sphere of the Sun and who has this sphere as well as the preceding ones under his control will not find it difficult to control the three spheres which follow.

The next sphere in the sequence of spheres is that of Mars. The Martian sphere is influenced by such powerful intelligences that it would be extremely dangerous for a magician to even dare to evoke these intelligences without first having the preceding spheres under his control. For this reason, and also because much mischief could be committed in a talismanological respect with the use of the seals of these intelligences as to their power, might and expression, I shall not publish the seals of the individual positive intelligences of Mars. However, I shall publish their names and their gradations, i.e. the division in degrees in the analogy of the zodiac. An experienced spheric magician will anyhow establish contact with the individual intelligences of the Martian sphere through mental travel in order to find out their seals and the extent of their sphere of influence. In this manner I discharge the responsibility that perhaps an immature person might misuse these seals, because if the intelligences of Mars are evoked carelessly without the appropriate preparations — even when they are positive intelligences — they could cause the sudden death of a human being, apart from the fact that many seals could be misused for erotic purposes. Whosoever is truly interested in pure knowledge will find it reasonable that I list only the names of the Mars intelligences, which will completely satisfy any mature person.

It should be well known to an astrologer that the Martian sphere in its effects predominantly pursues the Mars principle. Under the influence of the Martian sphere are the following: passionate love, erotica, superhuman strength, wars etc. It is also important to know that the negative intelligences of the sphere of the Sun and the Martian sphere are the most dangerous which exist in our cosmic hierarchy. Under their sphere of influence are the following: murder, manslaughter, robbery, fires, annihilation, destruction etc.

The Thirty-Six Intelligences Of The Martian Sphere

1. *Rarum*	1° – 10°	Aries
2. *Gibsir*	11° – 20°	Aries
3. *Rahol*	21° – 30°	Aries
4. *Adica*	1° – 10°	Taurus
5. *Agricol*	11° – 20°	Taurus
6. *Fifal*	21° – 30°	Taurus
7. *Imini*	1° – 10°	Gemini
8. *Kolluir*	11° – 20°	Gemini
9. *Ibnahim*	21° – 30°	Gemini
10. *Ititz*	1° – 10°	Cancer
11. *Urodu*	11° – 20°	Cancer
12. *Irkamon*	21° – 30°	Cancer
13. *Oksos*	1° – 10°	Leo
14. *Otobir*	11° – 20°	Leo
15. *Kutruc*	21° – 30°	Leo
16. *Idia*	1° – 10°	Virgo
17. *Abodir*	11° – 20°	Virgo
18. *Idida*	21° – 30°	Virgo
19. *Cibor*	1° – 10°	Libra
20. *Asor*	11° – 20°	Libra
21. *Abodil*	21° – 30°	Libra
22. *Skorpia*	1° – 10°	Scorpio
23. *Vilusia*	11° – 20°	Scorpio
24. *Koroum*	21° – 30°	Scorpio
25. *Sagitor*	1° – 10°	Sagittarius
26. *Agilah*	11° – 20°	Sagittarius
27. *Boram*	21° – 30°	Sagittarius
28. *Absolom*	1° – 10°	Capricorn
29. *Istriah*	11° – 20°	Capricorn

30. *Abdomon*	21° – 30° Capricorn
31. *Anator*	1° – 10° Aquarius
32. *Ilutria*	11° – 20° Aquarius
33. *Obola*	21° – 30° Aquarius
34. *Pisiar*	1° – 10° Pisces
35. *Filista*	11° – 21° Pisces
36. *Odorom*	21° – 30° Pisces

Chapter 9
The Genii Of
The Sphere Of Jupiter

The magician should not strive to establish any contact with the genii of the sphere of Jupiter until he has achieved complete success in getting at least a few intelligences of the Martian sphere under his absolute control. And it was mentioned in the previous chapter that each of these intelligences of Mars is very difficult to control. The vibrations of the sphere of Jupiter and its influences are considerably more bearable than the sphere of the Sun and the Martian sphere. Therefore, it will not be very difficult for the spheric magician to establish contact with the genii of the sphere of Jupiter. The extent of their sphere of influence is extremely large, and their influence, which is of a certain abstract nature, penetrates directly through all the subordinate spheres to our zone girdling the earth and as such it also affects our physical world on the mental, astral and physical planes.

A spheric magician who has properly and sequentially completed all the tasks in the preceding spheres in accordance with the instructions given, either through evocation or mental travel, and who has established contact with the individual beings, genii and intelligences of each sphere, must have come to the conclusion that through mental travel, i.e. traveling with his mental body to the individual spheres and now traveling also to the sphere of Jupiter, he is much more open to knowledge and wisdom and he gains considerably more than when he employs the methods of evocation and summons the entities to our earth. Certainly, this is not to imply that the magician should not practice evocation at all. On the contrary, it is quite appropriate to practice and master both methods equally. However, should the magician wish to consciously comprehend particular questions of a spiritual nature, subtleties etc. in a much better manner, he will always prefer to visit a particular sphere in his mental body. In this case it would be the sphere of Jupiter.

The consciousness of the magician expands through the influence of the vibrations of the sphere of Jupiter. He can penetrate more profoundly into the truths he has received from the genii and he can also understand them much more easily. After returning to his physical body on earth, the magician can transfer this truth to his physical consciousness without any great effort. Besides that, the magician will also be able to express the knowledge he has received in the sphere of Jupiter, in an understandable, intellectual language. Only through his practical experience will he be able to recognize which of the spheric inhabitants he should contact through evocation and which ones he should contact through mental travel.

The Twelve Genii Of
The Sphere Of Jupiter

In accordance with their unlimited sphere of influence of all the beings, angels and genii of the sphere of Jupiter, twelve genii rank as the highest. Their influence extends over the entire cosmic worldly order, i.e. to all spheres, planes and planets and to all its inhabitants. Each of the twelve arch-genii has a particular relationship to our signs of the zodiac, and their laws of analogy are identical with all spheres and planes of our cosmic hierarchy. For the first evocation, the seals of the genii of Jupiter are to be drawn in blue.

Fig. 1: *Malchjdael – Sign of the Zodiac: Aries.* He is the first arch-genius of the sphere of Jupiter. He keeps the electric fluid in the entire cosmic hierarchy in equilibrium. The enlivening of all things created in all three kingdoms on our earth and in the zone girdling the earth is among his duties. *Malchjdael* controls the will and the activity in human beings and in all other living beings. When a magician contacts this arch-genius he will instruct him completely in regards to these matters. In addition, he will familiarize the magician with magical and Kabbalistic methods which will enable him to increase and decrease activities at his discretion. With the help of instructions he receives from this genius the magician will be able to call forth such a manifested state of belief through magic and Kabbalah that he will be able to call forth miracles in the entire cosmic world order of which a lay person has no idea. Furthermore, *Malchjdael* can initiate the magician into the primary element of fire in all its aspects and analogies in the microcosm and macrocosm. He can also give the magician instructions and methods with which he can control this primary element through magic and the Kabbalah in all its phases, in order to become the absolute master of activity in the microcosm and macrocosm. Also, this arch-genius can familiarize the magician with many more laws, more wisdom and much more knowledge pertaining to activity, the electric fluid, the prime element of fire, the principles of light etc. Not only can this arch-genius familiarize the magician with these powers, he can also make all these powers accessible to him through an appropriate *abhisheka,* i.e. through a transfer of powers. When it comes to spheric magic this arch-genius is one of the most powerful, and no magician should neglect to establish contact with him. There is not a single intelligence in all the other spheres, with the possible exception of the Uranus intelligences, that can give the magician the amount of power in the cosmic hierarchy as does *Malchjdael.*

Fig. 2: *Asmodel – Sign of the Zodiac: Taurus. Asmodel* is the second arch-genius of the sphere of Jupiter. Under his jurisdiction is the control and guidance of the primary principle of love with all its aspects and analogies in all spheres, planes and on all planets of the entire cosmic worldly order. Any magician who establishes contact with this arch-genius will be able to understand the profoundest mysteries of love, not only emotionally and intellectually, but also from the point of view of wisdom. This arch-genius explains to the magician in which manner every cosmic love-vibration can be caused in any sphere through evocation or mental travel, through magic or Kabbalah. This genius can make all miracles which can be caused and realized in matters of love through magic and the Kabbalah accessible to the magician, not only in our physical world or in the zone girdling the earth, but also on all the other planets and in all the other spheres. *Asmodel* guides all paths of holiness which see the Divinity in the aspect of love. The conscious spheric magician is instructed theoretically and practically by *Asmodel* about all these aspects. Any magician who is interested in the mysteries of cosmic love in the entire cosmic world order will find in this genius one of the best arch-initiators.

Fig. 3: *Ambriel – Sign of the Zodiac: Gemini.* This is the third arch-genius of the sphere of Jupiter. Under his jurisdiction is all knowledge of the entire cosmic hierarchy. He monitors the intellect and therefore all theoretical knowledge, regardless of the particular field of knowledge. He directs the maturity of knowledge, the intellectual perceptive faculty of any being in the entire cosmic world order. This genius not only guides the intellectual perception and the intellectual talents of individuals in accordance with maturity and development, but also those of all the inhabitants of an entire planet. All sciences and arts on all planets which are in harmony with the intellect and reason are under the jurisdiction of this arch-genius. A magician who, in accordance with the level of his development, is in contact with this arch-genius can be gifted with knowledge that is only accessible to initiates who are able to work consciously with the Akasha Principle of the sphere of Jupiter.

Fig. 4: *Murjel – Sign of the Zodiac: Cancer.* The fourth arch-genius of the sphere of Jupiter is *Murjel*. He is the one who is in charge of the entire magnetic fluid in the cosmic hierarchy and who also has to keep it in equilibrium. The liquid state on all planets is under his jurisdiction, as well as the element of water in the entire cosmic world order, which also includes our world, namely physically, astrally and mentally. The magician can be thoroughly informed and instructed by this arch-genius about the primary element of water, its activities and effects in consideration of the entire cosmic lawfulness and in regards to magic and the Kabbalah. The magician can also be instructed as to how certain occult abilities can be awakened and developed in the mental body through the magnetic fluid, for example, transcendental vision in all spheres and on all planets. And there are many other things that the magician can learn from this arch-genius. A spheric magician who has the cosmic magnetic fluid completely under his control can achieve miraculous things with it, of which an uninitiated person has no idea.

Fig. 5: *Verchiel – Sign of the Zodiac: Leo.* This is the fifth arch-genius of the sphere of Jupiter. The entire vitalizing prime principle of the whole cosmic worldly order on all planets and in all spheres is under the protection of this arch-genius. *Verchiel* controls all life in all spheres, on all planets (including our earth), whether it concerns the life in the plant, animal or human kingdoms or whether it concerns the human being in his physical, astral or mental body. When the magician contacts this arch-genius, he will be instructed in the highest magic and Kabbalah; that applies to the entire cosmic worldly order. *Verchiel* entrusts the magician with special methods and practices in order to acquire the highest powers in the cosmic worldly order. Besides that, those miracles which are called forth through belief and through the power of conviction are also under the jurisdiction of the arch-genius.

Fig. 6: *Hamaliel – Sign of the Zodiac: Virgo.* This is the sixth arch-genius of the sphere of Jupiter. He is in charge of all chemical primary principles and primary elements in the entire cosmic worldly order. A magician who establishes contact with this arch-genius can receive detailed information regarding the chemical elements which are already known on our earth, but in addition he will also receive information pertaining to chemical elements which perhaps might be discovered in the distant future. Should it be of interest to the magician, he can learn about the elements of all the other planets in the entire cosmic worldly order. In addition, the magician can learn much more. He can learn through magic and Kabbalah how to make practical use of the radiation of the individual primary substances of our planetary system in a mental, astral and even in a physical form. Should the magician request it, he can be trained to become a consummate master of the chemical primary elements on the basis of precise methods and instructions which he will receive from this arch-genius. Therefore, he will become a magical-Kabbalistic alchemist, who will be endowed with knowledge whose applicability and key for practical use are only known to a very few adepts on our earth.

Fig. 7: *Zuriel – Sign of the Zodiac: Libra. Zuriel* is the seventh arch-genius of the sphere of Jupiter. On all planets *Zuriel* is in charge of the fertility principle as it applies to vegetation and living beings. As per *Zuriel's* instructions, the magician will fully comprehend the fertility principle of the entire worldly order. On the basis of special methods which this arch-initiator will entrust to the magician, he will be able to accomplish miracles through magic and the Kabbalah. For example, the magician could make water pour out of a rock, as did Moses, and he could turn desolate deserts into a paradise etc. However, a spheric magician who is initiated by this arch-genius could also do the exact opposite in a few seconds. In addition the magician has it at his discretion to cause many other miraculous things as they pertain to the fertility principle. It must also be obvious that *Zuriel* can also explain the cosmic sexual mysteries in all phases, in all kingdoms and spheres.

Fig. 8: *Carbiel – Sign of the Zodiac: Scorpio.* The eighth arch-genius of the sphere of Jupiter is *Carbiel.* He controls and directs the primary radiation principle in the entire cosmic worldly order in a mental, astral and physical manner. A magician who establishes contact with *Carbiel* can reveal any secret in the entire cosmic hierarchy through magic and Kabbalah. And through magical-Kabbalistic metaphysics, he will also find out how the laws of the primary radiation principle can be applied in practice. The magician will become the absolute ruler in the microcosmic and macrocosmic worldly order through controlling the primary radiation principle. It is entirely at the discretion of the magician to make practical use of these powers and the acquired might.

Fig. 9: *Aduachiel – Sign of the Zodiac: Sagittarius. Aduachiel* is the ninth arch-genius of the sphere of Jupiter. This genius has the primary legality, justness and equilibrium under his control and direction, i.e. that of the consummate harmony in the entire cosmic worldly order on all planets and in all spheres of our universe. A magician may be instructed by this genius about the highest wisdom and the unfathomable mysteries of divine lawfulness, justness and equilibrium. The magician will also learn from *Aduachiel* how to make use of all the laws in the universe through magic and Kabbalah without disturbing the equilibrium.

Fig. 10: *Hanael – Sign of the Zodiac: Capricorn. Hanael* is the tenth archgenius of the sphere of Jupiter. *Hanael* is in charge of the karmic primary principle of the entire worldly order on all planets and in all spheres. Should this be of interest to the magician, he can be taught by *Hanael* about the effects of the karmic laws on all planes and in all spheres. The magician will also gain knowledge from a magical-Kabbalistic point of view as to how the karmic primary principles and its laws are to be used for the various spheres.

Fig. 11: *Cambiel – Sign of the Zodiac: Aquarius.* This is the eleventh archgenius of the sphere of Jupiter. This arch-genius controls the crystalline primary principle, the primary principle of crystallization, condensation and hardening in the entire cosmic worldly order and therefore also in our entire solar system. *Cambiel* also controls the lawful orbit of all planets and in this connection he also controls gravity, i.e. the gravitational force. *Cambiel* can enlighten the magician about all the secrets of crystallization, not only as they pertain to our planet, but also as they pertain to all the other planets. The significance from a magical-Kabbalistic point of view is as follows: a magician learns through alchemy, magic and the Kabbalah how to change the principle of solidification by increasing or decreasing the vibration in accordance with the law and substance, as he wishes. The knowledge the magician will gain from *Cambiel* gives him the ability to change a pebble into a diamond and, vice versa, a diamond into a pebble. The magician is also taught by *Cambiel* the laws of alchemy in the highest form, especially the dry process, and the practical use of gravitation from a magical-Kabbalistic point of view. Should it be a spheric magician's wish, he can make the heaviest boulders as light as a feather or, vice versa, make the smallest things so heavy that no power can lift them. This makes it quite obvious that this arch-genius can answer all the magician's questions in regards to levitation. *Cambiel* also has at his disposal various methods with which the spheric magician can acquire this ability, and this arch-genius will gladly entrust these methods to him.

Fig. 12: *Jophaniel – Sign of the Zodiac: Pisces*. The twelfth arch-genius of the sphere of Jupiter is *Jophaniel*. Under his jurisdiction is the primary principle of evolution on all planets, in all spheres, in all kingdoms, mental, astral and material in the entire cosmic worldly order. This genius directs the ascent and maturity in all spheres and on all planets. It is quite difficult to describe in words the experience that a magician can gain through contact with this arch-genius. The magician will gain knowledge and wisdom of such profundity that it is almost impossible for an undeveloped person to grasp the immensity of it intellectually.

Chapter 10
The Saturnian Sphere

The description of the sphere of Jupiter does not bring us to the conclusion of our cosmic planetary system, as the Saturnian sphere is next. Similar to the Martian sphere, the Saturnian sphere is very difficult to establish contact with, and only a well-trained spheric magician should dare to set foot on it. He could, however, do this if he has worked his way with some of the arch-intelligences through various initiation systems and provided that for years he has mentally visited the individual spheres and gathered the necessary experiences and he is, as the saying goes, completely at home in these spheres.

Not everyone is equal to the task of withstanding the vibrations of the Saturnian sphere, which are as oppressive as a nightmare. The Saturnian sphere is the karmic sphere. The intelligences of this sphere are to be considered from the rational, intellectual point of view of a human being, as the judges of all beings, of all planets and spheres. Direct contact with any of these judges does not serve any practical purpose from a magical-Kabbalistic point of view. However, should a magician feel that he is mature enough and well acquainted with all the preceding spheres, he can endeavor to establish contact with the intelligences of the Saturnian sphere. I shall refrain from giving a description of the intelligences of Saturn, nor shall I state their names and seals, because under certain circumstances it could happen that some high-spirited magician would dare to evocate a Saturnian being without being aware of the consequences. If in this case the magician were unable to withstand the vibrations of an intelligence of Saturn, the consequence could be his physical as well as his astral death. That is why a description of the sphere will satisfy a wise and mature person and, on the basis of this brief description, he will be able to get a clear picture of the activities of the Saturnian sphere.

In some of the books written by Agrippa, Khunrath and other authors you will find the names of some Saturnian intelligences. However, these intelligences are not the highest beings of the Saturnian sphere, and, in comparison to the true Saturnian arch-intelligences, of which there are forty-nine, they only have a subordinate sphere of influence. The known intelligences are *Agiel, Arathron, Cassiel, Machatan, Uriel* etc. and they have only a limited sphere of influence in the Saturnian sphere and therefore they are not the arch-intelligences of this sphere. However, these subordinate intelligences have a certain fondness for the zone girdling our earth, and as such they are well disposed towards a magician and consequently it is easier to contact them. Whatever these intelligences have to offer the magician in regards to magic and Kabbalah can be obtained, to a much greater extent, from the intelligences of any other planetary sphere. I speak here from personal experience and any spheric magician can find out for himself whether this is true.

For example, whatever *Arathron* has to offer, every principal of the zone girdling the earth has in his possession, and, as you know, there are 360 such principals. Therefore it is not necessary that the magician visit the Saturnian sphere for that purpose. This also applies to *Agiel* and all the other Saturnian intelligences which are published in the grimoires. During my travels to the Saturnian sphere in my mental body I had a conversation with *Agiel* and *Arathron*, and the experiences I gained are stated here.

However, what could be said about the forty-nine intelligences of the Saturnian sphere is that all of them have in all spheres the karmic primary principle under their control. They pursue the activities and effects of all negative beings in all spheres, beginning with our physical world. In accordance with Divine Providence, they allow the activities and effects of negative beings. In the entire cosmic worldly order, they are the ones who rule over the effects and powers of the destructive principle. They make certain that justness is complied with and, through their subordinate beings, they permit negative effects to take place, provided it is in accordance with Divine Providence. The Saturnian intelligences allow wars to take place, not only on our planet but wherever love and hate exist. They allow the negative principle to have its effect to a certain limit, and the Saturnian intelligences are the ones who are the strict judges of human beings and the beings of all spheres in accordance with the Divine Order and lawfulness. That is why the Saturnian intelligences are considered to be the judges and the executors of destiny on the highest level. Furthermore, they make the decision as to how long a black magician who has entered into a pact with a negative or a positive being remains in the sphere of influence of that particular being.

Every arch-intelligence of the Saturnian sphere is responsible for a very particular sphere of influence. Every arch-intelligence has a particular planet and a particular sphere under his protection. Should it be of interest to the spheric magician to find out how one of these arch-initiators operates, how he makes his influence known and which sphere is under his jurisdiction, one of the subordinate intelligences, as for example *Agiel* or *Arathron* can give him this information. In accordance with what has been said thus far about the Saturnian intelligences, the spheric magician should not actually avoid the Saturnian sphere, but it should not be too significant for him to establish contact with the forty-nine arch-intelligences. It is not a pleasant sight to watch the activities of the negative beings spiritually, and how they are monitored and punished. This truly requires strong nerves and a very good mental steadfastness. This concludes the description of the Saturnian sphere. The seals of *Agiel, Arathron* and the other lower intelligences of the Saturnian sphere are commonly known. Any magician will take great care when it comes to the names and seals of the forty-nine arch-intelligences of the Saturnian sphere, and he will not entrust these names and seals to any immature person. He will also agree with me as to why I did not reveal any details about these arch-intelligences.

Chapter 11
The Spheres Of
Uranus And Pluto

With the Saturnian sphere the general spheric magic has come to its conclusion; the hierarchy of the seven spheres known to us has been explained in an understandable manner. However, a true initiate who moves about freely in the universe with his mental body and who has the ability to endure the various vibrations of all these spheres in his mental body must surely have noticed that there are other spheres beyond the Saturnian sphere. However, these spheres exert almost no direct influence upon our earth i.e., our zone girdling the earth, at least not to the extent that they could be considered worthwhile for working with magic or the Kabbalah.

After the Saturnian sphere, the first sphere that is worthy of mention is the Uranian sphere, whose minimal influence reaches no farther than the Moon sphere. Should a magician who is conversant with spheric magic be visiting the Moon sphere, he will still somewhat feel the effects of the Uranian sphere. In the zone girdling the earth the Uranian sphere is known, but the influence of this sphere has very little impact there, since the effects of the Uranian sphere were already waning considerably in the Moon sphere and these effects also end in the Moon sphere. Naturally, this realization and fact has nothing to do with the astrological interpretations of Uranus, about which I do not give any details. The Uranian sphere will not have any effect on our zone girdling the earth or on our planet until the next cycle of evolution. In any case, the magician, if he wishes, can contact the intelligences of the Uranian sphere, who can initiate him into macrocosmic magic and Kabbalah. It is not permitted to release any details in this respect, because the time to publish these details has not yet come. However, it can be mentioned that initiates refer to the actual Kabbalah as the Uranian language, i.e. the cosmic language. The intelligences of the Uranian sphere control and direct magic and the Kabbalah and their practical use in accordance with the universal laws that exist in the entire macrocosm, i.e. in our cosmic hierarchy. Therefore, these intelligences of Uranus control the extent to which any being and any arch-intelligence of the other spheres applies the various kinds of magic and Kabbalah and how they teach these methods to a magician.

For a spheric magician who gains a foothold in the Uranian sphere and establishes contact with the arch-intelligences and is initiated by them into magic and Kabbalah, no initiate, no arch-initiator, no matter to which kind of sphere he belongs, has anything more to offer to this magician, because he has become a consummate adept, a hierarchical magician and Kabbalist. He is not only lord over the zone girdling the earth, but also over all spheres and all kingdoms. Whoever has reached this level in spheric magic and has, so to speak, graduated from the Uranian sphere, can safely assume that he is a consummate adept, an initiate who completely and intellectually understands the Book of Wisdom with its 78 Tarot cards and who has its lawfulness in the microcosm and macrocosm completely under his control. Then I, for one, have nothing further to offer to such an initiate.

On the basis of this brief description of the Uranian sphere, the initiate finally sees how far he has to travel the path to perfection, because it is here where our hierarchy ends.

There is one more sphere, the Plutonian sphere. However, the magician at his present level of development cannot gain anything from this sphere, because the Plutonian sphere will not have an effect on our zone girdling the earth until the second day of Brahma or the next cycle of evolution. At that point our earth will be inhabited by an entirely different race of human beings with a different color of skin, and they will also be governed by different laws.

On my travels with my mental body, besides the aforementioned planetary spheres, I crossed several others, approximately thirty in number. In their present state of development these spheres have absolutely no significance for our zone girdling the earth and for us humans, and they are not integrated into the sphere of influence of our hierarchical analogy and its lawfulness. The extent of this work does not permit me to publish anything further on this subject.

A spheric magician who receives precise instructions in magic and Kabbalah and also from the arch-intelligences of the Uranian sphere will understand that besides our universe, our macrocosm, our planetary system, and besides the hierarchies and spheres described in this book, there are many more by far larger in size. These larger cosmos or universes have entirely different powers, different laws, and they also have different analogies than we have in our macrocosm. It would be impossible to describe all these macrocosms in more detail.

Chapter 12
Contact With Beings, Genii And Intelligences Of All Spheres Through Mental Travel

This chapter was not written for a spheric magician, but for the many readers who do not immediately begin with the practice, but instead want to extend their theoretical knowledge first with the content of these books. For these readers this chapter holds many incentives to increase their knowledge. My first work, *Initiation into Hermetics,* contains precise instructions about mental travel. In addition, it contains precise instructions about the exteriorization of the astral body, also known as astral projection. The magician will, at most, be able to visit the zone girdling the earth with his astral body, because the astral body is composed of the substances of the elements which will, if worse comes to worse, only endure the vibrations of the zone girdling the earth. Consequently, a spheric magician would not entertain the thought of traveling beyond the zone girdling the earth with his astral body. As a matter of fact, it would be impossible. A spheric magician knows from his own experiences that the astral body is bound by Divine Providence to the laws of the zone girdling the earth, and that he cannot violate these laws. Besides that, the astral body is also bound to the principle of space. The spheric magician can confirm this fact by visiting the zone girdling the earth.

However, the magician can visit the kingdoms of the elements with his astral body, and he can also visit any place on our planet, whether on the surface of the earth or below it. His astral body will even withstand the finest vibrations of the zone girdling the earth. However, the magician will soon realize that he cannot pass beyond this zone. In spite of this, if the magician dares to leave the zone girdling earth with his astral body while his physical body lies on our earthly plane and maintains contact through the astral matrix with the astral body, this futile attempt would immediately cause the astral matrix to sever, resulting in the instant death of the physical body. At this point the astral matrix could not be revived and any such attempt would prove unsuccessful. And then the physical body is subjected to the elements. Should it happen that, in spite of his physical death, the magician's astral body escaped, and the mental body together with the astral body forcibly crossed over the boundaries of the zone girdling the earth, this in turn would sever the mental matrix. The mental body would then separate from the astral body and the astral body would be subject to the elements in the astral world, and they would consume such an astral corpse in a very short time. It would be impossible for the spirit to return to the astral body, and such a spirit would then be banished to the sphere that corresponds to the magician's last phase of development. Such an act of violence is punished severely by the judges of the Saturnian sphere.

Such an act of violence and the conscious severance of the astral matrix from the physical body and the mental matrix from the mental body is a calamity. In the Bible it is stated as "a sin against the spirit." The actual meaning of the words "against the spirit" from a Hermetic point of view is only known to a very few. However, cases like this are quite rare indeed. Usually, the instinct of self-preservation is the reason why the bounds are not overstepped. Besides that, every magician has an intelligence at his side who guides him and warns him in time from such karmic intervention. This explanation examines in a certain respect the Faust tragedy, which every initiate clearly understands. Now we shall discuss a few matters regarding mental travel.

The spheric magician has learned in *Initiation into Hermetics* how to separate his mental body. In the beginning of this book he read and found it to be correct that it is a prerequisite to completely master the first book practically before he can begin with the practice of the second book. The magician learned how to loosen his mental body and, for the time being, how to move about the mental sphere of the physical world. After having practiced this sufficiently, the magician visits the astral plane of the physical world. Whereupon the magician crosses the entire physical world with his mental body wherever he wishes to go and to go wherever his spirit wishes to be. Then he visits the kingdoms of the elements and for this purpose he assumes the shape of the beings of the elements through the imagination, so that he can be seen, heard and felt by them. The magician first visits the kingdom of the gnomes, then the water kingdom or the undines, then he traverses the air region with the sylphs or fairies, and finally he visits the kingdom of the salamanders in order to get all these beings under his control. Subsequently, the magician learned to rise with his mental body into the planes by entertaining the fervent wish to reach the zone girdling the earth. After some practice, his mental body rose in a vertical position and the magician felt that he was transferred into this zone in accordance with his wish.

When the magician arrived in the zone girdling the earth, the vibration of which his mental body could quite easily tolerate, he was immediately surrounded by the beings of this zone. Following that, the magician had the possibility of getting to know the principals of the zone girdling the earth one by one, whose names and seals I have published in this book, and establish contact with them. They acquainted the magician with everything as far as the zone girdling the earth is concerned, and they gave him instructions on how he could proceed to the next higher sphere, i.e. the Moon sphere. The magician can proceed to the Moon sphere without a guide by influencing his mental body with the color of the Moon sphere, i.e. by coloring it silvery-white but slightly tinged with violet. As soon as the magician has finished impregnating his mental body with the light-accumulation in the appropriate coloration, he rises again in a vertical position with the wish to reach the Moon sphere. The first few times, the magician will experience a spinning motion when he elevates himself from the zone girdling the earth into the Moon sphere. However, this dizziness will cease after a few times and the pressure in the area of his solar plexus will also subside. This elevation into the Moon sphere occurs with lightning speed, and all of a sudden the magician will find himself in the Moon sphere in an ocean of light of a silvery-violet color vibration. His wish to meet with the intelligences of the Moon while he is there will also come true. If the magician calls out in the language of the imagination while he is in the silver vibration, one of the intelligences of the Moon described herein will soon appear to him. Contact is made in the same manner as in the zone girdling the earth.

Should it be the magician's intention to obtain something in particular from a being that inhabits another sphere, while still in the zone girdling the earth he should draw up his course of action and only after due consideration visit the particular sphere. During the initial operations and visits, the magician's consciousness is somewhat helpless because of the different kind of color vibration of the sphere. Only after several contacts with the same being will the magician become accustomed to the existing pressure in that sphere, and his independent thinking process will no longer be influenced by that sphere to that extent.

Once the magician has contacted all twenty-eight intelligences of the Moon sphere, he can be considered an absolute master of this sphere. Then he has gained the ability to change the influence of the Moon sphere within himself at his discretion by decreasing or increasing the vibrations of the Moon sphere, depending on whether he contacts a powerful or a less powerful being.

During his initial visits the magician will experience that the twenty-eight arch-intelligences possess such a power of emanation, an inner expansivity, which has an almost paralyzing effect on his mental body. In order to rise to the occasion and be able to withstand these vibrations, the magician must already prepare himself in the zone girdling the earth and, through the appropriate accumulation of light-power of the Moon sphere, assume a vibration that is acceptable to an arch-intelligence of this sphere. This allows the magician to establish contact with these intelligences without having to endure these paralyzing side effects.

Once the magician has become completely acquainted with the Moon sphere, he proceeds with his mental body to the next sphere by influencing his mental body with the yellow color-vibration of Mercury while he is still in the Moon sphere, i.e. he undertakes the accumulation of light-power of the Mercurian zone. The magician comes in contact with the individual genii of the Mercurian zone just as he came into contact with individual intelligences of the Moon sphere, one after the other. After the magician has elevated himself several times to the Mercurian zone, he no longer has to make his way through the Moon sphere. Instead, he can accomplish that from the zone girdling the earth by impregnating his mental body with the vibration of Mercury and elevating himself directly from the zone girdling the earth into the Mercurian zone. Once the magician has established contact with at least thirty genii of this zone, then he is ready to elevate himself into the Mercurian zone from the physical world. In other words, he can carry out the color impregnation, i.e. the accumulation of the light-power of the vibration of Mercury, right next to his physical body, and proceed directly from there into the Mercurian zone without a stopover in the zone girdling the earth or in the Moon sphere. During his contacts with the genii of Mercury the magician will not experience the same paralyzing feeling of their emanating powers as he did with the intelligences of the Moon, because the Mercurian zone is in a certain respect analogous to the mental body. However, this was already mentioned in the chapter dealing with the cosmic hierarchy. Not until the magician has become absolute master over these three spheres, the zone girdling the earth, the Moon sphere and the Mercurian zone, should he entertain the thought of elevating himself into the next higher sphere.

The reason that I pay so much attention to these three spheres, as I already mentioned, is that:

1. There is an analogous connection between the zone girdling the earth and the destiny of the physical body.
2. There is an analogous connection between the Moon sphere and the astral body in respect to the maturity of the astral body, the character, the equilibrium etc.
3. There is an analogous connection between the Mercurian zone and the mental body.

The Mercurian zone is, so to speak, the launching pad for the higher spheres. It is here that the spheric magician carries out the accumulation of the light-power before he elevates himself to the next sphere, in this case the Venusian sphere. The accumulation of light-power is carried out in a wonderful emerald green color. If the spheric magician has not fallen victim to the numerous temptations of the Venusian sphere and has thus become a master over love, he then proceeds directly from the physical world into the Venusian sphere by carrying out the accumulation of the light-power of the Venusian sphere in his mental body directly beside his physical body.

This also applies to the following sphere, the sphere of the Sun. The Sun sphere is, for the magician, the most difficult one to reach. This is so because the beings of this sphere are filled with such a tremendous amount of light-substance that he will not be able to withstand the vibrations of a Sun genius unless he has sufficiently accumulated enough light-power of the Sun, which must resemble a glaring sun. Should a magician come into contact with a Sun genius without having properly prepared and impregnated his mental body with light, then the glaring emanating light-power would thrust him back into his physical body, through which his mental matrix could severely lose its balance, which would inevitably result in disharmonies. These disharmonies would be noticeable through various side effects in the astral body and perhaps in the physical body as well. Under certain circumstances a severe nervous breakdown could also result, as well as disadvantages of a psychic nature. Therefore a magician will consider my warnings and deem them to be completely appropriate. He will realize that proceeding to the individual spheres is absolutely impossible without having knowledge of the laws of analogy and knowing how to practically employ these laws. Furthermore, he must have knowledge of evocative magic.

Once the magician has the sphere of the Sun completely under his control, he visits the adjacent sphere of Mars. As a precautionary measure I have only listed the names of the intelligences of this sphere, but not their seals. The Martian sphere has a ruby-red color light-vibration, which means that the accumulation of light-power of the mental body must have a ruby-red coloration. Any magician who has become master over the sphere of the Sun without encountering any danger can visit all the spheres beyond the sphere of the Sun in the proper order, with the obvious exception of the extremely dangerous Saturnian sphere.

When visiting the sphere of Jupiter, the previous methods apply; the accumulation of the light-power has to be carried out in a sky-blue color.

Should the magician also wish to visit the Saturnian sphere, then the accumulation of the light-power of his mental body must have a dark violet coloration.

When visiting the Uranian sphere, the accumulation of the light-power of the mental body must have a lilac coloration, whereas in the Plutonian sphere, as the last sphere, his mental body must have a light gray coloration.

All the spheres that follow are colorless. A magician who has reached this level in his development and who feels that he has risen to the level that he can accumulate the light-power which is required by these spheres can now proceed to the other spheres without having the proper coloration accumulated in advance in his mental body, and he can establish contact with the intelligences in these spheres. However, as soon as he approaches the sphere he wishes to visit, he will perceive in advance through his transcendental vision the color of that sphere, in order to carry out, without problems in the cosmos, the accumulation of light-power in the appropriate color before he enters the particular sphere. There are vibrations where the colors do not resemble any which are known to us and therefore a description of these cannot be given. Yet the transcendental eyes can see these colors and therefore call forth in the mental body the light-vibration of that particular sphere through which contact with the sphere and its beings is made possible.

This brief description should satisfy an initiate. Never before in Hermetic literature has anything been written about these details, and to this day only a few initiates are familiar with this knowledge. A spheric magician who masters all this in practice does not consider this chapter to be pure fantasy, because he can find out at any time if this is the truth. What I have described here are my own experiences.

Chapter 13
Magical Talismanology

In the first part of this book I gave brief instructions regarding the loading of talismans and amulets and how to make use of them in practice. At this point I find it appropriate to reiterate some of the instructions, since some of these instructions might be new to the magician. Be that as it may, I have chosen magical talismanology as the last chapter of this book, and I shall describe everything that has to be considered in this respect. Much has been written about talismanology, but even more could be said about this subject from a Hermetic point of view. But for technical reasons I shall be brief.

All information pertaining to this subject will be familiar and understandable to an experienced magician. Looking at a talisman from a Hermetic point of view, it is the means, the link or material form to which a power, an ability, a might, an influence, etc., can be attached or bound. The manner in which a power is bound varies. But first let us discuss talismans.

The magician has learned to contact a being, an intelligence, a genius, etc. Contact with these spiritual beings is established through (1) mental travel, (2) evocation, and (3) passive communication, as described in *Initiation into Hermetics* in the chapter on spiritism. The last method remains, which is establishing contact through a talisman.

As to the shape of a talisman, it can be a piece of jewelry, a ring, a gemstone, or an amulet, a pendant, and so forth. Other shapes can also be chosen, but those mentioned here are the ones that are usually considered as talismans. The best are the ones that the magician makes himself, starting with the metal that he smelts and then casts into a talisman and then loads. Should this not be possible, or if the magician does not possess the necessary skills, he should have the talisman made, but only in its basic form. Once the talisman is ready in the form chosen by the magician, he then begins with the actual talismanology, and out of this piece of jewelry he makes a true talisman, a link. The magician engraves the seal of the intelligence he wishes to contact into the metal. If he does not possess the ability to do so himself, then a trustworthy engraver or goldsmith can do this for him. The object to be used as a talisman or the amulet is now ready. The next step is the magical preparation. Should a magician wish to take the astrological signature into consideration when the talisman is to be manufactured or during the magical preparation, that is of course his choice. There is enough astrological literature available in order to calculate the most favorable influences of the constellations. The metal that is chosen for a talisman has to be in accordance with the astrological analogy of the particular sign of the zodiac. Below, the reader will find a chart. Since in the hierarchy of the spheres the signs of zodiac were taken into consideration, the particular metal must therefore be chosen which corresponds to the genius and his particular sign of the zodiac. However, the magician also has another choice: he can choose metals that are analogous to the planetary spheres.

The very best metal for all beings, genii and intelligences of all spheres is the electro-magicum. The electro-magicum is a compound that contains all the metals that correspond to all the planets. A detailed description of the electro-magicum can be found in *Initiation into Hermetics* in Step VIII, in the chapter dealing with solid fluid condensers. This alloy is best suited for beings of the zone girdling the earth and for the beings of the elements in kingdoms of the elements. Otherwise, for the zone girdling the earth, a hard wood or lead can be used.

For the Moon sphere and its twenty-eight intelligences, silver should be used in accordance with planetary laws of analogy when making a talisman.

For the

Mercurian zone	–	brass
Venusian sphere	–	copper
Sun sphere	–	gold
Martian sphere	–	iron
Jupiter sphere	–	tin
Saturnian sphere	–	lead

For the spheres that follow, tin or silver may be used. The analogies determining the choice of metals to produce a talisman are only of a general nature. It is only meant for those who wish to take the astrological analogies into consideration. For an experienced magician, two kinds of metal will suffice; he will choose gold for beings who are predominantly electric by nature, and for those who have a magnetic character he will use silver. For indifferent beings who are neither active nor passive, and who cannot be assigned to either the electric or the magnetic fluid, the magician uses both metals by soldering together two small plates, one made of gold and the other of silver. For example, should it have the shape of a pendant, one side consists of gold and the other of silver.

In reality, the choice of metal is not of great significance to a well-versed initiate and experienced spheric magician. He succeeds by magically impregnating any object with the intelligence, no matter which sphere the intelligence inhabits. Establishing magical contact and impregnating the chosen object depends entirely on the magical development and maturity of the particular magician.

Adepts mostly prefer only one metal, pure gold, when loading the metal with intelligences. Of course, this is not absolutely necessary. A common talisman that is well impregnated magically serves the same purpose as a talisman made from the purest gold or precious gemstones.

The next step is the magical impregnation, which is the most important work when it comes to loading a talisman, for only through this does an object turn into a real tool for the establishment of contact with the desired being or intelligence. With the help of an example, I shall explain to the magician the entire procedure for carrying out the operation of magical impregnation.

First the magician must choose the being, genius or intelligence, preferably from the zone girdling the earth, that best suits his purpose according to its magical attributes and other qualities. Once he has made this determination, he engraves its seal on the appropriate metal, and then, through the four elements, he has to cleanse the talisman from all unfavorable influences which may have been clinging to the talisman mentally when it was physically produced.

This is accomplished in the following manner: the magician swings the talisman several times over a burning candle, imagining that the fire of the candle annihilates all influences. This process is followed by immersing the talisman into a glass of pure water. The talisman has to remain immersed in the glass of water for an entire day with the wish-concentration that the water attracts all the bad influences from the talisman. Once the talisman has been in the glass of water for an entire day, the magician removes it from the glass, and pours out the water, meanwhile holding with the wish-concentration that all the unfavorable influences flow away with it. Then he swings the talisman through the air in a circular motion with the wish-concentration that the air element removes all the negative influences from the talisman. Then the magician takes a handful of earth and places it on a piece of filtering paper. Then he puts the talisman on the earth and rolls it up so that he can hold it in his hand, upon which the magician concentrates that the earth element that surrounds the talisman is drawing out all the negative influences. After very intensive wish-concentration, and having the firm conviction that all remaining unfavorable influences have finally been removed from the talisman, the magician removes it from the earth and cleanses it with a brand new cloth that has never been used for anything. Then he takes the talisman and wraps it in a dark violet piece of silk. The earth and the filtering paper are then to be buried in a place that is not easily accessible. Now the talisman is, from a Hermetic point of view, cleansed with the elements, i.e. not a single element is clinging to the talisman anymore, and therefore not one single element influences the loading of the talisman in any way.

Should it be the magician's intention to consider the astrological aspects, he then keeps the talisman in the dark violet silk until the astrological hour approaches. As soon as he is ready and the astrological hour approaches, he proceeds with the loading of the talisman. Taking a brand new needle, he traces the engraved seal with the firm wish-concentration that, by tracing the engraved seal, the interest and the attention of the chosen being is confined to the talisman. While the magician is emulating the engraving of the seal with the needle, he can repeat the name of the particular intelligence in his mind, and at the same time he can imagine that the intelligence transfers its influence to the talisman. The physical preparation, expressed Hermetically as establishing contact, has come to its conclusion with this procedure; the initial work of magical impregnation has been completed. However, there are many possibilities by which the talisman can be loaded.

The most effective manner of loading a talisman is when the magician, through an evocative operation and through the appropriate ritual, summons the intelligence in front of his magic circle. He asks the intelligence for the approval of the talisman that the magician keeps either in or in front of his magic circle; this is a promise to help the bearer of the talisman at any time. If the intelligence promises to grant the bearer of the talisman this favor, then as far as the magician is concerned the desired effect of the talisman has been achieved and it can be considered loaded. All the guidelines which the particular intelligence recommends when the operator uses the talisman must always be taken into consideration and followed. For example, the intelligence could take various precautions by instructing the bearer of the talisman to perform a daily ritual with the talisman, to utter particular formulas over it, to draw particular signs with it, to name particular names which are required for the effectiveness of the talisman, or also to keep certain things secret, etc.

If all the prerequisites are taken into consideration, then the bearer of the talisman can achieve the same effects with it as if he had established a personal contact with the intelligence through mental travel or evocation. The aforementioned method of loading is one of the most effective methods of talismanic impregnation for the purpose of establishing contact with an intelligence. However, when it comes to establishing contact in this manner, the particular intelligence usually places its subordinate servants at the disposal of the magician, which the intelligence then binds to the talisman and whose names are entrusted to the bearer of the talisman. When uttering the names or when an agreed upon sign is drawn, the desired effect is called forth by the being.

Another method of impregnating a talisman is when a contact is established by repeatedly imagining the attributes of the chosen intelligence. These attributes have to be concentrated into the metal and thus the termination of time, space and effect have to be considered. This method of concentration requires unshakable belief on the part of the magician, as well as a sufficient amount of magical power, enough to force the particular intelligence to obey the will of the owner of the talisman and to bring about the desired effects.

Another method of impregnation is accomplished with the help of a ritual, the procedure of which is as follows: The seal of the chosen intelligence is drawn in the air with the talisman and, while so doing, the magician concentrates on the realization of the desired effect. However, it is well known to the Kabbalist that a ritual of this kind must be repeated at least 462 times before a proper contact can be established in order to make the talisman actually effective.

The next method of impregnation is loading through magic volts with the electromagnetic fluid. After the volt is created, it is loaded with the electromagnetic fluid. The attributes of the chosen intelligence are transferred into the center of the volt through the imagination, a firm belief, and with a convincing power, and through sufficient repetition it becomes condensed to the extent that the metal of the talisman accepts the loaded volt. Wish-concentration is employed when the volt is loaded by repetition, i.e. the magician concentrates that the chosen intelligence is in contact with the volt and, through the volt, calls forth the desired causes in the Akasha world in order to achieve the desired effects.

There is yet another method of loading, namely a sexual-magical method, which I shall not describe in order to prevent any misuse. However, a magician who is initiated into the high mysteries and to whom everything remains pure and holy, certainly knows how to use the plus and the minus in a man and a woman to volt for the purpose of magically impregnating a talisman.

The last method of magically impregnating a talisman is a Kabbalistic loading which can be carried out by an initiate who is conversant with the Kabbalah. This is accomplished by uttering the name of the particular intelligence Kabbalistically over the talisman which is prepared to be loaded, and, in so doing, transferring the attributes of the intelligence into the talisman.

How a magical-Kabbalistic loading of a talisman is carried out in every detail is well known to every initiate who has followed all the instructions to this point in my works and who has established contact with an intelligence, regardless to which sphere the intelligence belongs, and provided he has been instructed by the individual intelligences about Kabbalistic knowledge.

In *The Key to the True Kabbalah* this subject is discussed in detail. This concludes this chapter about the impregnation and loading of talismans and about talismanology in general. The information given will completely satisfy a mature person, whereas to an immature person this knowledge will continue to remain a secret.

Epilogue

Now I present to the reader, to the practitioner and to the budding spheric magician, my second work. This work describes in an understandable manner the practice of the second Tarot card. I have repeatedly mentioned and emphasized that I could have written every chapter in much greater detail, but this was not possible for purely technical reasons. However, whosoever has acquired the necessary maturity through a conscientious study and diligent practical work on the basis of my first work, *Initiation into Hermetics*, will find what I have written in this work absolutely sufficient for any further practice. A mature magician is given the opportunity, through contact with the individual intelligences of the aforementioned spheres and whether through mental travel or evocation, to achieve the highest adepthood in magic and the Kabbalah, if he selects for his initiator an intelligence, genius or a being which appeals to him, and if he works in accordance to their instructions and with the practices which are entrusted to him. It should be obvious to the magician that he should not remain with one single intelligence and work only with that one intelligence; instead he should mentally travel through all spheres and he should also become acquainted with all the spheres through evocation.

I congratulate from the bottom of my heart any spheric magician who has visited all the spheres in a practical manner on the basis of this work and who has all the powers under his control and has established contacts. He has again progressed quite a distance on the path of perfection. It also gives me great satisfaction to have helped those readers who for the time being are interested only in the theory, because they have increased their theoretical knowledge considerably by just thoroughly reading this book. After reading this book, every reader, every theorist, and anyone who is interested in secret knowledge will come to the conclusion that magic and in particular spheric magic is not sorcery. Rather, it is the highest of knowledge on the whole, and it far surpasses all other intellectual sciences and in actuality is the true crown of wisdom.

Those who are not mature enough, and who do not understand this high knowledge theoretically and much less practically, will at least be conscious of their own immaturity and therefore they will refrain from any criticism.

My second work has completely fulfilled its purpose even if it is only granted to a few earthly human beings to practically finish all the tasks stated in this book.

At this point I would like to thank the publisher for taking on the task of making this work accessible to the public at large. My books are textbooks and they do not belong to the classification of literature that is only read once and afterwards gathers dust in libraries and bookcases. Instead, all my books will serve as guide and helper for centuries to come for those who have reached the level of maturity for Hermetics and for high adepthood. In the course of time millions of human beings will follow the teaching methods contained in these books, and they will also carry them out practically, in order to promote their own development and move constantly closer to perfection.

Franz Bardon

Part III
Seals Of The Principals, Intelligences, Genii And Beings

Illustrations

The Symbolism Of
The Second Tarot Card

The second Tarot card represents the temple of initiation. It is identical to the microcosm, the small world. The second Tarot card is frequently regarded as Solomon's temple. This temple is supported by four pillars which represent the four elements as well as knowledge, courage, volition and silence, i.e. the Kabbalistic Yod-Heh-Vau-Heh, the Tetragrammaton.

Each pillar rests upon a circular base or plinth of hewn stone which symbolizes that a magician who receives his initiation in this temple is already the absolute master of every element.

The black and white marble floor consists of the same size squares. This represents the positive and negative activities of the elements in the physical world. On a higher level it is the lawfulness — the sphere of Jupiter — of the physical plane with which the magician must also be completely conversant before he can be initiated.

The floor before the altar is covered with a carpet. The carpet is divided lengthwise into two equal parts (red and blue), which depicts the positive and negative activities of all powers of the planetary systems on our physical world. The magician must also be the absolute master of these powers, which are the electric and magnetic fluids.

On the carpet there is the magic circle which represents infinity, i.e. the alpha and omega. The reader will find the description of the magic circle in "Part I, Chapter 3" of this book. In the circle is the pentagram as a symbol of the microcosm, the small world. The magician must have his microcosm fully developed, i.e. he must be in complete harmony with the macrocosm. The pentagram is the symbol of the microcosm, whereas the macrocosm is usually symbolized by a hexagram.

The magician is dressed in a violet magical garment. As a symbol that he has attained a bond with God, Intuition, through the Akasha Principle, he holds in his left hand a sword, the symbol of victory, and in his raised right hand he holds conjuringly the magic wand as the symbol of his absolute will, his absolute might.

On a golden throne, to the right of the magician, sits the high priestess as the representative of Isis. As symbols of mastering the positive and the negative, she holds the Book of Wisdom in her left hand and the two keys of initiation in her right hand. She initiates the magician who has prepared himself for the evocation into the profound secrets of spheric magic. In some versions of the Tarot, the high priestess is also depicted as a female pope or an empress. Although this is the Tarot card which represents might and wisdom, in this case it does not necessarily indicate the female principle.

In front of the circle are three steps that lead to the altar. These steps indicate control over the three planes, the physical, astral and mental. The altar itself represents the symbol of reverence. The triangle in the center denotes the three-dimensional activities of the divine emanation in everything, in the plus and the minus principle.

As a symbol, the two censers indicate that the evoking magician has both the positive or good and the negative or evil beings under his control, and also that he has the ability to materialize these beings. The magical spheric mirror on the altar with the seven colors of the spheres indicates symbolically that the magician must not only be in contact with all beings of the seven planets in a divinatory manner and through mental travel, but he must also have the ability of summoning these beings in an evocative manner onto the physical world.

In the background on the wall are the ancient Egyptian symbols of the second Tarot card; they are pictures of the goddesses Isis and Nephthys.

1

The Beings
of the
Four Elements

1. Pyrhum

2. Aphtiph

3. Orudu

4. Itumo

5. Coroman

6. Tapheth

7. Oriman

8. Amtophul

9. Amasol

10. Ardiphne

11. Isaphil

12. Amue

13. Aposto

14. Ermot

15. Osipeh

16. Istiphul

17. Mentifil

18. Ordaphe

19. Orova

20. Idurah

21. Musar

22. Necas

23. Erami

24. Andimo

25. Parahim

26. Apilki

27. Erkeya

28. Dalep

29. Capisi

30. Drisophi

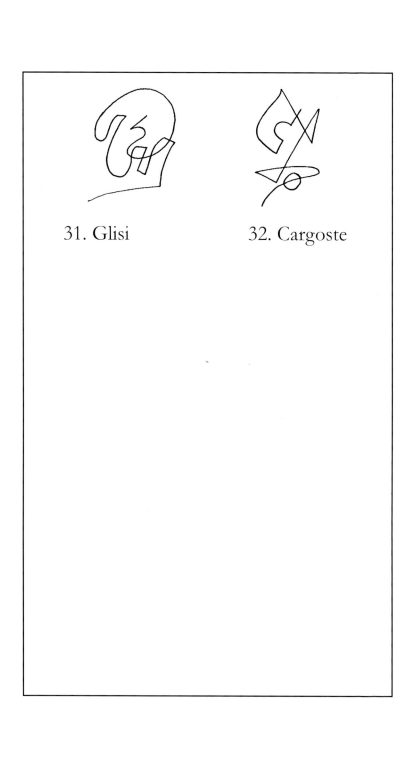

31. Glisi 32. Cargoste

2

Some original Intelligences
of the
Zone girdling the Earth

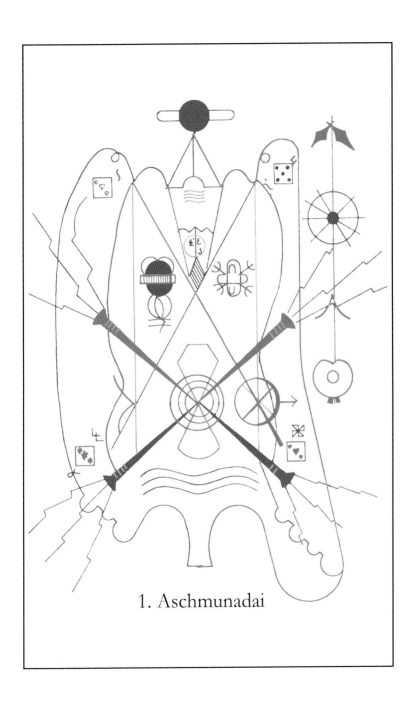

1. Aschmunadai

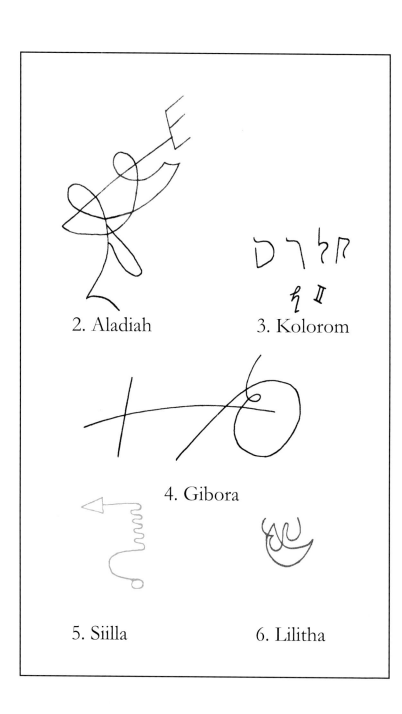

2. Aladiah

3. Kolorom

קלרם

4. Gibora

5. Siilla

6. Lilitha

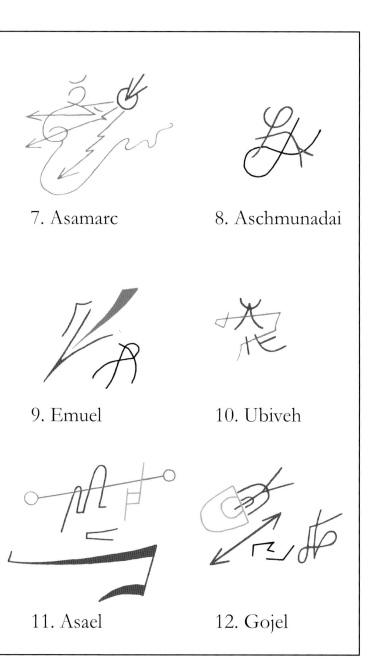

7. Asamarc

8. Aschmunadai

9. Emuel

10. Ubiveh

11. Asael

12. Gojel

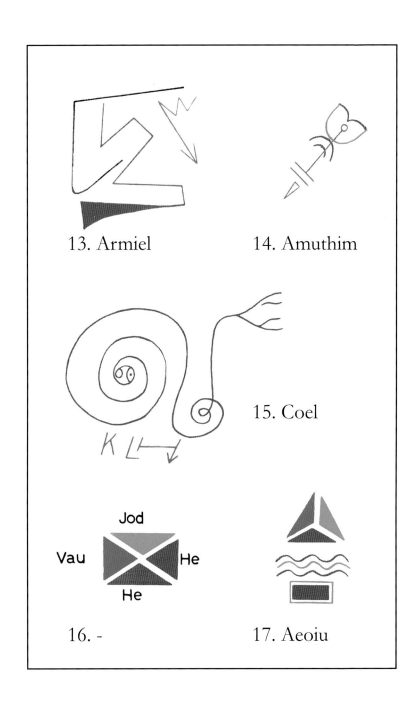

13. Armiel

14. Amuthim

15. Coel

Jod

Vau   He

He

16. -

17. Aeoiu

18. Juoea

19. Nahum

20. Immicat

21. Osrail

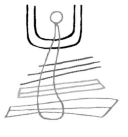

22. Ados

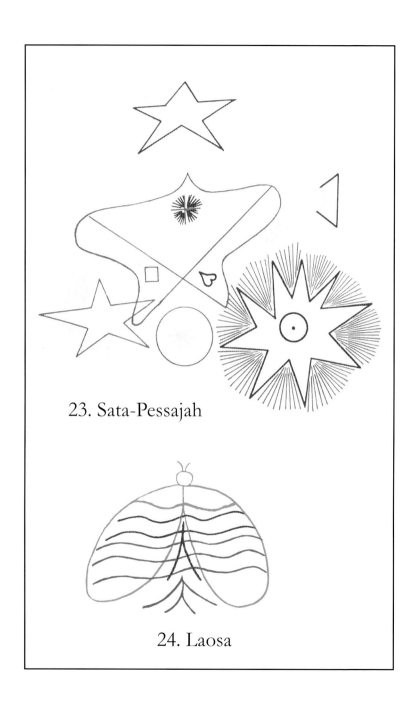

23. Sata-Pessajah

24. Laosa

3

The 360 Principals
of the
Zone girdling the Earth

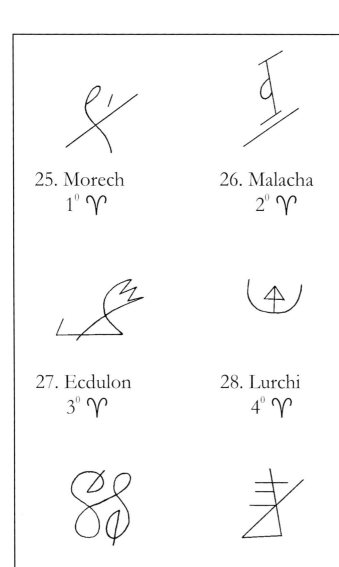

25. Morech
    1^0 ♈

26. Malacha
    2^0 ♈

27. Ecdulon
    3^0 ♈

28. Lurchi
    4^0 ♈

29. Aspadit
    5^0 ♈

30. Nascela
    6^0 ♈

31. Opollogon
7^0 ♈

32. Ramara
8^0 ♈

33. Anamil
9^0 ♈

34. Tabori
10^0 ♈

35. Igigi
11^0 ♈

36. Bialode
12^0 ♈

37. Opilon
13⁰ ♈

38. Jrachro
14⁰ ♈

39. Golog
15⁰ ♈

40. Argilo
16⁰ ♈

41. Barnel
17⁰ ♈

42. Sernpolo
18⁰ ♈

43. Hyris
19^0 ♈

44. Hahadu
20^0 ♈

45. Oromonas
21^0 ♈

46. Bekaro
22^0 ♈

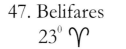

47. Belifares
23^0 ♈

48. Nadele
24^0 ♈

49. Yromus
25^0 ♈

50. Hadcu
26^0 ♈

51. Balachman
27^0 ♈

52. Jugula
28^0 ♈

53. Secabmi
29^0 ♈

54. Calacha
30^0 ♈

55. Serap
1^0 ♉

56. Molabeda
2^0 ♉

57. Manmes
3^0 ♉

58. Faluna
4^0 ♉

59. Nasi
5^0 ♉

60. Conioli
6^0 ♉

61. Carubot

7^0 ♉

62. Jajaregi

8^0 ♉

63. Orienell

9^0 ♉

64. Concario

10^0 ♉

65. Dosom

11^0 ♉

66. Galago

12^0 ♉

67. Paguldez
13⁰ ♉

68. Pafessa
14⁰ ♉

69. Jromoni
15⁰ ♉

70. Tardoe
16⁰ ♉

71. Ubarim
17⁰ ♉

72. Magelucha
18⁰ ♉

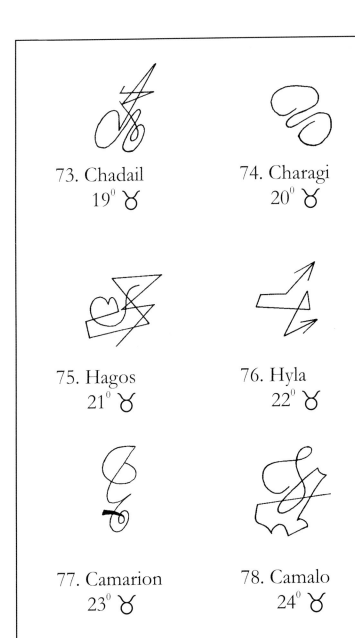

73. Chadail
19⁰ ♉

74. Charagi
20⁰ ♉

75. Hagos
21⁰ ♉

76. Hyla
22⁰ ♉

77. Camarion
23⁰ ♉

78. Camalo
24⁰ ♉

79. Baalto
25^0 ♉

80. Amalomi
26^0 ♉

81. Gagison
27^0 ♉

82. Carahami
28^0 ♉

83. Calamos
29^0 ♉

84. Sapasani
30^0 ♉

85. Proxones
1^0 ♊

86. Yparcha
2^0 ♊

87. Obedomah
3^0 ♊

88. Padidi
4^0 ♊

89. Peralit
5^0 ♊

90. Isnirki
6^0 ♊

91. Morilon
7^0 ♊

92. Golema
8^0 ♊

93. Timiran
9^0 ♊

94. Golemi
10^0 ♊

95. Darachin
11^0 ♊

96. Bagoloni
12^0 ♊

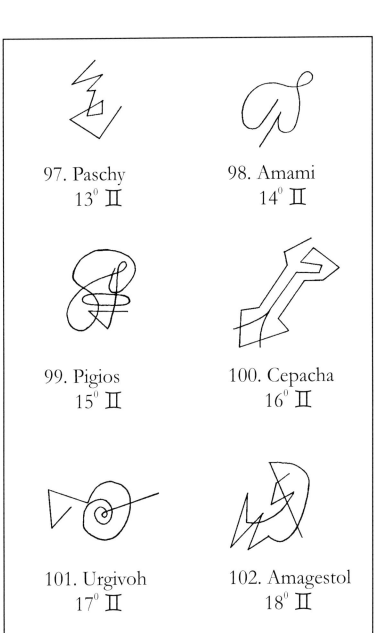

97. Paschy
13^0 ♊

98. Amami
14^0 ♊

99. Pigios
15^0 ♊

100. Cepacha
16^0 ♊

101. Urgivoh
17^0 ♊

102. Amagestol
18^0 ♊

103. Debam
19^0 ♊

104. Kolani
20^0 ♊

105. Mimosah
21^0 ♊

106. Eneki
22^0 ♊

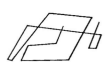

107. Corilon
23^0 ♊

108. Ygarimi
24^0 ♊

109. Jamaih
25^0 ♊

110. Bilifo
26^0 ♊

111. Mafalach
27^0 ♊

112. Kaflesi
28^0 ♊

113. Sibolas
29^0 ♊

114. Seneol
30^0 ♊

115. Nablum
1^0 ♋

116. Nudatoni
2^0 ♋

117. Jachil
3^0 ♋

118. Helali
4^0 ♋

119. Emfalion
5^0 ♋

120. Pliroki
6^0 ♋

121. Losimon
7^0 ♋

122. Kiliki
8^0 ♋

123. Oramos
9^0 ♋

124. Tarato
10^0 ♋

125. Horomor
11^0 ♋

126. Tmako
12^0 ♋

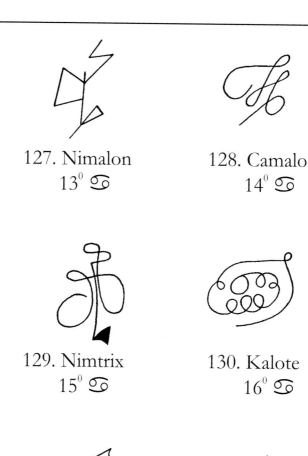

127. Nimalon
13⁰ ♋

128. Camalo
14⁰ ♋

129. Nimtrix
15⁰ ♋

130. Kalote
16⁰ ♋

131. Ysquiron
17⁰ ♋

132. Sikesti
18⁰ ♋

133. Abagrion
19^0 ♋

134. Kibigili
20^0 ♋

135. Arakuson
21^0 ♋

136. Maggio
22^0 ♋

137. Dirilisin
23^0 ♋

138. Akahimo
24^0 ♋

139. Aragor
25^0 ♋

140. Granona
26^0 ♋

141. Zagol
27^0 ♋

142. Mennolika
28^0 ♋

143. Forfasan
29^0 ♋

144. Charonthona
30^0 ♋

145. Kosem
1^0 ♌

146. Methaera
2^0 ♌

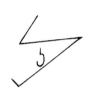

147. Jvar
3^0 ♌

148. Mahra
4^0 ♌

149. Paruch
5^0 ♌

150. Aslotama
6^0 ♌

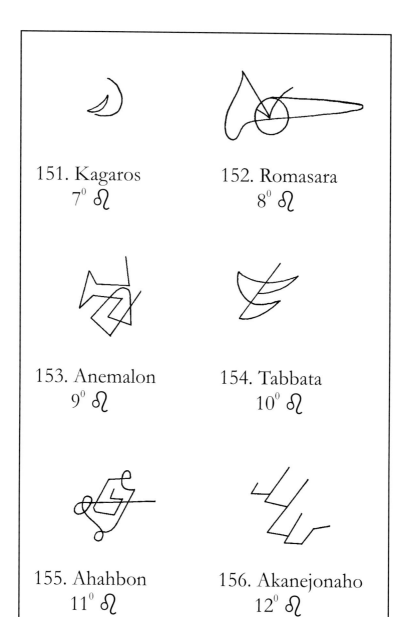

151. Kagaros
7^0 ♌

152. Romasara
8^0 ♌

153. Anemalon
9^0 ♌

154. Tabbata
10^0 ♌

155. Ahahbon
11^0 ♌

156. Akanejonaho
12^0 ♌

157. Horog
13^0 ♌

158. Texai
14^0 ♌

159. Herich
15^0 ♌

160. Ychniag
16^0 ♌

161. Odac
17^0 ♌

162. Mechebbera
18^0 ♌

163. Paschan
19^0 ♌

164. Corocona
20^0 ♌

165. Rimog
21^0 ♌

166. Abbetira
22^0 ♌

167. Eralicarison
23^0 ♌

168. Golopa
24^0 ♌

169. Jgakys
25^0 ♌

170. Pagalusta
26^0 ♌

171. Ichdison
27^0 ♌

172. Takarosa
28^0 ♌

173. Andrachor
29^0 ♌

174. Carona
30^0 ♌

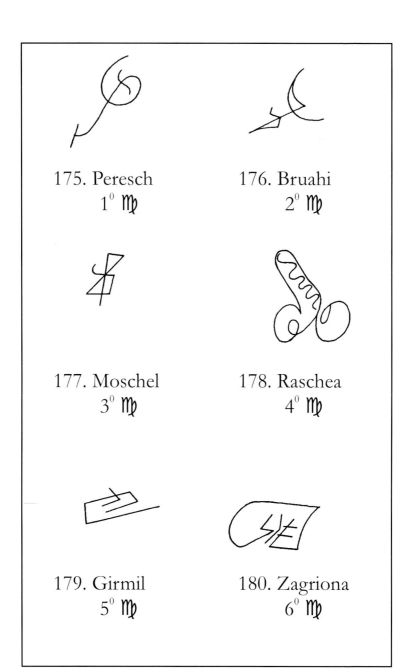

175. Peresch
1⁰ ♍

176. Bruahi
2⁰ ♍

177. Moschel
3⁰ ♍

178. Raschea
4⁰ ♍

179. Girmil
5⁰ ♍

180. Zagriona
6⁰ ♍

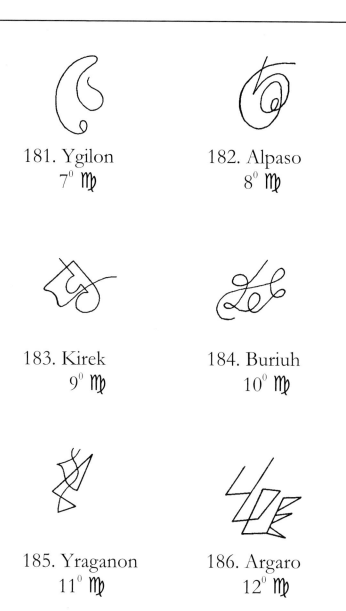

181. Ygilon
7^0 ♍

182. Alpaso
8^0 ♍

183. Kirek
9^0 ♍

184. Buriuh
10^0 ♍

185. Yraganon
11^0 ♍

186. Argaro
12^0 ♍

187. Algebol
13⁰ ♍

188. Karasa
14⁰ ♍

189. Akirgi
15⁰ ♍

190. Basanola
16⁰ ♍

191. Rotor
17⁰ ♍

192. Tigrapho
18⁰ ♍

193. Cobel
19^0 ♍

194. Hipogo
20^0 ♍

195. Iserag
21^0 ♍

196. Breffeo
22^0 ♍

197. Elipinon
23^0 ♍

198. Naniroa
24^0 ♍

199. Olaski
25^0 ♍

200. Hyrmiua
26^0 ♍

201. Sumuram
27^0 ♍

202. Astolitu
28^0 ♍

203. Notiser
29^0 ♍

204. Regerio
30^0 ♍

205. Thirana
1^0 ♎

206. Apollyon
2^0 ♎

207. Peekah
3^0 ♎

208. Nogah
4^0 ♎

209. Tolet
5^0 ♎

210. Parmasa
6^0 ♎

211. Gesegos
7^0 ♎

212. Soteri
8^0 ♎

213. Batamabub
9^0 ♎

214. Omana
10^0 ♎

215. Lagiros
11^0 ♎

216. Afrei
12^0 ♎

217. Rigolon
13^0 ♎

218. Riqita
14^0 ♎

219. Tapum
15^0 ♎

220. Nachero
16^0 ♎

221. Arator
17^0 ♎

222. Malata
18^0 ♎

223. Arioth
19^0 ♎

224. Agikus
20^0 ♎

225. Cheikaseph
21^0 ♎

226. Ornion
22^0 ♎

227. Gariniranus
23^0 ♎

228. Istaroth
24^0 ♎

229. Haiamon
25^0 ♎

230. Canali
26^0 ♎

231. Aglasis
27^0 ♎

232. Merki
28^0 ♎

233. Filakon
29^0 ♎

234. Megalogi
30^0 ♎

235. Aluph
1⁰ ♏

236. Schaluah
2⁰ ♏

237. Hasperim
3⁰ ♏

238. Adae
4⁰ ♏

239. Helmis
5⁰ ♏

240. Sarasi
6⁰ ♏

241. Ugefor
7^0 ♏

242. Armillee
8^0 ♏

243. Ranar
9^0 ♏

244. Caraschi
10^0 ♏

245. Eralier
11^0 ♏

246. Sagara
12^0 ♏

247. Trasorim
13^0 ♏

248. Schulego
14^0 ♏

249. Hipolopos
15^0 ♏

250. Natolisa
16^0 ♏

251. Butharusch
17^0 ♏

252. Tagora
18^0 ♏

253. Panari
19⁰ ♏

254. Nagar
20⁰ ♏

255. Kofan
21⁰ ♏

256. Schaluach
22⁰ ♏

257. Sipillipis
23⁰ ♏

258. Tedea
24⁰ ♏

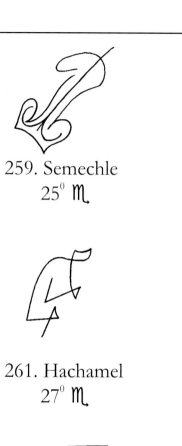

259. Semechle
25⁰ ♏

260. Radina
26⁰ ♏

261. Hachamel
27⁰ ♏

262. Anadi
28⁰ ♏

263. Horasul
29⁰ ♏

264. Irmano
30⁰ ♏

265. Neschamah
1^0 ♐

266. Myrmo
2^0 ♐

267. Kathim
3^0 ♐

268. Erimites
4^0 ♐

269. Asinel
5^0 ♐

270. Geriola
6^0 ♐

271. Asoreg
7^0 ♐

272. Ramage
8^0 ♐

273. Namalon
9^0 ♐

274. Dimurga
10^0 ♐

275. Golog
11^0 ♐

276. Ugali
12^0 ♐

277. Elason
13^0 ♐

278. Giria
14^0 ♐

279. Hosun
15^0 ♐

280. Mesah
16^0 ♐

281. Harkinon
17^0 ♐

282. Petuno
18^0 ♐

283. Caboneton
19⁰ ♐

285. Batirunos
21⁰ ♐

287. Ergomion
23⁰ ♐

284. Echagi
20⁰ ♐

286. Hillaro
22⁰ ♐

288. Ikon
24⁰ ♐

289. Alosom
25^0 ♐

290. Gezero
26^0 ♐

291. Agasoly
27^0 ♐

292. Ekore
28^0 ♐

293. Saris
29^0 ♐

294. Elami
30^0 ♐

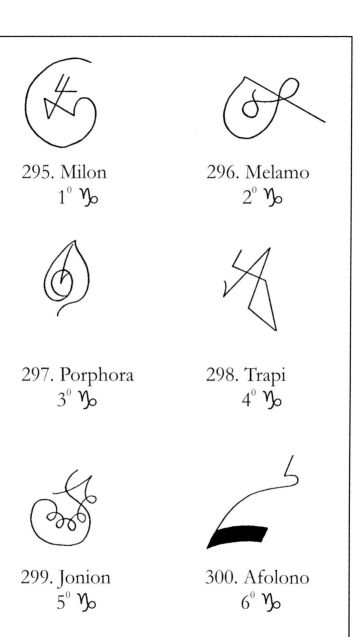

295. Milon
1^0 ♑

296. Melamo
2^0 ♑

297. Porphora
3^0 ♑

298. Trapi
4^0 ♑

299. Jonion
5^0 ♑

300. Afolono
6^0 ♑

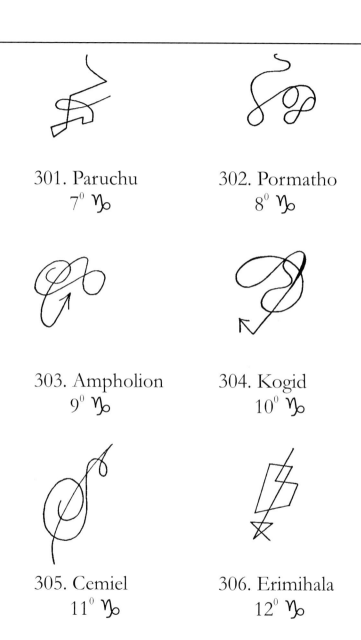

301. Paruchu
7^0 ♑

302. Pormatho
8^0 ♑

303. Ampholion
9^0 ♑

304. Kogid
10^0 ♑

305. Cemiel
11^0 ♑

306. Erimihala
12^0 ♑

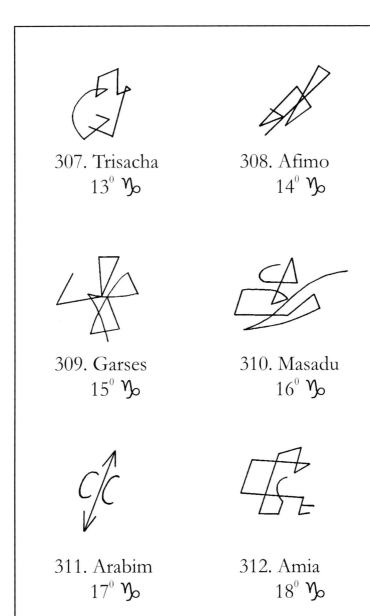

307. Trisacha
13^0 ♑

308. Afimo
14^0 ♑

309. Garses
15^0 ♑

310. Masadu
16^0 ♑

311. Arabim
17^0 ♑

312. Amia
18^0 ♑

313. Kamual
19^0 ♑

314. Parachmo
20^0 ♑

315. Cochaly
21^0 ♑

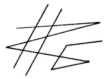

316. Ybario
22^0 ♑

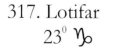

317. Lotifar
23^0 ♑

318. Kama
24^0 ♑

319. Segosel
25^0 ♑

320. Sarsiee
26^0 ♑

321. Kiliosa
27^0 ♑

322. Rosora
28^0 ♑

323. Ekorim
29^0 ♑

324. Ramgisa
30^0 ♑

325. Frasis

1^0 ♒

326. Pother

2^0 ♒

327. Badet

3^0 ♒

328. Naga

4^0 ♒

329. Asturel

5^0 ♒

330. Liriell

6^0 ♒

331. Siges
7^0 ♒

332. Metosee
8^0 ♒

333. Abusis
9^0 ♒

334. Panfodra
10^0 ♒

335. Hagus
11^0 ♒

336. Hatuny
12^0 ♒

337. Gagolchon
13^0 ≈

338. Bafa
14^0 ≈

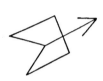

339. Ugirpon
15^0 ≈

340. Capipa
16^0 ≈

341. Koreh
17^0 ≈

342. Somi
18^0 ≈

343. Erytar
19^0 ♒

344. Kosirma
20^0 ♒

345. Jenuri
21^0 ♒

346. Altono
22^0 ♒

347. Chimirgu
23^0 ♒

348. Arisaka
24^0 ♒

349. Boreb
25^0 ♒

350. Soesma
26^0 ♒

351. Ebaron
27^0 ♒

352. Negani
28^0 ♒

353. Nelion
29^0 ♒

354. Sirigilis
30^0 ♒

355. Haja
1^0 ♓

356. Schad
2^0 ♓

357. Kohen
3^0 ♓

358. Echami
4^0 ♓

359. Flabison
5^0 ♓

360. Alagill
6^0 ♓

361. Atherom
7^0 ♓

362. Porascho
8^0 ♓

363. Egention
9^0 ♓

364. Siria
10^0 ♓

365. Vollman
11^0 ♓

366. Hagomi
12^0 ♓

367. Klorecha
13^0 ♓

368. Baroa
14^0 ♓

369. Gomognu
15^0 ♓

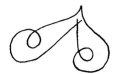

370. Fermetu
16^0 ♓

371. Forsteton
17^0 ♓

372. Lotogi
18^0 ♓

373. Nearah
19⁰ ♓

374. Dagio
20⁰ ♓

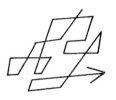

375. Nephasser
21⁰ ♓

376. Armefia
22⁰ ♓

377. Kaerlesa
23⁰ ♓

378. Bileka
24⁰ ♓

379. Ugolog
25^0 ♓

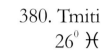

380. Tmiti
26^0 ♓

381. Zalones
27^0 ♓

382. Cigila
28^0 ♓

383. Ylemis
29^0 ♓

384. Boria
30^0 ♓

4

The Intelligences
of the Lunar Sphere

1. Ebvap

2. Emtircheyud

3. Ezhesekis

4. Emvatibe

5. Amzhere

6. Enchede

7. Emrudue

8. Eneye

9. Emzhebyp

10. Emnymar

11. Ebvep

12. Emkebpe

13. Emcheba

14. Ezhobar

15. Emnepe

16. Echotasa

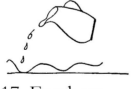

17. Emzhom

18. Emzhit

19. Ezheme

20. Etsacheye

21. Etamrezh

22. Rivatim

23. Liteviche

24. Zhevekiyev

25. Lavemezhu

26. Empebyn

27. Emzhabe

28. Emzher

5

The 72 Genii
of the Mercurial Zone

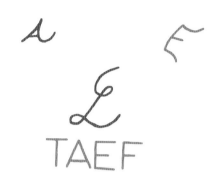

TAEF

1. Vehuiah $0^{0} - 5^{0}$ ♈

NTATE

2. Jeliel $6^{0} - 10^{0}$ ♈

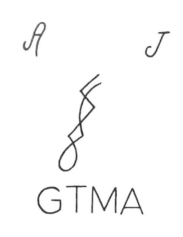

GTMA

3. Sitael $\qquad$ $11^0 - 15^0$ γ

(XALL)

4. Elemiah $\qquad$ $16^0 - 20^0$ γ

AFGFKH

5. Mahasiah 21^0 - 25^0
                                     ♈

GTRA

6. Lelahel 26^0 - 30^0
                                     ♈

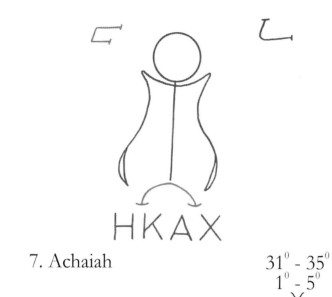

HKAX

7. Achaiah

$31^{0} - 35^{0}$
$1^{0} - 5^{0}$
♉

QKFA

8. Kahetel

$36^{0} - 40^{0}$
$6^{0} - 10^{0}$
♉

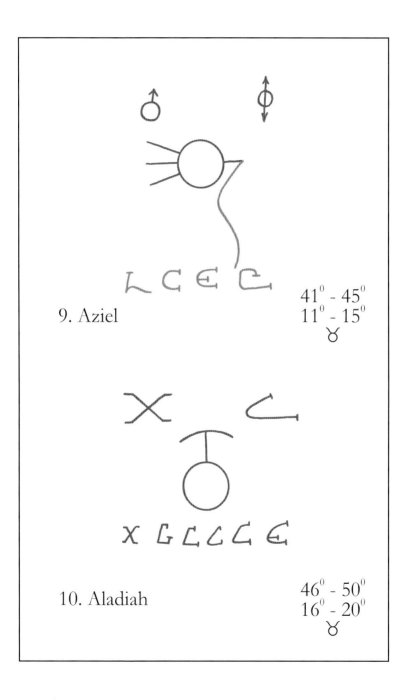

9. Aziel

$41^0 - 45^0$
$11^0 - 15^0$
♉

10. Aladiah

$46^0 - 50^0$
$16^0 - 20^0$
♉

THELA

11. Lauviah

$$51^0 - 55^0$$
$$21^0 - 25^0$$
♉

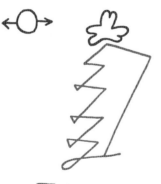

TAEEL

12. Hahaiah

$$56^0 - 60^0$$
$$26^0 - 30^0$$
♉

13. Jezalel

$61^0 - 65^0$
$1^0 - 5^0$
♊

Q ⚥ M

14. Mebahel

$66^0 - 70^0$
$6^0 - 10^0$
♊

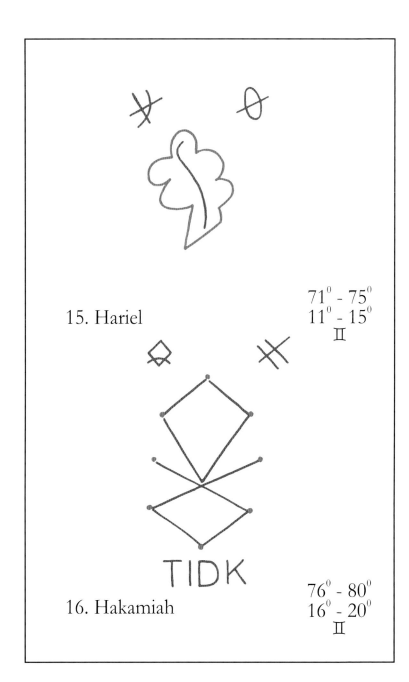

15. Hariel

$71^0 - 75^0$
$11^0 - 15^0$
♊

16. Hakamiah

$76^0 - 80^0$
$16^0 - 20^0$
♊

17. Lanoiah

$81^0 - 85^0$
$21^0 - 25^0$
♊

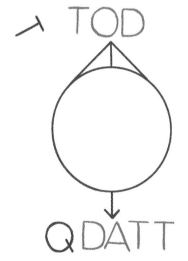

18. Kaliel

$86^0 - 90^0$
$26^0 - 30^0$
♊

EADF

XUTFA

19. Leuviah

$91^0 - 95^0$
$1^0 - 5^0$
♋

D   AEEU

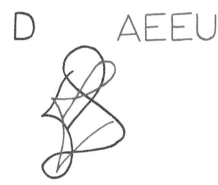

DT TFAN

20. Pahaliah

$96^0 - 100^0$
$6^0 - 10^0$
♋

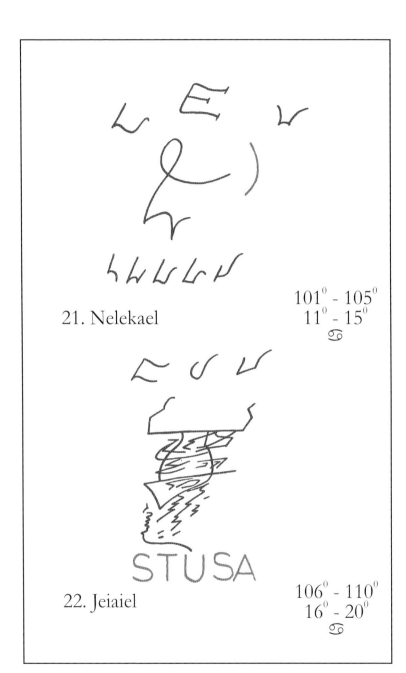

21. Nelekael

$101^0 - 105^0$
$11^0 - 15^0$
♋

22. Jeiaiel

$106^0 - 110^0$
$16^0 - 20^0$
♋

AQUFKH

23. Melahel

$111^0 - 115^0$
$21^0 - 25^0$
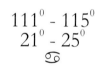

KBDTERE

24. Hahuiah

$116^0 - 120^0$
$26^0 - 30^0$
♋

25. Nith-Haiah

121^0 - 125^0
1^0 - 5^0
♌

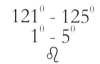

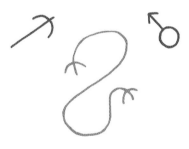

AFHPK

26. Haaiah

126^0 - 130^0
6^0 - 10^0
♌

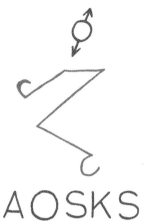

AOSKS

27. Jerathel

$131^0 - 135^0$
$11^0 - 15^0$
♌

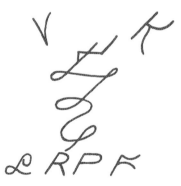

ℒ R P F

28. Seeiah

$136^0 - 140^0$
$16^0 - 20^0$
♌

FAFHFK

29. Reiiel

$141^0 - 145^0$
$21^0 - 25^0$
♌

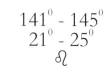

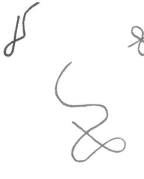

FTTSKF

30. Omael

$146^0 - 150^0$
$26^0 - 30^0$
♌

31. Lekabel

$151^0 - 155^0$
$1^0 - 5^0$
♍

TFHKOE

32. Vasariah

$156^0 - 160^0$
$6^0 - 10^0$
♍

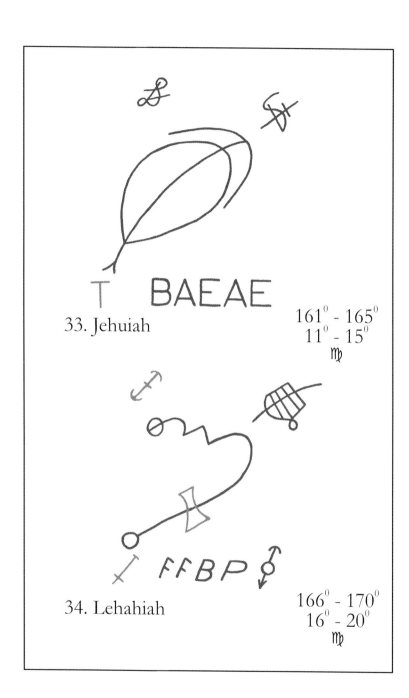

33. Jehuiah

BAEAE

161^{0} - 165^{0}
11^{0} - 15^{0}
♍

34. Lehahiah

FFBP

166^{0} - 170^{0}
16^{0} - 20^{0}
♍

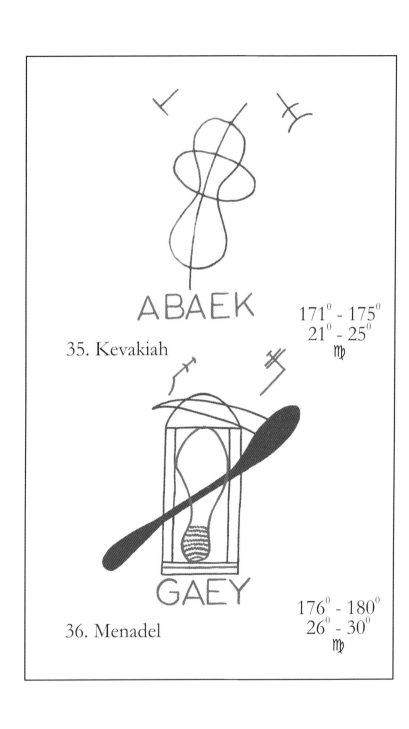

ABAEK

35. Kevakiah

$171^{0} - 175^{0}$
$21^{0} - 25^{0}$
♍

GAEY

36. Menadel

$176^{0} - 180^{0}$
$26^{0} - 30^{0}$
♍

FEAEY

37. Aniel

$181^{0} - 185^{0}$
$1^{0} - 5^{0}$
♎

HARRE

38. Haamiah

$186^{0} - 190^{0}$
$6^{0} - 10^{0}$
♎

FAAHK

39. Rehael

$191^{0} - 195^{0}$
$11^{0} - 15^{0}$
♎

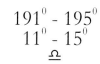

DATTEYE

40. Ieiazel

$196^{0} - 200^{0}$
$16^{0} - 20^{0}$
♎

OKTUY

41. Hahahel

$201^{0} - 205^{0}$
$21^{0} - 25^{0}$
♎

DEAFYO

42. Mikael

$206^{0} - 210^{0}$
$26^{0} - 30^{0}$
♎

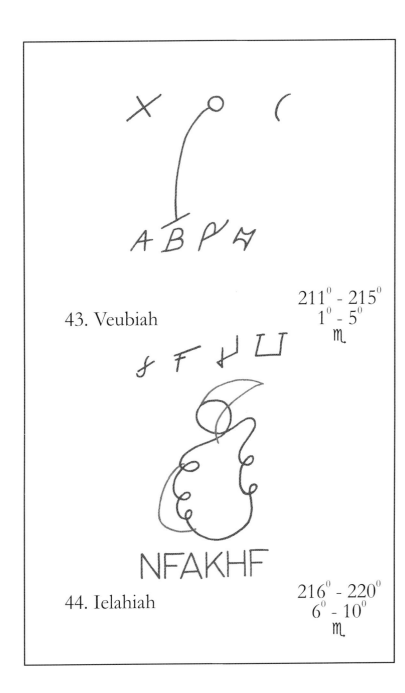

43. Veubiah

$211^0 - 215^0$
$1^0 - 5^0$
♏

44. Ielahiah

$216^0 - 220^0$
$6^0 - 10^0$
♏

NFAKHF

45. Sealiah

$221^0 - 225^0$
$11^0 - 15^0$
♏

TNEFY

46. Ariel

$226^0 - 230^0$
$16^0 - 20^0$
♏

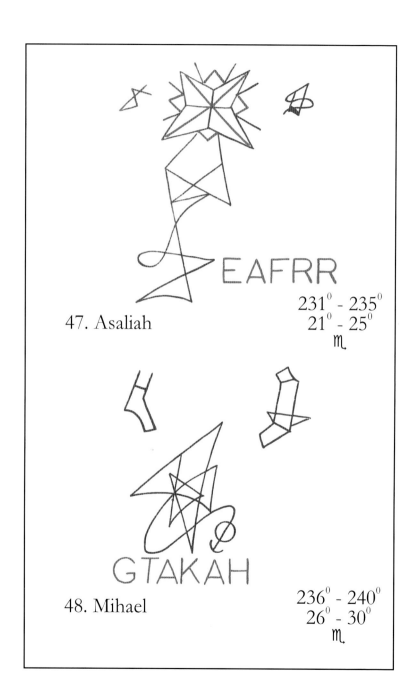

EAFRR

47. Asaliah

$231^{0} - 235^{0}$
$21^{0} - 25^{0}$
♏

GTAKAH

48. Mihael

$236^{0} - 240^{0}$
$26^{0} - 30^{0}$
♏

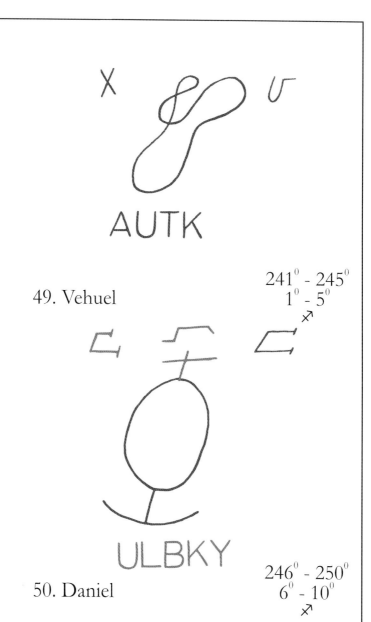

AUTK

49. Vehuel

$241^0 - 245^0$
$1^0 - 5^0$
♐

ULBKY

50. Daniel

$246^0 - 250^0$
$6^0 - 10^0$
♐

KHUXS

51. Hahasiah
$251^0 - 255^0$
$11^0 - 15^0$
♐

—EKUU

THEKUS—

52. Imamiah
$256^0 - 260^0$
$16^0 - 20^0$
♐

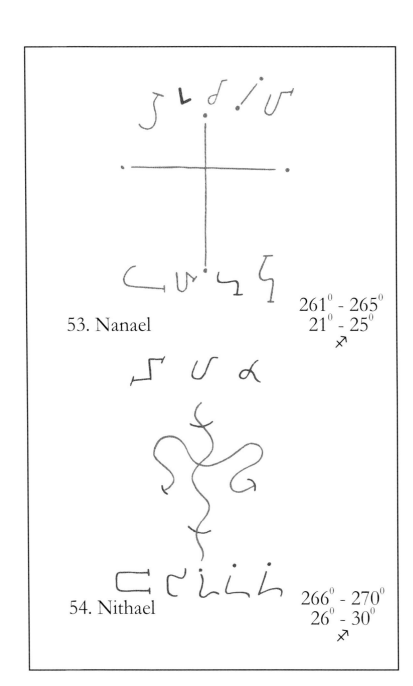

53. Nanael

$261^0 - 265^0$
$21^0 - 25^0$
♐

54. Nithael

$266^0 - 270^0$
$26^0 - 30^0$
♐

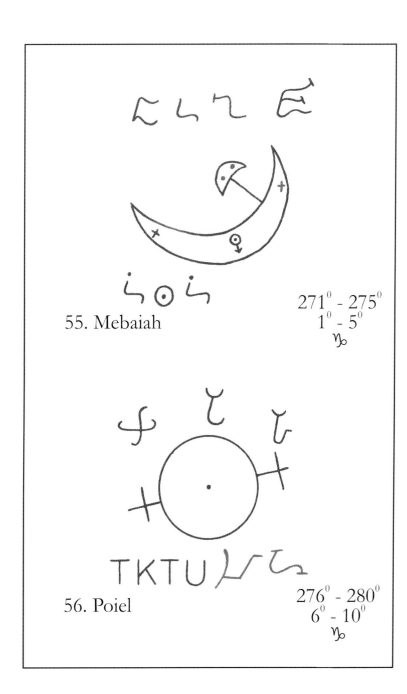

55. Mebaiah

271^{0} - 275^{0}
1^{0} - 5^{0}
♑

56. Poiel

276^{0} - 280^{0}
6^{0} - 10^{0}
♑

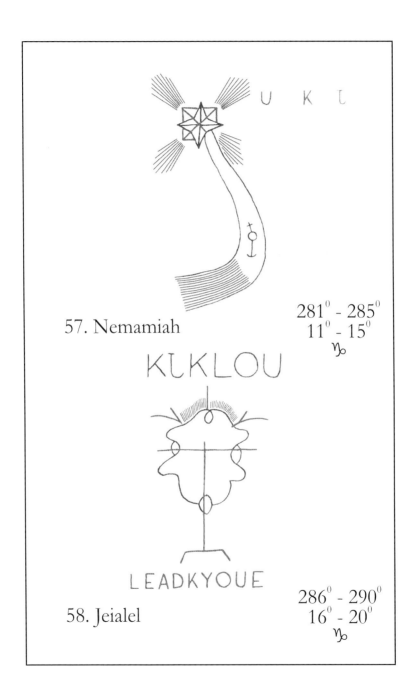

U K L

57. Nemamiah

$281^{0} - 285^{0}$
$11^{0} - 15^{0}$
♑

KLKLOU

LEADKYOUE

58. Jeialel

$286^{0} - 290^{0}$
$16^{0} - 20^{0}$
♑

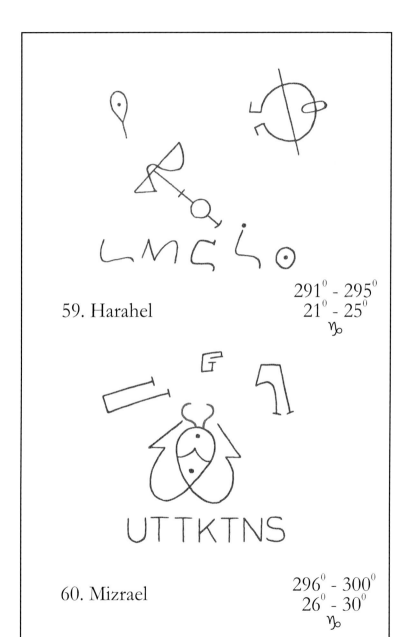

59. Harahel

$$291^0 - 295^0$$
$$21^0 - 25^0$$
♑

60. Mizrael

UTTKTNS

$$296^0 - 300^0$$
$$26^0 - 30^0$$
♑

KFUiNNE

301^0 - 305^0

61. Umabel

1^0 - 5^0

ꞮMNSKELL

62. Jah-Hel

306^0 - 310^0

6^0 - 10^0

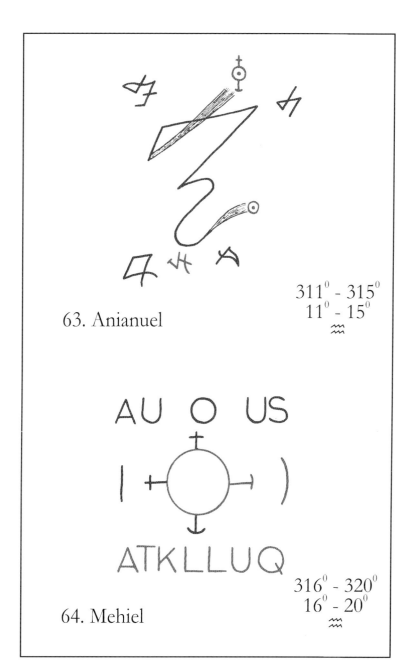

63. Anianuel

$311^0 - 315^0$
$11^0 - 15^0$

64. Mehiel

$316^0 - 320^0$
$16^0 - 20^0$

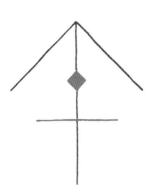

65. Damabiah

$321^0 - 325^0$
$21^0 - 25^0$
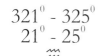

66. Manakel

$326^0 - 330^0$
$26^0 - 30^0$

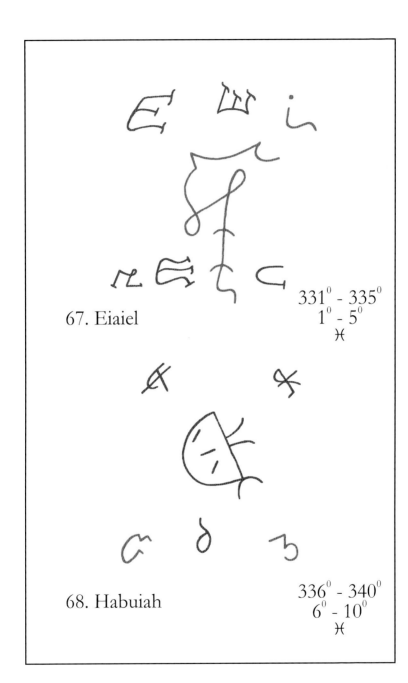

67. Eiaiel

$$331^0 - 335^0$$
$$1^0 - 5^0$$
♓

68. Habuiah

$$336^0 - 340^0$$
$$6^0 - 10^0$$
♓

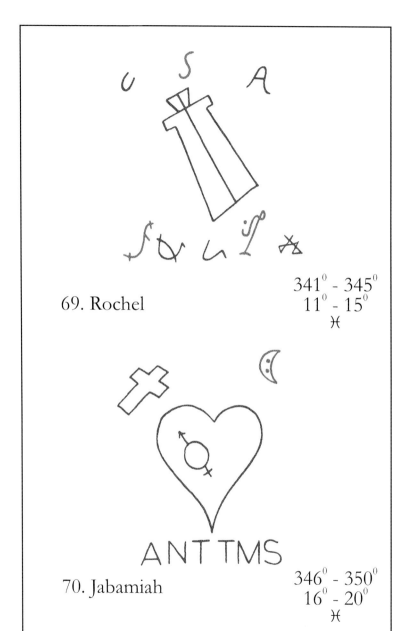

69. Rochel

$341^0 - 345^0$
$11^0 - 15^0$
♓

70. Jabamiah

$346^0 - 350^0$
$16^0 - 20^0$
♓

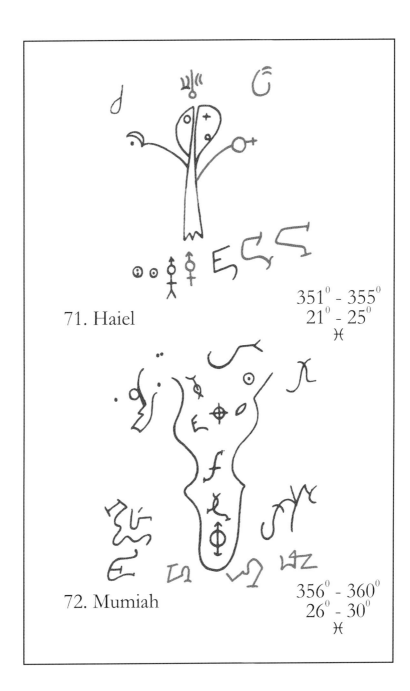

71. Haiel

$351^0 - 355^0$
$21^0 - 25^0$
♓

72. Mumiah

$356^0 - 360^0$
$26^0 - 30^0$
♓

6

The Intelligences
of the
Venusian Sphere

1. Omah
$1^0 - 4^0 \gamma$

2. Odujo
$5^0 - 8^0 \gamma$

3. Obideh
$9^0 - 12^0 \gamma$

4. Onami
$13^0 - 16^0 \gamma$

5. Osphe
$17^0 - 20^0 \gamma$

6. Orif
$21^0 - 24^0 \gamma$

7. Obaneh
$25^0 - 28^0 \gamma$

8. Odumi
$29^0 \gamma - 2^0 \forall$

9. Orula
$3^0 - 6^0 \forall$

10. Osoa
$7^0 - 10^0 \forall$

11. Owina
$11^0 - 14^0 \forall$

12. Obata
$15^0 - 18^0 \forall$

13. Ogieh
$19^0 - 22^0 \, \text{♉}$

14. Obche
$23^0 - 26^0 \, \text{♉}$

15. Otra
$27^0 - 30^0 \, \text{♉}$

16. Alam
$1^0 - 4^0 \, \text{♊}$

17. Agum
$5^0 - 8^0 \, \text{♊}$

18. Albadi
$9^0 - 12^0 \, \text{♊}$

19. Aogum
$13^0 - 16^0 \text{♊}$

20. Acolom
$17^0 - 20^0 \text{♊}$

21. Achadiel
$21^0 - 24^0 \text{♊}$

22. Adimil
$25^0 - 28^0 \text{♊}$

23. Aser
$29^0 \text{♊} - 2^0 \text{♋}$

24. Aahum
$3^0 - 6^0 \text{♋}$

25. Acho
7^0 - 10^0 ♋

26. Arohim
11^0 - 14^0 ♋

27. Ardho
15^0 - 18^0 ♋

28. Asam
19^0 - 22^0 ♋

29. Astoph
23^0 - 26^0 ♋

30. Aosid
27^0 - 30^0 ♋

31. Iseh
$1^0 - 4^0 \, \mathcal{\Omega}$

32. Isodeh
$5^0 - 8^0 \, \mathcal{\Omega}$

33. Idmuh
$9^0 - 12^0 \, \mathcal{\Omega}$

34. Irumiah
$13^0 - 16^0 \, \mathcal{\Omega}$

35. Idea
$17^0 - 20^0 \, \mathcal{\Omega}$

36. Idovi
$21^0 - 24^0 \, \mathcal{\Omega}$

37. Isill
$25^0 - 28^0 \, \Omega$

38. Ismee
$29^0 \, \Omega - 2^0 \, \text{m}$

39. Inea
$3^0 - 6^0 \, \text{m}$

40. Ihom
$7^0 - 10^0 \, \text{m}$

41. Iomi
$11^0 - 14^0 \, \text{m}$

42. Ibladi
$15^0 - 18^0 \, \text{m}$

43. Idioh
19^0 - 22^0 ♍

44. Ischoa
23^0 - 26^0 ♍

45. Igea
27^0 - 30^0 ♍

46. Orro
1^0 - 4^0 ♎

47. Oposah
5^0 - 8^0 ♎

48. Odlo
9^0 - 12^0 ♎

49. Olo
$13^0 - 16^0 \, ♎$

50. Odedo
$17^0 - 20^0 \, ♎$

51. Omo
$21^0 - 24^0 \, ♎$

52. Osaso
$25^0 - 28^0 \, ♎$

53. Ogego
$29^0 ♎ - 2^0 \, ♏$

54. Okaf
$3^0 - 6^0 \, ♏$

55. Ofmir
$7^0 - 10^0$ ♏

56. Otuo
$11^0 - 14^0$ ♏

57. Ohoah
$15^0 - 18^0$ ♏

58. Ocher
$19^0 - 22^0$ ♏

59. Otlur
$23^0 - 26^0$ ♏

60. Ogileh
$27^0 - 30^0$ ♏

61. Gega
$1^0 - 4^0$ ♐

62. Gema
$5^0 - 8^0$ ♐

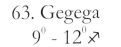

63. Gegega
$9^0 - 12^0$ ♐

64. Garieh
$13^0 - 16^0$ ♐

65. Gesa
$17^0 - 20^0$ ♐

66. Geswi
$21^0 - 24^0$ ♐

67. Godeah
$25^0 - 28^0 ♐$

68. Guru
$29^0 ♐ - 2^0 ♑$

69. Gomah
$3^0 - 6^0 ♑$

70. Goldro
$7^0 - 10^0 ♑$

71. Gesdri
$11^0 - 14^0 ♑$

72. Gesoah
$15^0 - 18^0 ♑$

73. Gescheh
$19^0 - 22^0$ ♑

74. Gehela
$23^0 - 26^0$ ♑

75. Gercha
$27^0 - 30^0$ ♑

76. Purol
$1^0 - 4^0$ ♒

77. Podme
$5^0 - 8^0$ ♒

78. Podumar
$9^0 - 12^0$ ♒

79. Pirr
$13^0 - 16^0$ ♒

80. Puer
$17^0 - 20^0$ ♒

81. Pliseh
$21^0 - 24^0$ ♒

82. Padcheh
$25^0 - 28^0$ ♒

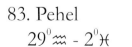

83. Pehel
29^0 ♒ $- 2^0$ ♓

84. Pomanp
$3^0 - 6^0$ ♓

85. Pitofil
7^0 - 10^0 ⅋

86. Pirmen
11^0 - 14^0 ⅋

87. Piomal
15^0 - 18^0 ⅋

88. Piseph
19^0 - 22^0 ⅋

89. Pidioeh
23^0 - 26^0 ⅋

90. Pimel
27^0 - 30^0 ⅋

7

The Genii of the Solar Sphere

1. Emnasut
1^0 - $8^0 \gamma$

2. Lubech
9^0 - $16^0 \gamma$

3. Teras
17^0 - $24^0 \gamma$

4. Dubezh
$25^0 \gamma$ - $2^0 \vartheta$

5. Amser
3^0 - $10^0 \vartheta$

6. Emedetz
11^0 - $18^0 \vartheta$

7. Kesbetz
19^0 - 26^0 ♉

8. Emayisa
27^0♉ - 4^0 ♊

9. Emvetas
5^0 - 12^0 ♊

10. Bunam
13^0 - 20^0 ♊

11. Serytz
21^0 - 28^0 ♊

12. Wybiol
29^0♊ - 6^0 ♋

13. Lubuyil
7^0 - 14^0 ♋

14. Geler
15^0 - 22^0 ♋

15. Wybitzis
23^0 - 30^0 ♋

16. Wybalap
1^0 - 8^0 ♌

17. Tzizhet
9^0 - 16^0 ♌

18. Dabetz
17^0 - 24^0 ♌

19. Banamol
$25^0 \text{♌} - 2^0 \text{♍}$

20. Emuyir
$3^0 - 10^0 \text{♍}$

21. Dukeb
$11^0 - 18^0 \text{♍}$

22. Emtzel
$19^0 - 26^0 \text{♍}$

23. Tasar
$27^0 \text{♍} - 4^0 \text{♎}$

24. Fusradu
$5^0 - 12^0 \text{♎}$

25. Firul
$13^0 - 20^0 \triangleq$

26. Ebytzyril
$21^0 - 28^0 \triangleq$

27. Lhomtab
$29^0 \triangleq - 6^0 \mathfrak{m}$

28. Tzybayol
$7^0 - 14^0 \mathfrak{m}$

29. Gena
$15^0 - 22^0 \mathfrak{m}$

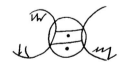

30. Kasreyobu
$23^0 - 30^0 \mathfrak{m}$

31. Etzybet
$1^0 - 8^0 \nearrow$

32. Balem
$9^0 - 16^0 \nearrow$

33. Belemche
$17^0 - 24^0 \nearrow$

34. Aresut
$25^0 \nearrow - 2^0 \text{♑}$

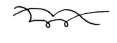

35. Tinas
$3^0 - 10^0 \text{♑}$

36. Gane
$11^0 - 18^0 \text{♑}$

37. Emtub
$19^0 - 26^0$ ♑

38. Erab
27^0 ♑ $- 4^0$ ♒

39. Tybolyr
$5^0 - 12^0$ ♒

40. Chibys
$13^0 - 20^0$ ♒

41. Selhube
$21^0 - 28^0$ ♒

42. Levum
29^0 ♒ $- 6^0$ ♓

43. Vasat
7^0 - 14^0♓

44. Ezhabsab
15^0 - 22^0♓

45. Debytzet
23^0 - 30^0♓

8

The Seals
of the Intelligences
of the
Martian Sphere
are not listed

9

The Genii
of the
Jovian Sphere

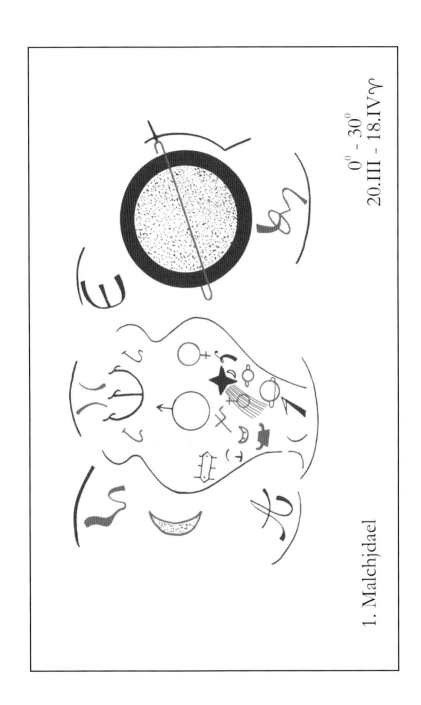

$0^0 - 30^0$
20.III – 18.IV♈

1. Malchjdael

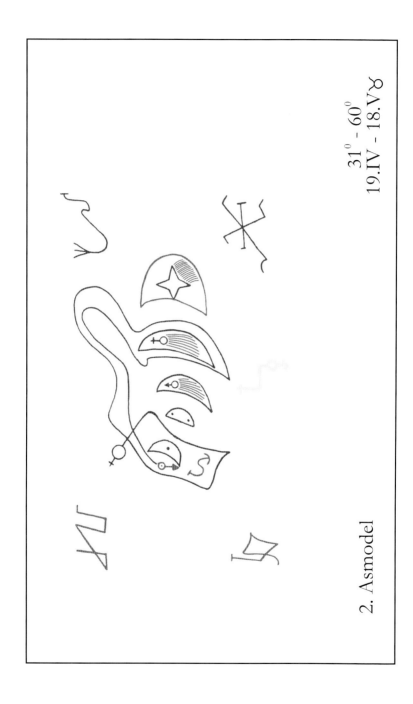

31⁰ - 60⁰
19.IV - 18.V♉

2. Asmodel

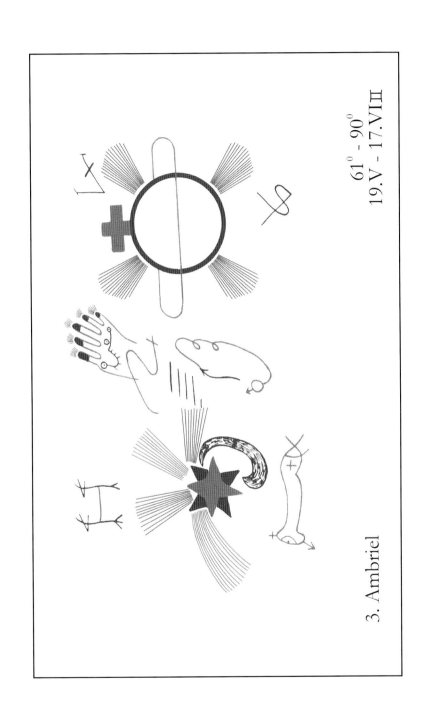

$61^0 - 90^0$
19.V – 17.VI⫫

3. Ambriel

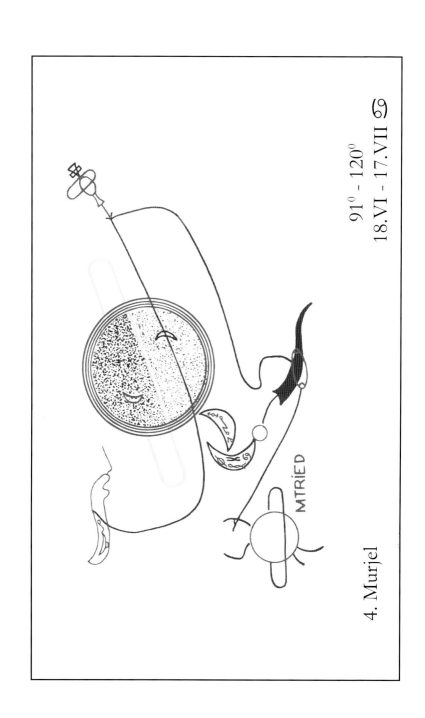

4. Murjel

91^0 - 120^0
18.VI - 17.VII ♋

$121^0 - 150^0$
18.VII - 17.VIII♌

5. Verchiel

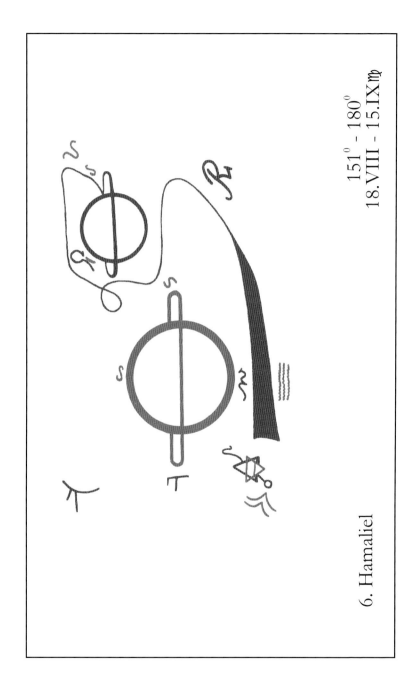

151⁰ - 180⁰
18.VIII - 15.IX ♍

6. Hamaliel

7. Zuriel

$181^0 - 210^0$
16.IX - 15.X ♎

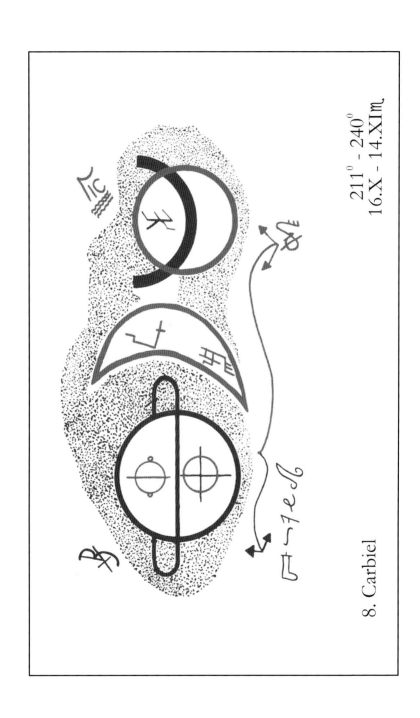

$211^0 - 240^0$
16.X - 14.XIm.

8. Carbiel

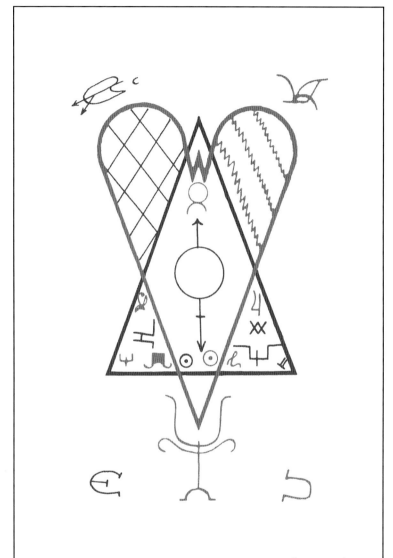

9. Aduachiel

$241^0 - 270^0$
15.XI - 14.XII ↗

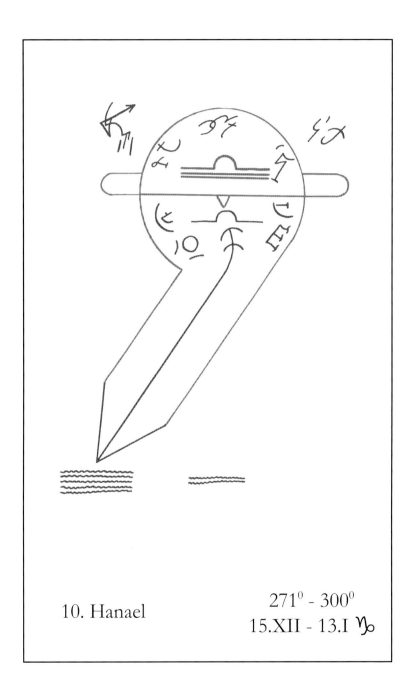

10. Hanael

271⁰ - 300⁰

15.XII - 13.I ♑

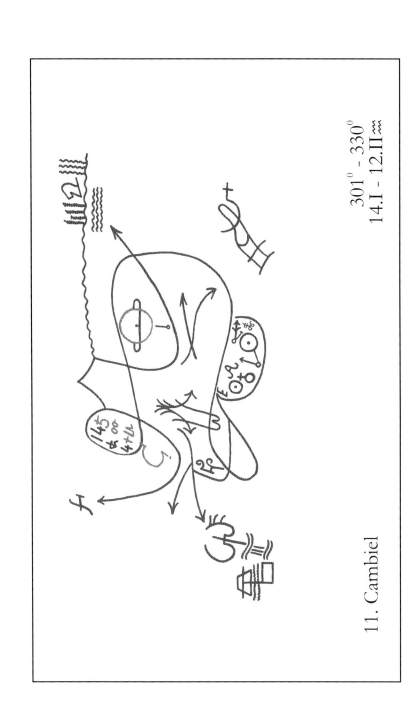

$301^0 - 330^0$

14.I - 12.II ♒

11. Cambiel

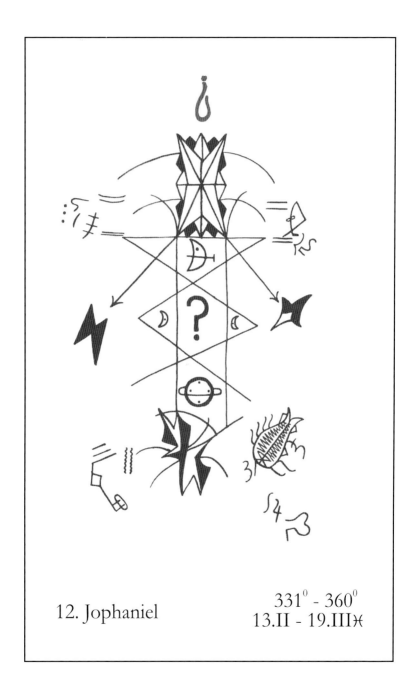

12. Jophaniel

331^{0} - 360^{0}
13.II - 19.III♓

The series of books on Hermetics (Alchemy) by Franz Bardon reveals the Holy Mysteries. They are unique in that they contain theory and practice. It is also important that these works be read and practiced in the proper sequence. Should the reader not do so, he will have great difficulties in understanding the content, even from a philosophical view point; as for the practitioner, he will not progress at all. Therefore, it is advisable for everyone to follow this sequence:

Frabato The Magician
(Introduction)

Though cast in the form of a novel, Frabato the Magician is in fact the spiritual autobiography of Franz Bardon, one of the greatest adepts in the universe.

Set in Dresden, Germany, in the early 1930s, the story chronicles Bardon's magical battles with the members of a powerful black lodge, his escape from Germany during the final days of the Weimar Republic, and the beginning of the spiritual mission which was to culminate in Bardon's classic books on Hermetic magic.

Also included are fragments of The Golden Book of Wisdom, the fourth Tarot card. Photos, $19.95, 173 pages, hardbound, ISBN 1-885928-03-3.

Initiation Into Hermetics
(Volume I)

A course of magical instruction in ten steps. Theory and practice. Complete revelation of the first Tarot card. From the index:

Part I: Theory

The picture of the magician.	The astral plane.
The elements Fire, Air, Water and Earth.	The spirit.
Light.	The mental plane.
The Akasha or Etheric principle.	Truth.
Karma, the law of cause and effect.	Religion and God.
The soul or astral body.	

Part II: Practice

(1)   Though control. Subordination of unwanted thoughts. Self-knowledge or introspection. Conscious breathing and reception of food.

(2)   Autosuggestion. Concentration exercises with the five senses. Meditations. Attaining astral and magical balance with respect to the elements. Transmutation of character and temperament.

(3)   Concentration exercises with two or three senses at once. Inhaling the elements through the entire body. Impregnation of space.

(4)   Transference of consciousness. Accumulation of elements. Production of elemental harmony. Rituals and their practical application.

(5)   Space magic. Outward projection of the elements. Preparation for passive communication with the invisible ones.

(6)   Preparation to master the Akasha principle. Deliberate induction of trance by means of the Akasha. Deliberate creation of different beings (elementals, larvae, phantoms).

(7)   Development of the astral senses by means of the elements: clairvoyance, clairaudience, clairsentience. Creation of elementaries. Magical animation of pictures.

(8)   The practice of mental wandering. Mastering the electric and magnetic fluids. Magical influence by means of the elements Preparation of a magic mirror.

(9)   The practical use of the magic mirror: clairvoyance, distant effects, different tasks of projection, etc. Deliberate separation of the astral body from the physical one. Magical charging of talismans, amulets and gems.

(10)   Elevation of the spirit to higher spheres or worlds. Conscious communication with God. Communication with spirit beings.

One picture of the first Tarot card. One photo of the author. $24.95, 356 pages, softbound, ISBN 1-885928-12-2.

The Key To The True Kabbalah
(Volume III)

Complete revelation of the third Tarot card. The cosmic language in theory and practice. The Kabbalist as a sovereign in the micro- and macrocosm.

Part I: Theory — The Kabbalah
Man as a Kabbalist. The laws of analogy. Esotericism of letters. The cosmic language. The magical or Kabbalistic word. The Tetragrammaton. The mantras and tantras. Magical formulas. Theory of Kabbalistic mysticism. Kabbalistic magic.

Part II: Practice
Mysticism of letters. Kabbalistic incantation. Aqua vitae kabbalisticae. Kabbalisticae elementorum. The ten Kabbalistic keys. The Tetragrammaton: Yod-Heh-Vau-Heh. The Kabbalistic fourfold key. The Kabbalistic mysticism of the alphabet. The first key — the simple letters.

Part III: The Magic of Formulas
The Kabbalistic alphabet. The twofold key. The use of the threefold key. The use of the fourfold key. Formulas of the elements. Kabbalistic use of divine names and beings. The Kabbalist as absolute master of the micro- and macrocosm. Through the ages, he who was called "The Master of the Word" was always the highest initiate, the highest priest and the true representative of God.
One picture of the third Tarot card. One photo of the author. $35.95, 286 pages, hardbound, ISBN 1-885928-05-X.

Franz Bardon: Questions & Answers
By Dieter Rüggeberg

This most recent volume is the first complete new work to appear since Bardon's famous series of books on Hermetics. Compiled by Dieter Rüggeberg from the notes of Bardon's students in Prague, it represents his oral teachings on the nature of the magical universe. Set in the form of questions and answers, this book is an invaluable addition to the Bardon material. $14.95, 99 pages, soft cover, ISBN 1-885928-11-4.

Recommended reading for students of Hermetics:
Alchemy Unveiled by Johannes Helmond, ISBN 1-885928-08-4, $19.95
Seven Hermetic Letters by Dr. Georg Lomer, ISBN 1-885928-09-2, $16.95
Saturn by Jakob Lorber, ISBN 1-885928-07-6, $14.95
Earth & Moon, by Jakob Lorber, ISBN 1-885928-01-7, $19.95